ALSO BY B. S. JOHNSON

FICTION

TRAVELLING PEOPLE

ALBERT ANGELO

TRAWL

THE UNFORTUNATES

HOUSE MOTHER NORMAL

CHRISTIE MALRY'S OWN DOUBLE-ENTRY

POETRY

POEMS

POEMS TWO

NON-FICTION

STATEMENTS AGAINST CORPSES
(WITH ZULFIKAR GHOSE)

AREN'T YOU RATHER YOUNG TO BE WRITING YOUR MEMOIRS?

EDITED ANTHOLOGIES

THE EVACUEES

ALL BULL: THE NATIONAL SERVICEMEN

MISCELLANEOUS

STREET CHILDREN

B. S. JOHNSON OMNIBUS

ALBERT ANGELO

TRAWL

HOUSE MOTHER NORMAL

PICADOR

This omnibus edition first published 2004 by Picador
an imprint of Pan Macmillan Ltd
Pan Macmillan, 20 New Wharf Road, London N1 9RR
Basingstoke and Oxford
Associated companies throughout the world
www.panmacmillan.com

ISBN 0 330 35332 2

3 5 7 9 8 6 4 2

A CIP catalogue record for this book is available from
the British Library.

Printed and bound in Great Britain by
Mackays of Chatham plc, Chatham, Kent

Publisher's Note

B. S. Johnson took an active interest in the design of his books, and the original settings of these novels have been retained.

CONTENTS

1 / ALBERT ANGELO

2 / TRAWL

3 / HOUSE MOTHER NORMAL

ALBERT ANGELO

When I think, that is to say, no, let it stand, when I think of the time I've wasted with these bran-dips, beginning with Murphy, who wasn't even the first, when I had me, on the premises, within easy reach, tottering under my own skin and bones, real ones, rotting with solitude and neglect, till I doubted my own existence, and even still, today, I have no faith in it, none, so that I have to say, when I speak, Who speaks, and seek, and so on and similarly for all the other things that happen to me and for which someone must be found, for things that happen must have someone to happen to, someone must stop them. But Murphy and the others, and last but not least the two old buffers here present, could not stop them, the things that happened to me, nothing could happen to them, of the things that happened to me, and nothing else either, there is nothing else, let us be lucid for once, nothing else but what happens to me, such as speaking, and such as seeking, and which cannot happen to me, which prowl round me, like bodies in torment, the torment of no abode, no repose, no, like hyenas, screeching and laughing, no, no better, no matter, I've shut my doors against them, I'm not at home to anything, my doors are shut against them, perhaps that's how I'll find silence, and peace at last, by opening my doors and letting myself be devoured, they'll stop howling, they'll start eating, the maws now howling. Open up, open up, you'll be all right, you'll see.

from *The Unnamable*
by Samuel Beckett

for Virginia

This novel has five parts:

Prologue	9
Exposition	17
Development	61
Disintegration	165
Coda	177

ONE: Prologue

Joseph said: Cocoa needs cooking in a saucepan.

Luke said: Don't be comic.

Albert said: They put hormones or silicones or stormcones or something in it now so's it'll mix easily in the mug.

Joseph said: Whose cocoa is it, then?

Luke said: Why are you cooking cocoa when we haven't had any nosh anyway?

Joseph said: Sustaining, cocoa is, they give it you inside to help you suffer.

Albert said: I'll cook while you sustain us, then. I think Graham's left some odds and ends.

Joseph said: That's it. A noshup of the lot.

Luke said: Did you know Graham then?

Albert said: Oh, yes, I knew Graham. Well.

Joseph said: Graham once called me a pathetic pseudo-disciple of Them.

Albert said: A double-yolker! How about that, then?

Joseph said: I thought they weren't allowed any more by the egg manufacturers?

Albert said: That's made my day! A double-yolker!

Joseph said: What happens with them? D'you get two chickens out?

Luke said: Y'know, I reckon that Graham was off his trolley. I mean, I've been here some evenings and you should have heard what was going on upstairs!

Joseph said: All through the bloody night, too.

Albert said: He was certainly unusual . . . eccentric. . . .

Luke said: Eccentric! He was bleeding round the twist, mate, straight round the twist, no doubt about that!

Joseph said: I got used to it.

Luke said: Well, I wouldn't have got used to it. Bleeding groaning and saying his prayers with beads —and the music he used to play!

Joseph said: I liked it, I liked it. I didn't understand it, but I liked it.

Albert said: Well, I shan't make a lot of noise. I like quiet. I spend a lot of time working at a drawing-board.

Luke said: You an artist, then?

Albert said: Well, sort of. I'm an architect—that is, I'm a teacher really, but I want to be an architect. No, that's the wrong way round, I'm an architect but I have to earn my living by teaching.

Joseph said: What, you do drawings of buildings and things?

Albert said: Yes.

Luke said: What buildings have you done, then?

Albert said: Ones that have actually been built?

Luke said: Yes.

Albert said: None. I just design them.

Joseph said: Sounds a bit useless to me, mate. What's the use of designing buildings if no one's going to build them?

Albert said: I do it for its own sake. You have to do something for its own sake.

Luke said: Won't anyone ever build your buildings, then?

Albert said: Oh yes, one day they'll all be built, I know.

Joseph said: When you're dead, like.

Luke said: Like poets, after they're dead.

Albert said: Like poets, just.

Luke said: Fucking lot of good that is, mate. I mean, when you're dead you're fucking dead, aren't you?

Albert said: No.

*   *   *   *   *

The first thing you see about Percy Circus is that it stands most of the way up a hill, sideways, leaning upright against the slope like a practised seaman. And then the next thing is that half of it is not there. There are trees in the circular railinged area in the middle: planes mostly, but one or two oaks and a long, hanging willow, oddly twisted like a one-legged circus tumbler. There is a little grass there, too, and rubbish of various kinds littered around—bicycle wheels, bottomless enamel buckets, tins, rotting cardboard. Some of the houses have patches where new London stocks show up yellow against the older blackened ones; then you know what happened to the rest of the Circus. New flats abut at an angle, awkwardly. A blue plaque tells you that Lenin once lived at number sixteen.

Percy Circus can be dated early Victorian by the windows, which have stucco surrounds as wide as the reveals are deep, with a scroll-bracket on either side at the top. The proportions are quite good, though the move away from Georgian is obvious except in the top and leadflashed dormers. There is stucco channelled jointing up to the bottom of the first-floor windows, which have little cast-iron balconies swelling enceintely. Each house is subtly different in its detail from each of its neighbours. The paintwork is everywhere brown and old and peeling.

Albert lived at number twenty-nine. He had one huge room on the ground floor. His drawing-board he set up overlooking the Circus, facing south, to take benefit of the light.

The previous tenant was named Graham. Joseph lived underneath, in the basement, of twenty-nine Percy Circus. Albert had a bathroom, a lavatory, and a kitchen in common with Joseph. Luke was a friend to Joseph, who happened to be visiting him at the time that the conversation already related took place. Joseph had oh many other friends, but on this particular occasion it happened to be Luke who happened to be visiting Joseph on the first evening of Albert's tenure of the room in Percy Circus. On the very special occasion of Albert's coming to number twenty-nine it happened to be Luke: Luke, to give him a name pregnant with significance.

Someone lived upstairs, above Albert. Albert did not know who lived upstairs, above him. This was enough for

Albert, to know that someone lived upstairs but not to know who it was who lived upstairs. For many it would not have been enough. They would have been out at many times, on many occasions, contriving coincidences in the hall and in the passageways and other common places, in their first week at Percy Circus. But not Albert. He heard the toings and the comings and the froings, but did not worry himself with identities. It was enough, for Albert, to know that someone lived upstairs.

TWO: Exposition

I think I shall visit my parents every Saturday, as a rule, as a habit. Occasionally Sundays: instead, though, not as well. But usually Saturdays, as a rule, as a habit almost. Yes.

I think that they are my parents, at least, yes. They have always told me that they are my parents, my father and my mother, no inconsistency on their parts. I have been fairly content to think of them as my father and my mother. Naturally, I have only their words for it. Unless you count physical resemblances. But those I have, physical resemblances, to others who do not tell me they are my father, or my mother. Not that I could not have grown like them, for I could, people do grow like other people around them, in looks, and like their animals, too: Jim Wells grew to look like a greyhound in just the couple of years he kept them. And traits, too, physical traits, and mental traits, as well, these resemble some of those of my mother and more particularly some of those of my father. But traits, traits, both physical and mental, traits one picks up from anyone. Anyone.

I shall call them my parents, in any event, it seems right to call them my parents, my mother and my father. My parents, to give them a name with which to be going on.

Every Saturday morning in the normal way I shall visit my parents. In the normal way.

They live at Hammersmith, my parents. I walk down the hill from Percy Circus, along Kings Cross Road, into Pentonville Road, towards Kings Cross. The station has two great squat stock-brick arches, their yellow uncommonly unblackened; Cubitt, the youngest, Lewis. Then there are the pseudo-Gothic excrescences of Scott's St. Pancras. I wonder shall I come to accept St. Pancras station, living so near? Or even to like it? Perhaps it is fatal to live so near to St. Pancras for an architect? Certainly it would be to bring up children here: their aesthetic would be blighted. But it seems unlikely that I shall be allowed to bring up children here.

Kings Cross is crowded, the tube station, with non-Londoners, foreigners, who do not know their ways, upfortheweekenders who stand on both sides of the escalator with too much luggage and go as far as Piccadilly.

The monotonous, regular sag and rise in the cable lines through the window opposite lulls me into drowsiness. I mean, had meant, to read. Sunlight as the train emerges before Barons Court rouses me. The first wintry unsure sunlight of spring.

This sun on St. Paul's Hammersmith lifts me. Its proportions are miraculous, miraculous. Who did it . . . Gough, yes, Gough and Roumieu, and someone else. Forget the other. My first real isometric drawing was of St. Paul's. My first real. Miraculous. And my parents (whatever that may mean) were married there, at St. Paul's. The flyover, Hammersmith flyover, too, pleases me. It sets off the church, is a fine piece of architecture itself. Graceful, curving away as though on tiptoe. But the sun emphasises which is the better.

Under, along, down towards the river. Towards the house of my parents.

I meet the Vicar. He looks the way he was looking before he saw me. I look the way I was looking before I saw him. The Christian Fellowship of Youth used to run a football team, and we used to belong. We never used to go to church, though. And one day he was so disgusted with us, the Vicar, that he called us a lot of little heathens. So the team broke away from the church and we called ourselves Little Heathens F.C. He used to let us practise in the church school playground, but we did not miss it much, afterwards, we used the streets instead. It was difficult though to transfer your skills to grass, but as a result we all became good at the unexpected-angle ball. Particularly Gerry in goal. There was an enormous manhole cover and a kerb in front of the yardgates we used as a goal. Gerry got so used to expecting difficult angles at short notice that he became one of the best goalkeepers in the junior league. Gerry actually went on and played regularly in the Combination side for Fulham. I had a trial for Chelsea myself, when I was about sixteen, up near the Welsh Harp at Hendon it was, their trial ground. But I had a wet dream the night before because I had been saving up for a week beforehand, and I played far below my best. Not that I really think that I would have made the pro game anyway: no concentration if I was not completely interested. Start of a season, I would play well because I was interested, because I cared. Then after a few games my interest would go, though I still wanted to play well, and my game would go right off. Used to play left-half or left-back. Worked out a great understanding with Stan, our left-winger. He was as fast as a whippet. He could do the hundred yards in evens without really trying. Stan still lives near and has a fat wife and two whippety kids. I still see him sometimes, but hardly ever to speak to. The Vicar I see even less often. He looks the way he was looking before he saw me. I look the way I was looking before I saw him.

They rent it, my parents, the house, squarish 1880-looking, so undistinguished that I have never bothered to find out who built it and exactly when. Undistinguished, that is, except for the comic portico over the door: nine steps leading up to it, two plain columns with cushion capitals and a severely-moulded entablature. The grey stucco is cracked off in some places, but painted over regardless by my father. But this portico I am very fond of since I used to use it as a permanent set in my film day-dreams and acts: I would make exits and entrances and imagine a vast audience watching every movement I made. This behaving as though an audience were watching has become part of me, is my character, is me, and on one level I am always thinking and acting in a film for such a film audience.

In this house, in my parents' house, my parents' home, all affection is channelled through the dog. No one is affectionate to anyone else except through the dog. I make a fuss of the dog. Fortunately he is a sensible and a lovable dog.

I accept a mug of instant coffee from my mother.

"It's made with all milk," she says, my mother, and she is proud.

All milk, I query literally in my mind, all *milk*, and remember the war. She has a new hat, and puts it on to show me. Then she comes to asking me what she had wanted to blurt out as soon as she saw me.

"And how are you looking after yourself in your new flat?"

I answer formally. She seems reassured, perhaps unwillingly.

"Have you got another school yet?"

I point out to her that the holidays are still on, and that they therefore do not know what vacancies there will be for supply teachers.

"Why don't you take a permanent job, Albert? You've been doing this supply now for three years. You're twenty-eight, now, you know."

I know that very well, today, though there are days when I know it far less well. I answer her question as I have answered it many times before: I am an architect, not a teacher, and I will not tie myself to a term's notice even though it does mean the insecurity and constant changing of schools involved in supply work. She does not understand. She did not understand before. She has never understood. I do not mind that she does not understand, now, now I do not care that she does not understand. There was a time when I was concerned that she should understand.

I ask her where my father is.

"On the dyke."

I wander out into the little garden. My father comes out, clipping together the two halves of his Boy Scout belt. He wears braces as well, my father, not exactly a pessimist, but always prepared.

"Wotcher, mate," he says, my father, and he grins.

One of the few warm things I remember about the war was my father calling me 'mate' in his letters home.

I play cricket with my father, in the little garden. We use a watering-can, a broom, and a practice golfball he found down along the towpath. I give him first innings and cannot get him out. Eventually he gives me an easy catch. Then he has me out third ball. He uses his off-spinner. Incredible, it is, his golfball offspinner, but I should know it by now. He pretends he did not see it beat me or hear the hollow clunk on the can. I draw his attention to both. He is still batting when my mother comes out to call us in to lunch.

My father liked my mother because she turned up for their first assignation even though it was raining. Here was reliability. And fortitude.

For lunch we have beef. I enjoy lunch. I offer the dog a piece of gristly beef for which I have no use.

"You'll make him sick," says my mother.

"You'll make him constipated," says my father.

The dog accepts my offer, swallows it without chewing, and sits back confused about whether sickness or constipation is now expected of him.

I go to football with my father in the afternoon, after my mother has fed us, has fulfilled her function, has performed her duty, as she sees it, as mothers see it. I catch a number eleven bus with my father as far as Fulham Broadway. Walham Green it used to be called, when I first came here, and when my father first came here, too, I suppose, that long ago. I and my father join thousands of others jostling along Fulham Road at a pointlessly fast pace. My father buys two programmes. I pay for us both at the turnstiles.

First I and then my father climb the steep concrete steps

behind the main terrace. I note again the *ad hoc*, piecemeal construction of the terrace: a huge earth mound formed from the excavated centre with a steeply cantilevered shell on it. Badly finished, shuttering marks: not that such marks are not of the nature of the material, of the nature of concrete, for they are, but they can be well left or ill left. Here they are ill left.

Chelsea's play is intensely aggravating, by turns appallingly bad and supremely skilful. They always play like this. Chelsea supporters are men of a special cast of mind, and widely cosmopolitan: all they have in common is this need to become emotionally involved with a team which can play as well as any and worse than any. Men who need to experience a wildly fluctuating range of emotions within ninety minutes. They would not come to Stamford Bridge if the team played any differently. Whoever manages the team, whoever plays in the team, the tradition is the same, is perpetuated.

I remember, in swearing, shouting, and roaring with the rest, today, the first time I heard my father swear, at a football match, how somehow it made us closer, me having heard him swear, as though against the women, the two of us, closer.

In the interval it is cold. I feel the cold, my father feels the cold. I can see my father feels the cold badly. I promise to buy him a season ticket for a seat in the stand when I get my first big commission. He does not answer. I know that he regards this as about as likely as him winning the pools. He gives me an apple, and polishes one for himself against the lapel of his old raincoat.

The second half begins. And ends. Chelsea lose three–two after leading two–nil at one point. Satisfied with our dissatisfaction, I and my father and the crowd squirm away from Stamford Bridge. I blame myself for the defeat, since I lost interest ten minutes after half-time, stopped willing them to win. I had been trying to find an original solution for a stadium to hold a hundred thousand which did not crib from Nervi.

A bus is not caught by either my father or myself, a number eleven, that is, the one we came by, on our return. We walk down the whole length of North End Road. We always do this. We enjoy the street market. Occasionally my father buys something. Usually it is vegetables. Today he buys some Felixmeat for the dog. The dog is a perverse dog. Felixmeat is his delight, nothing can make earth seem more like heaven than Felixmeat, in his view. I feel it is fortunate that not more of us have views like this.

I catch with my father a number twenty-seven bus several minutes after arriving at the bus-stop in Hammer-smith Road at the end of North End Road. The northern end of North End Road, that is. We could have caught a number nine or a number seventy-three, to place them in numerical order, had either of these splendid numbers been opportune. But we catch a number twenty-seven back to Hammersmith, my father, and I. The numbers are related: the square root of nine, three, multiplied by nine gives you twenty-seven; and seven added to three brings you back to nine again, if you take one off. Further-more, there is a three in seventy-three. The numbers of these three (*again!*) buses running along the Hammersmith Road are not related by accident, these things are no co-incidences. Anyone who thinks they are accidents or coincidences probably does not believe in parthogenesis either. To say nothing of god. But no one ever says nothing of god. I feel that this may well be a large part of the trouble.

My father talks to me on the twenty-seven.

"Have you been to see about teaching up at the Angel?"

I tell him almost exactly what I told my mother earlier.

"It's a tough area, mate, I shouldn't think they get many teachers to stay. The kids are very tough."

I tell him that I think he must be exaggerating, and that the children I have been teaching in West London have not been easy to control. I feel fairly confident about taking any class after the variety of three years' supply.

"It's really your mother who worries about you not having a job."

I tell him I have a job: I am an architect.

My mother has a special tea ready. I can see my father is very glad to be indoors out of the cold.

"Taters," he says. "Taters in the mould."

But there are kippers and hot rolls and English butter and fancy cream cakes. She is being good to me, my mother. I do not know whether it is because she wants to make me welcome after missing me or because she wants to make me regret leaving home.

When Jenny left me, betrayed me for a cripple whom she imagined to need her more, my mother said never mind, perhaps he would die and then I could have her back again.

*   *   *   *   *

You have a phone call from them sometimes, but usually you have to go to the office and wait until someone wants **you.**

You have a phone call from them this first morning. The woman at the office gives you directions to the school, and you look it up in your *A to Z* to make quite sure. You put in a briefcase those textbooks experience has suggested will cover most of the subjects you are likely to be required to teach.

You walk out of Percy Circus down past the doctor's surgery. Vernon Baptist Church, rosebushbeds, the public patch with the public seats, traffic, traffic, at the one-way system intersection, across Kings Cross Road, the Hansler Arms, Grove Fisheries, Connaught Dairy, Express Dining Rooms, the Northumberland Arms, the sun on Cobden Buildings with their curious half-exposed central stairway and castiron ornament, *Sausage Cases* (The Oppenheimer Casing Co. (U.K.) Ltd.), Caxton Printing Co. (Kings Cross) Ltd., The Susan Lawrence Hostel, the back of the Welsh Chapel, Ladies, Gentlemen, Radios, Launderette, Suits....

You catch a number 214 bus outside Henekey's, past St. James's, which reminds you of Adam, but you realise that he can hardly have had anything to do with it, to the top of Pentonville Road. The end of a Georgian terrace against the skyline, stacks and terracotta, graceful, peaceful, very right. Flowers on a surprising bank to the right, a grass mound with shrubs, flowering yellow and leaved laurelgreen, walled with broken glass and coiled barbed wire on top; you wonder what it is. It is in the centre of a square with tall late Georgian second-ratings with mansard roofs: the pitch of the mansards is particularly well-chosen, subtle. It pleases you. Claremont Square, it was, you notice, as the bus passes the farther side. You will walk that way, you decide, soon.

Angel Mews, another garden. Colebrooke Row, lovely,

backs of fourth-ratings, all pleases you this morning by its grace and proportion, in the sunlight, down the City Road, to City Road Basin, the bus takes you, you leave the bus, you walk through sidestreets for nearly ten minutes before you find the school.

You open a blackiron door into the playground, and go down a flight of steps. The wall you have just come through forms one side; the school forms another; and tall factory buildings, with heavy wire shields over their windows, complete the other two sides of the playground's quadrilateral. At this level the building is partly open, supported on great blackened stockbrick piers, and providing dark shelter. Down the centre runs a fletton wall broken in its length only by a door, later than the rest of the building but well on its way to becoming as blackened, dividing the sexes. Against opposite walls, projecting little more than three feet, are identically-built lavatories, a postern for each sex. They look like air-raid shelter entrances, narrow, claustrophobic. The asphalt surface of the playground has a very noticeable slope.

You see a girl of about nine come out from a postern, still hitching herself comfortable, and you ask her to take you to the Headmaster.

The Headmaster is formal, apart, preoccupied. He introduces you to his Deputy Head, Mr. Coulter. Mr. Coulter does not like you. He does not like any supply teacher. Supply teachers mean inconvenience to him. They upset his timetable and they are often untrained and incompetent.

As he takes you along square stonefloored tunnels to your classroom he expresses his dislike, oh so politely, by finding out why you are not in a permanent teaching post when he hears that you are trained and qualified.

"Ah, an architect *manqué*," he smiles unpleasurably,

opening a classroom door and requiring almost impera-
tively that you enter first.

The class is relatively quiet. Mr. Coulter calls them to
attention.

"Thank you, 3B, for helping us by behaving yourselves
while left alone. I shall see that you gain five Merit Points
for it. Now, as you know, Mr. MacKenzie is away ill, and
Mr. . . . what is your name?"

You tell him, although the Headmaster had told him
when he introduced you.

". . . and Mr. Albert is going to take you until Mr.
MacKenzie is quite well again. I'm sure that you will do
everything you can to help Mr. Albert while he is here.
If anyone does misbehave, then Mr. Albert will tell me,
won't you, Mr. Albert—and you know what that means,
don't you? Christopher Arbor does, don't you, Christopher? You ask Christopher what happens to those who
make a nuisance of themselves!"

He turns to you.

"I don't think you'll have much trouble with them,
Albert," he says in a lowered voice. "MacKenzie keeps
them very much under his thumb. Now the register and
dinner money haven't been done. I'll lend you my red pen,
if you'll be a good man and be sure to let me have it back
at playtime."

You have a red pen. They love you to have your own
red pen.

"Oh. Well, in that case I'll leave you to it, to sink or
swim. If you need me, my classroom is one floor up, at the
end of the corridor right above the one we came along.
Fit, then?"

You smile your fitness to teach 3B. He goes to the door,
and then remembers something.

"Oh, MacKenzie does dinner duty on Mondays, when he's here, that is, Albert. I trust you have no objections to dinner duty?"

Yes, you have. But you always do it just the same.

"Ah, Albert," he says, "you're too young to have been a teacher before the war. Then we had to bring our own food and cook it in the staffroom. Or go out to dinner, which few of us could afford. Now there's none of that. And the children then often didn't see a square meal from one week's end to the next."

You are not objecting to there being school dinners. You were a child at a London school yourself just before the war. You think the scheme is admirable. But it should be run by non-teaching staff.

"Well, the union has been advocating that for many years now, Albert, many years," Mr. Coulter says.

You restrain your contempt for the union with difficulty.

"It'll come, Albert, it'll come," he says. "Meanwhile— one floor up, at the end of the corridor right above the one we came along."

You are glad he is gone. You smile and look at the class.

"Right, 3B," you say, "just until I get used to things, I'd like you to read quietly to yourselves. You all have your own reading books, don't you?"

Brightly yes.

"Until playtime, then, read. Or look at the pictures if reading is not your best subject. When is playtime, by the way? Christopher Arbor?"

Give him responsibility; he should be on your side if he is a troublemaker. Perhaps in a sense prove Coulter wrong, too.

"Five past eleven, sir," a boy says. ⌐Potato face, potential boxer's, wide eyes, retroussé nose, wellblack hair, blue pullover. ⌐

"Thanks, Chris," you say. He looks pleased at attention being paid to him that is not threatening; or perhaps he thinks he has found a soft teacher.

You sit down. You are glad to sit down. You open the single central drawer of the scored and inkstained desk. Under the register and the dinner book is a litter of schoolchildren's valuables: marbles, sweets, plastic whistles, a spring balance, razorblades, three thimbles, handkerchiefs, keys, chewed rubbers, brushes, pens, pencils, useless plastic parts, ballpen refills, cereal manufacturers' lures, a Durex packet, and a long blunt sheathknife.

You open the register, and glance down the names. Several Greek-looking ones, a Mustapha, and half a dozen Irish. Not a West Indian district, apparently. You look for special notes: there is only one, Linda Taylor, mild epileptic, besides three with 'S' against their names for spectacles. You look round, and see that only two children are wearing glasses: both are boys, and looking again at the names you see the third to be a girl. You decide to demonstrate that you have knowledge of them, and therefore a certain mysterious professional power over them.

"Gloria Canning: why aren't you wearing your glasses this morning?" you demand.

"Please, sir, I left them at home. My mum forgot to remind me." ⌐Small, dark, ovoid face, squareset eyes, block chin, homepermed hair, whitelace blouse.⌐

"Please don't forget tomorrow, then. And you're old enough now not to need your mother to remind you."

3B. Third year, second stream, nine-to-ten-year-olds. How many streams in this school? Difficult to tell how many. 3B will not be the brightest, anyway. Taking J.L.E. next January. Only another nine months, so you should do a fair proportion of formal work with them.

Oversquare room with high, pocked ceiling. White-flaking decoration. Brown up to dado, a green line, then chalky green to ceiling. Woodblock floor treated shinily to prevent splinters. Furniture old, apart from new pair of cupboards. White sashes, three large lights on one side. Reproduction on opposite wall of winsome girl, red-cheeked at embroidery. Vertical sliding blackboards, worn, messy. Boardrubber bald.

"You two, stop talking! You were told to read. What're your names? And stand up!"

You must always start harder than you intend to go on: never the other way round.

"Please, sir, they don't know what you say to them."

"They're Cypriots, sir."

"They can't understand, sir."

"Oh. Thank you."

⌐Dark hair, olive faces, rounded, a little simian, beautifully-shaped heads, remarkably alike.

"How many of the others do not understand English?"

Four.

Give them games to play with in the formal lessons, books to look at, and personal coaching, ha, and try to give as many other lessons as possible that do not involve reading or writing without depriving the other children. Like painting. Yes, you can give a painting lesson after play.

"Now, will you all please answer your names as I call them. Rita Allen."

"Yes, sir."

"Hilary Bullivant."

"Yes, sir."

"Jaclynne Caylor."

"Here, sir."

"Gloria Canning."

"Here."
"Sherry Clift."
"Yes, sir."
"Janet Collings."
"Present."
"Anne Foley."
"Here."
"Nevin Georgiou."
"Yes."

She knows one word of English, at least.

"Doreen Langley."
"Yes, sir."
"Ann Liddiard."
"Present, sir."
"Denise Murphy."
"Yes, sir."
"Felicity Murphy."
"Yes, sir."
"Are you two cousins? No? Related in any way?"
"No, sir."
"Oh. Kate O'Reilly. Kate O'Reilly?"
"Absent, sir."
"Sir, I saw her up Old Street yesterday, with her mum."
"Do you know why she isn't here?"
"No, sir."
"Then there wasn't much point in telling me you saw her up Old Street yesterday with her mum, then, was there? Stella Riordan."
"Here, sir."
"Gladys Saintly."
"Present."
"Linda Salter."

"Yes, sir."

"Sonia Smith."

"Here, sir."

"Georgina Stoneham."

"Here, sir."

"Yvonne Stonehouse."

"Here, sir."

"Linda Taylor. Linda Taylor? Anyone know why Linda's away?"

"Please, sir, she's got fits."

"She had one in class, sir."

"She bit Mr. MacKenzie, sir."

"That's enough! Brenda Trussell."

"Yes, sir."

"Elaine Vaughan."

"Yes, sir."

"Lynn Waters."

"Yes."

"Now the boys. Christopher Arbor."

"Yerp!"

> *You look hard at him. You decide to let him get away with it this time.*

"David Bufton."

"Yerp. Sir."

"Alan Burdick."

"Yer-r-r-r-r-p!"

"Look, the next boy who tries to be funny while I'm calling the register is going to regret it. Georgiou Constantenou."

"Yes, sir."

"James Day. James Day?"

> *You will risk a joke.*

"James Day seems away."

Good, they laughed a little.

"Owen Evans."

"Here, sir."

"George Ellett."

"Here, sir."

"John Hammett."

"Yes, sir."

"Barry Hilton."

"Present, sir."

"Roger Lord."

"Present."

"Eray Mustapha."

"Yes, sir."

"Eray? Which one's Eray? Can you understand any more English, Eray?"

"Yes, sir."

Accent like any other North Londoner's. Must have been born here.

"Good. John Nash."

John Nash and Regent Street and the Quadrant and All Souls' and the Prince Regent and the Haymarket Theatre and bits of Buckingham Palace, you think, John Nash.

"Yes, sir."

"Andreas Neo . . . Neophytos."

"Yes, sir."

"Derek Pearce."

"Present."

"Alan Pearson."

"Present. Sir."

"William Rollings. William Rollings. Away?"

"Yes, sir."

"Away, sir."

"Fedros Stavrikes."

"Yes, sir."

"Daniel Williams."

"Here, sir."

"James Wilson."

"Yes, sir."

"Right. Thank you."

Twenty-one girls here. Seventeen boys.

"Now I want all those who are staying to lunch, dinner, that is, today, to bring out their money when I call their names."

This takes you until nearly playtime. You fail to avoid awkwardness, embarrassment, shame, over those who do not bring money out but have free dinners. Not for the first time.

At eleven you remember to direct that the milk be given out. At playtime you dismiss them and Christopher Arbor shows you the way to the staffroom.

You face the staff, an outsider. No one talks to you except Mr. Coulter, briefly, and an old woman of about thirty, at length. She talks sweetly to you, who would rather be left alone, the professional supply. Through your talking you listen to the rest of the staff. The men are noisily discussing their combined perm entry which narrowly failed to win the week before. The women are shy, the other unmarried ones, and the married ones are aggressive and make loud remarks about the Headmaster's laziness and criminal unfitness.

You are given a cup of tea, and charged twopence for it. Always in supply there is this mysterious figure whom you are replacing. You try to build up your own conception of him from what the others let fall in conversation, from his room, his desk, his children. Mr. MacKenzie. Whom you are replacing.

Your painting lesson goes well, though there is a lot of noise. You pin a piece of sugarpaper to the board and show them the elements of a simple landscape. On the top three-fifths of the paper you lay a greyblue wash, and on the bottom two-fifths an earthbrown one. You run some black mountains across the division. The children murmur then as they see, as the mountains make the picture stand out, become real to them. You are pleased at their reaction. You add a full moon, and then tell them that once they have reached this stage themselves then they may put whatever they wish in the foreground.

You walk around, watching them working. Some start with the moon. You try to remain patient, kind. It begins to be a strain. You go back for relief to your own painting, and quickly rough in a Doric portico flanked by colonnades. You enjoy it. You hear some giggling going on, and turn. A group of boys. They quickly split up, and one tries to hide a painting as they see you noticing. You walk slowly up and demand the painting. In the foreground are hardly identifiable animals with television aerials on their heads, yoked to a sleigh. Underneath each is a series of brown splodges, and, leaving no room for dubiety as to what was represented, an arrow and the word *shit*. You conceal your amusement with difficulty, confiscate the drawing for your collection, and stand the boys out in the front facing the board.

Mr. Coulter comes to fetch you just before the bell for

lunch. The children are still painting. You tell them to clear up now. They do so readily: you are not sure whether it is because you have control over them or because Mr. Coulter is there. You cover up the painting of the incontinent animals with the register as Mr. Coulter moves towards your desk.

Mr. Coulter takes you down to the dining-hall. Long rows of cream Formica-topped skeletal tables, skeletal chairs with steam-moulded laminated wooden seats and backs, lines of children at two closed hatches. The noise is tremendous, due largely to the acoustic properties of the hall. Mr. Coulter goes to the dais, picks up a large brass handbell and rings it violently. Most of the children stop talking.

"*When* you stop chattering, *then* you can have your dinners!" he bellows. He picks on a child at random. "Gerald Thompson, you can't stop talking so you'll have to wait until the end. Go to the very back of the queue. Go on, *move*, boy! Anyone else?"

They are silent now.

"Mrs. Goodman, I think we are just about ready to start dinner now."

The hatches open, and in a remarkably short time the lines have disappeared and the tables have filled with small children, eating and talking. The noise is worse than before, there now being added the clatter of knives and forks. Mr. Coulter tells you to go around giving permission to those who have finished and are sitting up straight with their arms folded to take their plates out and collect their puddings.

The tablemanners are appalling by Mr. Coulter's standards. You notice him correcting one eight-year-old girl for some time. You do not attempt to do anything similar

yourself: these children and their manners are the product
of their environment, and therefore suit that environment.
You are not sure enough of your own standards to take the
responsibility of imposing them on these children for
whom they would probably be quite inappropriate.

You do, however, very surely deal with two boys who
are delightedly spattering each other with mashed potato.

School dinner is finished in just over fifteen minutes, the
slower eaters being chivvied and forced. Mr. Coulter tells
you how they pride themselves on this speed.

"So even if you do consider it an imposition, Albert," he
says as you climb back towards the staffroom and your own
meal, "you can see that at this school we make dinner duty
as painless as possible."

The staffroom is on the top floor. There is a view from
it out to the south-east, over the city. You are grateful for
it. Some of the tower blocks are very good in their own
right, though too many of them have services untidily
designed on their roofs. After lunch you sit sketching it in
your notebook, the skyline: blocks, spires, St. Paul's. The
blocks set off the cathedral: none are as tall: their rectangu-
larity against the dome's sweet curve.

The rest of the staff chattter and laugh: the air becomes
polluted with the smoke of their camaraderie. They think
you are unsociable. Even the woman of thirty does not
talk to you after she has given you another cup of tea and
charged you another twopence for it. You do not mind.

You teach them simple sentence construction during
the first session of the afternoon.

You read them a story during the second session of the
afternoon.

You feel exhausted at the end of the afternoon.

You decide to walk home slowly, up the City Road,

towards the Angel. City Arms; St. Mark's Hospital for Fistula &c.; Mona Lisa Cafe Restaurant; vast anonymous factory block shouldering Georgian first-ratings mainly used for light industries; Albion House with two lovely bow-fronts spoilt by nursery stickers inside the windows and two comically sentimental plaster dogs guarding the steps.

Sale Closing Down. Aspenville wallpaper. Claremont Mission. Overgrown gardens this side. Claremont Square. The bank again, yellow, saffron, green. Across Amwell Street, down Great Percy Street, to the Circus.

You feel far less tired when you reach your flat.

You walk to school as well the next morning, for your second day at St. Sepulchre's. You look forward to teaching. You think of it as a great privilege, to be allowed to work amongst children. Very worthwhile, very satisfying. You think of these as commonplaces, but true and relevant, and remember that this is how you always feel, enthusiastic and dedicated, at the start of a term. Then disenchantment sets in, after perhaps two weeks.

But this second morning you look forward to teaching. You arrive early. You talk with the early children as friends, interesting yourself in their interests. When the class has assembled you say good morning to them, smiling, and they respond readily.

You try the standard jokes:

"All those who are absent please put up their hands."

They are allowed to laugh at this.

And, later:

"Now who's going to have super delicious school dinners?"

They are allowed to groan at this, in a derisive manner.

You like your class. You want to teach them well, as a result. Mr. Coulter interrupts your first lesson, ostensibly to tell you that you are on playground duty today, but really, you are sure, to check up on you. The class is working quietly, and you are giving personal attention to one child when he comes in. You are pleased he has not caught you out. He tells you that no ballgames are allowed in the playground because children have too frequently been knocked over and injured whilst playing them.

When you see them in the confined area of the playground, you can understand why. But, deprived of ballgames, the boys have evolved other ways of playing. The playground has a slope of perhaps one in twelve in its fifteen-yard length, and groups of boys link arms against the factory wall at the back and rush down it. Anyone in their way is knocked down. This game they call Chariots. You stop them, feeling a spoilsport as you do so. Even so, you notice that at any given moment there seem to be just as many boys on the ground, fighting, or being tripped, or falling.

You go through the door in the fletton wall to the girls' side. You notice that the wall is badly laid. You presume that this was once one playground, and that, divided, it now serves for more children.

Many of the girls are standing in small groups, talking. Others chase round these groups. Some of those from your class run over to you and cling to your arms looking up at you and smiling and laughing. You are pleased with their attention, but quite relieved at the same time that no adult can see you; especially no adult who knows you.

➤Dark, red cheeks, dirty mouth.↩   ➤So fair, skin pale as white vitriolite, one incisor broken at the corner.↩ ➤Strong, neat, curiously twisted smile.↩   ➤Tall, shy, never taking her eyes from you. ↩

You shiver slightly; you wish you had put on your

overcoat. You wonder how the wind penetrates such an enclosed space.

You wonder why there is no woman teacher on duty in this playground.

⤳ Jenny! Just like Jenny. Not in your class. That square set of the shoulders, the same type of face, but coarser, oh, far coarser than Jenny's. But eyes just as lovely, just as treacherous. ⤶

A boy comes running through the door up to you and says that someone is hurt. Gently, you make the girls leave hold of you and go through to see. A boy has grazed his hand against the wall. You ask who attends to such things in this school, and then send the boy with two of his friends to the school secretary.

You see by your watch that playtime has ended, but you give them three minutes more before blowing your whistle. They line up reasonably quickly, and do not talk. You are surprised. You stand in the doorway attempting to control the files in both playgrounds at once.

The first period after lunch you feel relaxed, completely in control of your class. You begin a geography lesson which turns into a lesson on London then into a lesson on architecture. You try very hard to make it interesting and understandable to your children. That they are quiet seems to indicate that you are succeeding: there is only one slight disturbance when Bufton, toying with a pencil, sends it skittering across the classroom; and this you deal with patiently. Even the Greek Cypriots seem to be watching and listening, though presumably they can understand very little of what you are saying. The bell cuts short your lesson while they are still attentive and not restive.

Before going down to the playground you ask Mr. Coulter what special arrangements there are for teaching the Cypriots. He is non-committal about it, resents your asking the question, and implies that it is not really the concern of a supply teacher.

⌐Face of a failed saint, boyblue eyes, hair like a drummer's brush.⌐   ⌐Ochre smudge of a face, narrow eyes, soft black hair, lace collar and white press-stud shoes.⌐

"'Ere, sir, d'you know some boy, 'e said there was a pole frough the norf and souf poles!"

Your arms ache where they drag on you.

You set the rest of your class to read, and have the Cypriots out as a group. Eray Mustapha, whom you had hoped to use as an interpreter, you find speaks Turkish and can no more communicate with the Greeks than you can. You take a simple reading book with large coloured pictures in it, and, from a slight knowledge of classical Greek, you identify such objects and ideas as you can for them: φίλος, χωρα, μουσα, νησος, λεω, λογος, πολί, έρως, πατερ, γενες.

Fedros and particularly Andreas are quick to pick up the words, and point to other objects and give them their Greek names in return for your giving their English ones; but the girl Nevin is shy, and you have great difficulty in persuading her to join in.

At the end of the afternoon you feel very tired. You have tripled your Greek vocabulary. You catch a bus home.

The next day it is raining. On going into your class you find a stranger there. You assume he is Mr. MacKenzie, though he does not introduce himself. He does not seem curious about the work you have been doing with his class. Mr. Coulter comes in to tell you that they have phoned from the office to tell you to go on to Wormwood Street Junior Boys' School. Mr. Coulter does not say goodbye to you, and you are overpolite to him. On your way out you see some more of your class, and you smile at them but do not stop to talk.

In your *A to Z* you find that Wormwood Street is in the City, just to the south of Liverpool Street Station. You catch a bus to Finsbury Circus and walk through crowds of crowdressed men and artificially coloured officebirds. It pleases you to walk slowly, to be going about something so totally different from these people.

The school does not look like a school; it is scarcely distinguishable from the commercial buildings around it. Inside, you can hear a hymn being sung somewhere on the floors above, and an odd slishing sound of traffic on the wet road outside.

The school secretary seats you in the Headmaster's room until assembly is over. He is a round, meaty man, the Headmaster, when he comes. The school is a small one, and you are to take the single first-year class in place of a teacher who has been released for two days to attend a course.

All boys. Superbly natural haircuts. Real. ⌐ Perpetually grinning eyes, skijump nose, thin lips. ⌐ ⌐Blacker than you would think possible, starred by teeth white as the weathered western face of Portland stone, eyes brown as brazil nuts. ⌐ ⌐Blue eyes, staring, postbox mouth, ears like open cardoors. ⌐

A new desk, hardly kicked. A worn dirty cushion upon which you feel unable to bring yourself to sit. Grey cupboards, pitted blackboard, no decoration at all on the walls except for a frayed canvas map of the world as Mercator projected it. A lean budgerigar in a rusting cage making untimely interruptions.

The modern method: tables grouped in threes, so that some children have to turn their heads to face you. Should be grouped according to relative intelligence. You look round to try to see which is which. There is an art which can tell something of the mind's construction in the face.

You set them to read, to start with, the opening gambit, unchanging. They are used to having a woman teacher, but they are not well disciplined. They begin to get on top of you. You must clamp down on them. You hit one of them. It is the wrong one to hit: he has a bad ear, the others tell you, in chorus, and you have hit it. He stares through the window to hide his tears from you, infinitely pathetic, for the rest of the lesson. You feel guilty, but suppress the feeling. It is an enormous effort. You worry about the boy, quietly, for the rest of the morning.

You use eccentrically coloured chalks, for relief.

At lunchtime you do not stay in the staffroom after you have eaten. You go back to your classroom and teach obscenities to the budgie. He does not learn: either.

At the end of the day you are depressed. It is at such times that you feel the loss of Jenny most. Somehow, she represents the depression, is responsible for it in a basic but indirect way; but responsible in a way that you admit is not her fault. Paradox. At such times she should be here to solace you.

You walk home despondently.

The second day at Wormwood is worse. You despair of being able to teach. Even when you try to entertain you evoke little response from the boys. Yet you like them. You hate yourself. By midday the strain of being responsible for every child whose nose is bleeding is almost at breaking-point.

You are very glad and very tired when the end of the day comes and you leave Wormwood.

They send you the next day, on the Friday, the last day of the first week, to Crane Grove Secondary, up past

Highbury Corner, off the Holloway Road. The five- and six-storey schools in this part stand above the three-storey streets like chaotic castellations. Dead cinemas and a musichall sadden corners, abandoned. Only Arsenal Stadium, older-looking in its outdated modernity than last century's houses, competes in height with the dark red brick, stonedressed schools. Swart sleek diesels shaped as functionally as otters pass and re-pass solemnly between strips of houses at eaves-level pulling trains of rust-stained wagons.

You spend all day teaching simple English to the third-year classes, fourteen-year-olds who have very little interest in learning: they are waiting only to leave school. You try to arouse their interest by pointing out how basic a knowledge of at least English must be. One boy says he can read the racing, and that that's enough for him.

⌐A mulatta, next to him, with negroid features, coffee-coloured, frizzy hair tending towards fairness.⌐

They sit, large and awkward at the aluminium-framed tables and chairs, men and women, physically, whom you are for today trying to help to teach to take places in a society you do not believe in, in which their values already prevail rather than yours. Most will be wives and husbands, some will be whores and ponces: it's all the same; any who think will be unhappy, all who don't think will die.

Even the lavatory-gothic of the Union Chapel in Compton Terrace cannot make you smile on your way back home, nor the glimpse of Barry's Holy Trinity in Cloudesley Square encourage you by a reminder that a good architect's early work may be poor.

The end of the last day of the first week.

*   *   *   *   *

He must have seen her on the first day at college, but the earliest clear recollection that he had was of noticing as she passed in the corridor, once, the just too large and hooked nose, her only fault. He was pleased about this fault: for otherwise she was so very fine, a woman of nineteen, holding herself very squarely, with wide shoulders, long arms and legs which tapered subtly and gracefully, and breasts to just the right proportion. Dark-haired, she seemed proud, haughty, and unattainable to him at first, and he hated her for being these to him, and was glad about her nose.

She thought him arrogant, and sensed that he felt himself superior to the rest of their year. She noticed his neat suits, and that he always wore white shirts with stiff collars and unpatterned ties. This formality in his dress was counterpointed by an intellectual eccentricity which at first she resented, then admired, and finally came almost to worship. She found herself taking his side in defending the indefensible propositions and situations into which his originality of thought had taken him. And physically she felt he was her equal, right for her, big, hard, everything physically about him was big and hard.

It grew between, love, of a kind, love, more in him than in her, but love, a good love, of its kind.

He felt it as a desire to absorb her yet to become lost in her, for as long as he could see, for as long as he could feel, to merge with her, completely, utterly, achieve the completion of his self in her.

She felt it as a triumph for her self, that she could win him, as she had recently failed to win a lover host to an incurable crippling disease, as a temporary and transitional absorption in which she could destroy the image of this former love.

It was created, fostered, nurtured, cultured, maintained by the situation, this love, by the being together within college, each day. For him, it had as great an existence outside, too; for her, it had a place, but a small place, in the background when she was at home with her parents.

He was used by it; she used it; it, this love between.

He had talked with her about architecture, had given some of his enthusiasm for it to her, and had one day invited her to a lecture on modern architecture at the I.C.A. The first time alone together, he and she, having always before been in the company of other people at college. He was nervous, and talked too much and too quickly. She listened, too conscious of wanting to hear, and tried to make him feel easier.

But by the end of the evening it was warm and good between them.

He walked with her, she walked with him, along Piccadilly, down Lower Regent Street, through the Palladian-Greek vista formed by Smirke's Royal College of Physicians, Wilkins' National Gallery, and Gibbs' St. Martin's-in-the-Fields. Then he showed her Hungerford Lane, under the rsjs, past the doorways of arch-lockups, the several smells of various different storages, and the roofline through the gap up to the right like a random clerestory mullioned by fire escapes and black leaning stacks: and where he would have kissed her, there in the winedark shadows beneath the groined arches before they turned out through the garage into Villiers Street, but for his need to do so anti-romantically, to prove it, the romance, the love. So he waited until they were in the well-lit vaulted approaches to the footpath of Hungerford Bridge, and then in the middle of a sentence he stopped and turned her towards him, and she was waiting for him and ready and he kissed her and then moved his head to kiss her neck and she put down her handbag and held him to her and he kissed her fully and felt her lips grow warm and knew and gently used his tongue as he ended the kiss to tell her more of him and when she felt him leave go of her she felt she knew his body already, hard and solid, big and hard, and he felt he knew her body already, as well, warm and pliant, smooth and warm.

And he and she had linked arms tightly and naturally and walked off across the Bridge in step, his body and her body complementary, to Waterloo where she was to catch a train to her home in Sutton.

He made her miss one train to catch a later one; then she made him wait for her while she missed the next one; and finally she caught her last train that night; he saw her on to her last train that night.

"There will be other times," she said, Jenny.

"All the other times in the world," he said, Albert.

*   *   *   *   *

We see much more of each other now: at about the same time as I moved up to the Angel, Terry's wife Janine left him and he came back to live with his parents in Clerkenwell.

We have an odd sort of reluctant friendship in which each of us depends on the other for things the other does not really know he is giving. Physically, we are very disparate, but we think the same way about many things: and we were both London kids.

We go out fairly late: after nine, say, and have a few drinks, and then after they close we go searching for various places which stay open all night.

Most usually we head down City Road, then sharp left at Old Street Station, bear right into Great Eastern Street and Commercial Street, down to Whitechapel. Sometimes we stop there at Aldgate for cockles or prawns at Tubby Isaacs', but more often we will go straight on down to Cable Street, and Terry will park this Fiat he runs in Wellclose Square.

Visually, architecturally, Cable Street, Cablestrasse, The Strasse, at night excites us: everywhere we go in this part of Stepney there are Georgian façades in all stages of repair, from the one beautifully-kept house in Wellclose Square to others with skeletal dormers from which the lead and boards have been stripped. There are bomb-derelict warehouses, too, one with a thick first-storey drawbridge suspended from chains above a gulf.

But we really come down Cable Street because of the allnight cafés, because there we can always be sure of something going on that may possibly help to distract us. We can, most of all, be sure of no one interfering with us. We can just stand or sit in any of the cafés, and talk and look. There must be cafés for ten or a dozen nationalities— Maltese, West Indians, Somalis, West Africans, Turkish and Greek Cypriots, and so on—and we usually go in a West Indian or a Somali one. There's always a jukebox with their own pop music in it. One particular one we like has a dicegame on the ground floor and a club underneath it. Another has a football game we can play for sixpence. The Strasse has a reputation for all sorts of vice: but we never see much, and would be disappointed if we were merely tourists seeking it.

No, Cable Street for us is a place to come to remind us that other people are suffering life when most of London seems dead. It is, too, a place for outcasts, misfits, where we feel something in common, however else we differ.

Mostly we talk about women: and mostly about this cow Janine who's done Terry down, as Jenny did me down. This is the chief bond between us: as we have this need to talk and equally as we have this need to listen.

But we also talk about teaching, for instance, for he still teaches over at some grammar at Sidcup near where he used to live with her. We compare his experience with mine, so totally dissimilar though we teach only a few miles apart. And we talk about how education is so desperately old-fashioned, of such very low productivity, and of the waste, the waste, and of the ineffectual cosiness of our colleagues, of the other teachers, and of what we would ideally do in education. This breeds such frustration in us that in revolt, in desperation almost, we become like delinquent teachers in going to places like the Strasse and doing various other things (or thinking about doing them) which would blight our laughable teaching careers if they were known.

Anyway, we talk, we listen and watch, several nights a week. And I'll suddenly want to see some building or other, and off we will go in the Fiat, Terry talking perhaps, me listening and looking at the architecture on the way, or playing solo pontoon with car numbers. That's how it so often is. I'll say I want to see Wren's Observatory at Greenwich Park again, and we go: to find the Park is shut at that time of night, but we have a marvellous prospect across London by night. And to all sorts of other places we go on these night journeys, for all sorts of reasons, or non-reasons, or for no reasons, having coffee occasionally at anywhere we happen to find open: to save the loneliness, the oneness, of being in bed alone at night, for each of us.

There is a very good Greek Cypriot place about equidistant from Terry's and mine, up the Liverpool Road, and we often end up there. Georgiou seems to have a different waitress every time we go in: they get the sack if they won't sleep with him. They're never Cypriot girls, either, and we kid him about this, saying they all go about in total black as soon as they're sixteen, as though in mourning for a lost innocence. Georgiou's place has a steep flight of wooden steps down to it from the street, covered by an awning, and the outside walls have a vitriolite crazy mosaic all over them, shiny pastel colours and black. Inside, the walls have murals which incongruously incorporate the room's projections and abutments. Terry thinks they picture something like a decadent nineteenth-century Bari. I don't quite know what he means by this, as with a number of his remarks: they, like himself, are sort of offset to reality, as mine are, too, but it's a different offset. Anyway, one of the noble heads reminds me of Robert Graves, and there are Norman-type castles, and some blocks of what look like modern flats but which might equally be Roman *insulæ*.

Georgiou sells marvellous Turkish coffee, and great *shish-kebab*—flat, floury envelopes of bread stuffed with spitted veal, chopped onion, parsley, and tomato, with a segment of lemon to squeeze into it. We usually, almost as a ritual, have a coffee and a *kebab* each, and play the jukebox, which has mostly Greek popular music in it. Sometimes we will also have a *paklava*, or a *kataifi*, or a *galatopoureko*, to finish with, and play on the fruit machines

Georgiou has in the little barrel-vaulted room which forms a crosspiece to the longer shape of the main one. *ΑΠΑΓΟΡΕΥΕΤΑΙ Ο ΧΟROS—COSMAS* it warns, and perhaps fortunately we rarely feel like dancing anyway.

The curtains of the window beside the counter are always left undrawn to reveal a section of the wooden steps outside: this is Georgiou's private legshow, to which he is very partial.

So there we sit, Terry and I, in this eighteenth-century cellar, while the smart hairy Cypriot boys preen and look arrogantly in the mirrors, Londoners like us.

And we talk, talk, talk, talk, talk. As though it could make some difference.

*   *   *   *   *

You all must have been told about God in previous R.I. lessons with your own teacher, you must have talked about God as though it was certain that he existed, as though his existence was a fact. I want this morning briefly not to question the existence of God—the law wouldn't approve of my doing that in any case in this classroom—but I do want to ask some questions about a few of the things which follow from accepting, as we do, of course, in this classroom, that there is a God.

You have all been taught, for instance, that God is good, that God is love: yet from your own experience, limited as it is to your own twelve or thirteen years of life, you must all have seen that this is hardly likely to be true, or, if it is true at all, true only in a very special and in a very limited way. How can you think that God is good when you learn in History lessons about terrible wars which have killed thousands of people, and made thousands more, and even millions more, suffer? Some of which wars, like the Crusades, have been undertaken in God's name? If God created everything, must he not then have created war, as well? And disease, too, and suffering, and death, and poverty, and all the unpleasant things in the world? Can such a God be called good, then, can such a God be called the God of *love*? Perhaps only when he is being good, perhaps only when he is being loving?

You have been told, too, that he is a God who knows everything: *omniscient* is the word we use to mean 'knows everything', *om – ni – sci – ent*, it's a Latin word. I'll put it on the board. But does God know everything? *Everything*? Does he really? Everything that's going on, everything that there is? Does he know, for instance, how many specks of chalkdust there are on the board? Or in this classroom? Or in the school? Or in the whole world? And why should he be interested, anyway, in how many specks of chalkdust there are?

All these are really questions about what sort of a God he is, then, assuming, as we do, that he does exist; they are questions about what we can know about him. Is there any reason why he should not be a bad God, for instance, an evil God, if he made all the evil things in the world too? Do you think that he might actually have made a mess of creating the world, and that the bad things were mistakes he couldn't put right? Even if he was capable of thinking up the idea of creating the world, does that mean as well that he was capable of actually doing it? What if he saw that he'd bitten off more than he could chew, and

then just gave up the world as a bad job—or a bad joke—
and went off to try to do better somewhere else? Yet if he
is capable of better, why didn't he do it on earth? Perhaps
some of you know how, if you make a bad job of something,
then you hate it and everything connected with it. Is that
how God feels about us, and about the world? And has
he just deserted us, left us to get on as best we can in his
mess? Has he just gone away? Gone off in disgust, perhaps,
if not in hatred, to somewhere else, just not interested any
more in us? Or perhaps he is dead—how do we know that
he couldn't die, that he didn't die, that he couldn't be
dead?

You cannot, I cannot, no one can *know*, truly *know*, the
answers to these questions. What is certain is that you are
here on this earth and that there are some good things and
some bad things, and that you enjoy the good things and
that you suffer the bad things. This is what is called the
human predicament, or the human condition, or the human
situation. 'Predicament', 'condition', and 'situation', in
this case are all words which mean something like 'fix',
'jam', 'awkward position'. And being human as you all are
means that you are in this 'awkward fix' of enjoying the
good things whilst at the same time having to suffer the
bad things, whether or not anyone or any God created it.
Whether or not, remember, whether or not.

Faced with this human situation, then, what do you do?
What can you do? The main thing is to behave with dignity, dignity: human dignity is your greatest refuge, your
greatest comfort. *Accept* the human situation, do not go
blaming the bad things on to God, or, equally, thanking
him for the good things; accept that fire burns you and
that stone is hard when you run up against, come into
contact with, either of them, accept that wom . . . that

other people are treacherous to you and hurt you: and remember that fire is good for warmth, for instance, and pavements for walking on, and other people—often the same people—are also kind and warm and loving sometimes. You can accept it all with dignity, dignity, the greatest, the most godlike, of all human qualities. You can accept responsibility for everything, but absolutely everything, that happens to you: for who else is there to do so?

And call nothing human, inhuman: this man in the papers who cut up his wife and sent her in bits through the post to her relatives, for instance, is not inhuman. How could his actions, being those of a human being, be called inhuman? They are encompassed by humanity, they even have a comic side to them, and the comic goes a long way towards making up for anything. He did no harm to you, did he, nor to me? What unthinking people mean by calling him 'inhuman' is really that he offended against the best in humanity, that he failed to achieve the good, the best, of which humanity is capable. But he's still a human being, in the same condition as you are, in the same condition as I am. He lost his dignity, you could say of him and of his actions, he could not accept the suffering with dignity: and that is perhaps the lowest state of humanity, that is certainly a crime against humankind.

In the end, all you are left with is the dignity of humankind.

You have heard me ask a great many questions this morning, and heard me give one answer. You must go away and think about what I have said for yourselves. Some of my questions may seem silly to you, some may not even seem to be real questions at all, to you. What you must not do is to think that these *are* real questions and yet still think you know anything about God. In other words, don't let there be a difference between what you believe because you have been told it, and what you have seen and felt for yourselves. Whether you decide there is or is not a God, or whether you refuse to decide, face up to being human, to being in the human predicament, and accept with dignity everything, but everything, that happens to you in any way whatsoever.

And think, tomorrow morning when you're singing the hymn in assembly, think what the words *mean*, and whether you believe them to be true: and, if you do not believe them to be true, then think why you are singing them.

*   *   *   *   *

They had had to walk on the third day, but by then they had arrived: to Fishguard it had been easy, a lucky straight hitch, and then the boat to Cork with a night's loving and sleeping in a cabin that was like their first home, transitory as it was; then walking through the coldmorning city, and three lifts to Tralee by way of Macroom and Killarney; and finally, on that third day, the walking north after a bus to Dingle.

They had had rain about three o'clock, when they were walking along an unmetalled road parallel to the sea. There had been mountains like hooded Fathers rising to their south, and a sea like tarnished hammered pewter in Brandon Bay to their north. This had been the first rain they had had on the whole journey from London, and they felt that to complain about it would have been ungrateful.

Lead-underbellied clouds had come from the north-west, had cut off up to the haunches the purple mountains and had foreshortened the horizon. They had brought umbrellas, firstly as a gimmick for lifts, but then they had been glad to use them seriously.

They had decided that it would be as well to pitch their tent at the first place suitable, because of the set-in rain, rather than go on farther eastwards as they had at first intended. They had come down a path towards a lough and had turned inland along it: everywhere the land had been sodden and marshy, with peat digs here and there. They had walked about a mile alongside the lough without finding a large enough area of firm grass, drinking water from the bitter lough to ease unusual thirsts, before they had decided to turn back towards the sea. A stream had led out of the lough, down through striated rocks, and amongst these rocks they had found a small area of thick, close grass, green as spring, as unexpected as if it had been a hotel, and more welcome, where they had set their camp. When they were warm and comfortable they had realised that their love had come through its most severe trying yet: that miserable walk in the heavy rain with no know-ledge of where they would that night sleep.

The lower slopes of the mountains at their backs had been enforested, the regular patterns of the plantations counterpointing the wildness of the summits' outlines against the sky. From the skin of earth and grass had protruded enormous rock outcrops, red like contusions when the sun in the evening had fallen upon them.

They had spent six days at this place, which had no name on their maps: but they had called it Balgy, for no reason other than that it had come to them, Balgy. They had built a kitchen area protected by rocks, and dug a pit in which to bury their detritus, and had defined an area where they could comfortably and civilisedly defecate, and had found a thicket where they could collect wood for a fire.

Gneiss had been exposed in two great slabs at acute angles, the fault cut wider by the stream, the sides showing glacial striation. They had sketched the mountains, and had talked, had cooked and eaten enormous meals, and had never been as close. They had designed and drawn a house to be built for them over this stream, founded on the gneiss, inspired by Frank Lloyd Wright but more beautiful than his *Falling Water*, they had thought, and they had called it *Above the Fault*.

On the ninth day they had left their Balgy, regretfully, and had walked eastwards to Tralee, twenty miles in that one day, on that warm day, and with heavy packs: and this journey and its physical exhaustion had drawn them the closest they were ever to be, for its length. Well before they had reached London they had both known that they had passed the pitch of their loving.

THREE: Development

The Fight

One day of last term I had a fight with a second year boy, quiet by accident I threw a stone and caught him on his head, I at once apologised but this wasnt enough for him he struck me, I hit back and hurt my fist. After the fight was over I went down the hospital and had a brocken finger, my arm was put in plaster. And next day the boy laughed at me so I hit him on the head with my plaster and squirted ink from my pen onto his face and went to my form room and I was sent to mr. Harrison and he made us be friends and from that day on we were friends. Next day we had a friendly fight and I busted is nose. FIN

A Night Out

The night was cold, with slight patches of fog or mist surrounding the city. As the night drew on rime formed on the back street roads, there was too much traffic on the main roads for frost to form.

My friend Jim and I went for a ride on a bus to New Oxford Street, after looking in the shop windows we went round to the "Moulin Rouge", it was not open so we went for a walk around the back streets, such as Drury Lane and Grape Street. After walking back to Bloomsbury Square we got on a bus, in this three Greeks or Italians were sitting next to two girls, one turned round and licked his lips, I don't know what he meant but when most of the people had left he started kissing her.

When we got off I got a dirty look from one of the men, I think it was because I kept on looking at them in the bus.

We saw that same woman with another man a few nights later and I made my own conclusion from that. She was a prostitute Many people do those sort of things, Just for a kick, and it is on the increase. Now, instead of the girls walking the street, they stand on doorsteps, or the doors of night clubs, some even stand on their own step! Most people who do those things are between twenty and forty. Teenagers do it for nothing!

What a scrap.

One day as my mates and I were coming home from a long game of football we all stopped to buy an ice-cream. As we waited our turn at the van we saw some toughs walking towards us. Mind out the way so we can get our ice-creams first they said. Why should we, we all said. And in reply they said "Because we said so. "Oh move along you bunch of jungle bunnies," as most of them were darkies. The ice-cream man laughed at this remark. "What did you call us," they said. "Jungle Bunnies," we answered. You ought to get you're ear-oles cleaned. You might be able to hear better. As soon as we had said this the toughs charged us. I landed a punch on an on-running darkie which made his nose even more flat. I then turned round to see how my mates were getting on. They were doing okay as I see one punch one of the toughs in the eye. The bundle went on for quite a while. All the time the ice-cream man was laughing his head off. "What do you think you're laughing at," I said. At that moment everybody stopped fighting. We all started throwing stones and anything in hands reach. We then after made friends with the toughs.

The Killer Master

On the first day back from the holidays we had a new French teacher, he had a sort of a dull look with spec's hanging over his nose. When he first took us for french I hated his guts. He set lots of homework, and if he did not get the homework he had a size ten slipper with which he applied maximum pain. When he was puting work on the Blackboard for us to do we used to fire ink pellets at his back. At the end of the lesson his back was covered in ink. For this he called us all back one night and asked who fire them. A deadly Huss fell over the class as he walked up and down the gang ways. Suddenly the boy behind me said something to the boy next to him. The Master in a deadly rage got hold of the boy by his hair, and dragged him to the front of the class where he brutally hit him the boy fell to the floor moaning then master kicked him, the class by then were shouting their heads off. With that he walked out of the class and that was the last we ever saw of him

*　*　*　*　*

"2. The Development of the Gothic Style seen as an Immanent Process. The improvement of Romanesque groin-vaults came about as a result of a rational consideration of the geometric construction of the arches and the surfaces of the cells; the building technique employed, that is, the centering; their statics, both during and after construction; and also the economic problems which they presented. But all these considerations always went hand in hand with the aim of producing an aesthetically satisfying result. The changes had nothing to do with the Crusades, which began only

later, or with the liturgy, or with philosophy. The architects were intent simply upon making necessary improvements. As far as can be reconstructed, this was a process of trial and error which led to the replacement of diagonal, wooden centering arches by the stone cintre permanent, *that is the rib.*

Here, the question must indeed have arisen as to whether the architectural patrons of this time, the clergy, were in agreement with the introduction of this innovation; but this question can be ignored for the moment. The development which was described in the first part of this book shows that the rib-vault, in its turn, was further improved by a combination of rational considerations and aesthetic criticism, which resulted in the introduction of pointed arches, first over the four sides of each bay, and finally in the diagonals also. This process, too, was an im-

manent, or an internal one. Just as master-masons did not determine the form of the liturgy or indulge in metaphysics, so the clergy did not build scaffolding, or draw designs for arches or for the profiles of ribs. These are different spheres, different jobs, requiring special skills, and it need hardly be said that no amount of knowledge of metaphysics can help one to build a rib-vault, and that on the other hand the ability of an architect to build a vault cannot help him to decide whether general . . ."

——No, but I will do!

——. . . then he came round to my place and you know what my Dad is, I mean, he wouldn't . . .

——Rah!

——. . . than I thought it would be, just went in easy like, and . . .

Get out! Out! What d'you mean by coming into my class and making such a hell of a row? Eh? Eh! Get out and line up outside, and be dead quiet until I tell you

Damn! Knew I shouldn't have started another section. Bloody sharp on the breaks here. Not a minute over all the week.

to come in. DEAD quiet,
d'you understand?
——Albie'll 'ave t' go if 'e's
goin' t' be like this all the
time, 'e'll 'ave t' go!
——'E's got 'ead on 'im like
a side of bacon, en 'e?
I said QUIET! QUIET!
You! What was that about
bacon?
——Nothing.
Well whatever it was,
keep it for later.
——Albert's got new suedes
on.
——Cor, dig them broffel-
creepers!

Marvellous phrase. Try not to laugh.

That's enough!
——No, but I will do.
Right, you, once more
and you'll get thumped.
——You ent allowed to 'it
kids.
And you're not allowed
to talk when I tell you not to.
You break rules, and then so
shall I.

Perfect answer. But works only once, usually. Next time?

Right. Now file in
quietly and sit down. Without talking!

——No, but I will do.

All right, little one, come out here. You did hear me say 'no talking', didn't you?

I asked you a question! Did you hear me say 'no talking'?
——No, but I w... oh! You ent sposed to 'it kids on the 'ead!

Just go and sit down and don't let me hear another word from you unless I ask for it. And what's your name? What's your name! name!
——Langley.
Langley.

——'E'll 'ave to go, then, them suedes 'n' all, the lot!
Right, settle down, I

Stupid truculence. Have to hit him now.

⌐Eyes narrowly, skin very white, hands just like trotters and dirty, nicotine-stained.⌐

All violence rebounds on society. He'll take it out on another kid. Or on something.

But what hurt did I just now pass on? It must stop somewhere, but why with me? Or is there a constant quantity of violence in the world, continually circulating?

know it's the last lesson of the day and you can't wait to get home, but first you're going to listen very carefully to a Geology lesson. What's Geology? Langley? Anyone else?

——It's to do with dirt and stones and stuff like that.

Yes, that's nearly right. Geology is the study of earth and stones and everything that goes to make up the world except for the living things like plants and animals. And ourselves. Have you learnt anything about this subject before?

——No.

——No.

——Don't want to now.

——No.

Not in Geography lessons? Nothing at all?

Then I'll have to start right from the beginning. You all know what stone is, and that there are different

Nor can I, for that matter.

Thick. Or resentful. And. Can't get any response today. Either. Haven't tried very hard. Guilt. But tiredness. C-stream, too, christ knows what the H-stream must be like!

Even that assuming too much? Cynical, cynical.

sorts of stone—you can see that in the houses you live in: there's the slate on the roof, and the stone of the window cills and the doorstep, and some of you may have marble mantelpieces, and the bricks are made of clay, which is really very tiny pieces of stone mixed up with other things that I'll tell you about in due course. Coal is yet another kind of stone. All these different sorts of stones came from underneath the ground—that is, from underneath the grass and earth. In some places the stone sticks out of the earth and only has to be cut or broken off to be used, but in other places men have to dig or quarry for it. Anyone seen a quarry when they've been on holiday in the country?

No? Well, next time you do go out of London keep your eyes open for quarries. Anyway, when you look at the country you see that most of it is covered

More likely Coade round here, or some other composition.

Nóthing. This class is a nothing.

And I'm a nothing teacher.

with grass and soil. But this is only a thin topcoat, like the skin on a rice-pudding, say, while underneath lies rock, solid rock.

——Give me that rice-pudding rock, daddy-o.

Quick enough when they want to be. Then the teaching has been at fault. Mine must not be.

Right, joke over. In Geography you must have been told of all the different kinds of countryside there are in Great Britain—mountains, barren heaths, uplands, wide fertile plains— and the importance of Geology is that each of these regions, and the others . . .

Sentence getting tortuous.

The reason why each region is different from the others is because of the different kind of rock or stone which lies underneath the soil, where there is soil, that is.

Too simple for fourteen-year-olds? Can't be if they've never done any before. Constant problem.

Now, Geology is a science, and in the sciences one of our chief methods of going about things is by classification. That is to say, we put things in order, we make them tidy, by grouping them into their different kinds. Take out your rough notebooks, and copy down the following different sorts or classes of rocks.

Aristotle.

And you can do it without talking!

They don't like that. Means they'll have to work.

How I hate this perpetual nagging. Ninety percent of teaching is nagging. Someone won't have a pencil.

——Mr. Albert, I need a new roughbook.

Thick, virginal, sensuous pile of new books. A small pleasure.

Here.
Now, has everyone got a pencil? Or something to . . . with which to write?

Amazing. Now what to say next, no respite?

Put the heading 'Geology' just as I'm spelling it on the board.
Now, different sorts of

stone have different ages, and I'm going to start with the oldest. The earth was once a ball of flame, its surface a mass of material so hot that we can hardly imagine it. The sun is like this today, and the centre of the earth is, too. The heat was so great that it melted . . .

——'Ow does 'e know about the sun and the middle of the earth? 'As 'e bin there?

True, how do I bloody well know? Might have been a ball of shit for all I know, a ball of stinking shit. So? You don't have to believe in anything to teach it?

. . . the rocks so that . . . Just be quiet and listen, for the moment, and you'll have a chance to ask questions later.

To which I shall be pleased to invent answers.

Now, this heat was so enormous that it melted the rocks, it made them so hot that they flowed like water. You've all seen solder when it's melted, the way it flows, well that's what happened to the rocks of the earth, in the beginning . . .

Biblical. And who said that was the beginning anyway?

Now, those rocks which were melted in this way are the oldest, and as they gradually cooled they set into shapes that . . .

These rocks we call igneous rocks, the oldest ones that were once very hot, in the beginning. Igneous is a word which means 'fiery'. So copy down this word igneous and the number 'one' against it.

This is the first class of rocks, the igneous rocks, which were formed by great heat many millions of years ago—about five thousand million years ago, scientists seem to think. So copy all this down, now.

It's about bloody time they gave us something less primitive than blackboard and chalk.

Right, Langley, why are you talking again? As soon as my back is turned you talk.

I ought to clobber him again. They'll think I'm weak if I don't. But don't want to hit him. So shan't.

Just get on with what you were told to do. How

far have you got? Get on with it!

Igneous, igneous, 'ideous rocks.

You haven't done much.

⌐ *Soft, starched collar, bitten nails, squat.* ⌐

You haven't even started!
——Ent got no pencil.

⌐*Hair fine, saffron mist, neck scarred.* ⌐

I asked ten minutes ago whether you all had something to write with! Go out and get one from my desk.
Why can't you get on? Laziness!

⌐*Eyes like grapes, mouth a melon segment.* ⌐

——'E'll 'ave t' go.
What was that?
——I'll 'ave t'go to the toilet. Please, sir, Mr. Albert?
No. Wait.

They always ask twice if they really want to.

Now: have you all done that? Come on then!
Now what makes igneous rocks different from the other sorts? How can you specially tell? Well, first of all, igneous rocks are very hard, very hard indeed. And they are often shiny, as well, if you break a piece and look

at a surface that has not been made dull by the weather. This is because igneous rocks are made up of crystals, which are shiny themselves, lots of crystals of all different sizes. The sorts of crystals in each different igneous rock . . .

Doubt if anyone is following. My fault. Know what I want to say, but haven't prepared the lesson well enough to say it effectively. Guilt. But if all my spare time spent preparing lessons shouldn't have time for designing. And I am after all an architect, not a teacher, a creator, not a passer-on.

. . . make the difference between each sort. That is, some have crystals like felspar, mica, or quartz . . .

Useless. Abandon it.

Right now. I've given you two ways you can tell igneous rocks—they're very hard, and they're shiny when you break them. Now who can tell me the name of an igneous rock? Come on, think. Think.
——Sarfend Rock?

Quite funny.

And your name? Name!
——Gloria Stenning.

Please don't speak again unless you put up your hand and are asked to speak.

Bathos! Stock response— just bloody ludicrous. They should have laughed more. Don't tell you how to teach a class like this. At least, they tell you it is ultimately the Head's responsibility, you can go to him. But what if the Head doesn't give a damn? Didn't back my authority yesterday when I sent a boy to him.

——No, but I will do!

Langley again. This must be a stock phrase, one he trots out hopefully. Perhaps it once made kids laugh. Once in twenty times it will be hilarious: that's the time, that once, I've got to watch out for.

Friend Langley . . .

The shock approach.

. . . stuffit!
——Oooh, Mr. Albert sir!
——Oooh!
——You try!
——No, but I will do!
——Ooh, and he's supposed to be a teacher, too.

Not supposed to be human if you're a teacher.

Lesson appalling. For cris-sake pull it together.

Right! If you don't settle down and listen you'll find yourselves here after school until six o'clock.

The only sanction that may have some effect.

——You can't keep kids in more than half an hour.
——It's a rule.
——The L.C.C. says so.

The bastards know it all!

Can't I keep you in? Just watch me! And I've already explained that if you break rules, then so shall I.

Some effect.

Now: igneous rocks. I asked you if you knew the names of any rocks which were very hard and shiny.
——Sir?

⌐Indian, thin face, oiled hair, intelligent eyes. ⌐

Yes?
——Is one of them granite, sir?

Yes, indeed, granite is one of them. That's the one I was hoping most of you would know. What's your name?
——Navin Bhatia, sir.

Very good, Bhatia. How many of you others had

heard of granite? Come on, don't be lazy, put your hands up if you'd ever heard the word before.

A dozen of them.

 I'm surprised at you not having heard of granite before, Langley. After all, your head's made of it.
——Ha. Ha.

Sarcasm, least effective and most vicious weapon, they tell you. But least easy to avoid, and most enjoyable.

 Well, those of you who had heard of granite now know that it is a rock formed by intense heat many millions of years ago. You can see granite very often in London, because many buildings, especially big public buildings like banks and some offices, are faced with it. That is, a thin layer of granite is used to cover the brick or nowadays ferro-concrete structure. We call this thin facing layer 'ashlar'.

Illegitimately: form should be honest, should be honestly exposed.

 Granite can be polished to a very high, shiny, that is, finish, and it is found in many different colours. In some places it is almost white, in others it is all shades of grey, green, a kind of blue, pink, deep red, brown and black. There's a particularly lovely grey-blue one which comes from Penmaenmawr in North Wales, which is . . .

Irrelevant.

Another place you can often see granite in all sorts of different colours is in cemeteries, where, because it is . . .

——Ooh!

——Eerh!

——You bin wandrin' round any cemeteries lately?

——My dad just 'ad wood.

——'E's right orf it.

Ignore. Louder.

. . . because granite is such a very hard stone I suppose people think their names cut in it will last that much longer.

Bloody stupid remark. Must go over and see Zulf and his fearful cemetery this week.

But granite is not the only igneous rock, though it is the most commonly used one . . . .

Definite evidence for that remark? None. Never mind.

There are some places where the crystals that go to make up igneous rocks are found in more or less pure states, where you get layers or seams or strata of almost pure quartz, or felspar or mica. Then, too, there are different impurities which give you different sorts of igneous rock. Two of these other sorts are basalt and gneiss. Basalt and gneiss: spelt like . . .

——Basil is nice?

Name? What's your name? You! I know it was you! And stand up! Name?

——Stenning.

You can't hold your tongue any more than your female namesake over here, can you?

——She's my sister.

You don't look like twins.

——We're not twins.

Oh.

Don't make stupid remarks,

On.

I'll get that fucking kid and beat . . . No, I won't.
⌐*Orange sweater, over-grown it, flopping hair, un-washed look, twists lips.*⌐

What a bloody stupid, trite, readymade euphemism!

Two in the same year? Have to be bloody quick off the mark to get two in the same year. Must have been got at as soon as she'd had the first.

Stenning, or you'll find yourself in trouble.
——Ha-ha-ha.

*Pointless threat. Deserved
derision. Just look at them
threateningly.*

Basalt and gneiss. This
g is silent as in gnat. So now
we know three igneous
rocks: granite, basalt, and
gneiss, all of which were
formed by the action of heat
at a very early stage in the
earth's history.

*Sheer bloody repetition of
teaching gets me. Once I've
learnt something I want to
go on, I want to build on it,
not go on repeating it.*

Granite is the only one
used widely as a building
material. In an unpolished
state it is used for kerbs and
gutters. The kerbs and gutters of the street outside are
made of granite. Basalt is
often too hard to use for
building, and is chiefly
known for the spectacular
natural effects it creates
at the Giant's Causeway
in Northern Ireland, for
instance, and at Fingal's
Cave on the island of Staffa
in Scotland. Anyone ever

Is it?

been to either of these places? No? The composer Mendelssohn wrote a well-known piece of music, an overture, called after Fingal's Cave. Perhaps I'll play a record of it to you in a music lesson when we next have one. Well, as the basalt in these places cooled it split into interesting shapes: regular shapes. Into hexag ... into six-sided columns.

Gneiss is hardly used at all in building, mainly because it is laminated or foliated. That is, it is made up of thin layers which fairly easily split apart. Not that it isn't hard, however, for it is, but its strength lies only one way. You could build a house on gneiss, however, if the layers went the right way.

Above the Fault, Falling Water, Balgy, Jenny, oh Jenny!

Now: I happen to have with me a piece of gneiss, that I brought back with me from the west of Ireland, and I'm going to pass it round the class now so that you can see what it looks like. This was part of a huge outcrop of gneiss and I knocked this piece off it as a sort of souvenir, you might say . . .

——Albie's knocked off some ice . . .

Quiet! Quiet! When it comes to you, feel how hard it is, and you can see the crystals glinting in it, and you can see the layers as well. You won't be able to split any off, though, as the piece is too small to get enough leverage on it. Right, until the piece comes to you, get on with writing down from the board these three types of igneous rock, and against each one write down what you can remember of what I've said about it.

Which isn't much. But a respite for me. Sit down.

We came back from collecting wood, yes, dragging branches over the peat and turf, and reached our place by the fault just after rain began, laughing as we ran

the last stretch, and fell in-
side the spread entrance of
the tent. Soft filtered light,
unnaturally green through
the light canvas. Out of
breath, leaving the firewood
out in the rain, and we made
love, beautifully, suddenly;
remember Jenny's almost-
closed eyes and the half-
caught intense sounds she
made, and the way she held
me within her, and the way
I surpassed myself in pleas-
ing her, and she, me. And—
oh god!—we ran out naked
as we were into the rain and
down into the deep pool
below the fault and swam
the four and a half strokes
there were room for again
and again and—oh god,
how every thought of Jenny
hurts, how such pleasure
has now become such pain,
in the remembering, yet is
still pleasure, the greatest I

——No, but I will do!

ever, the pleasure and the
pain inextricably together!
Shouting and holding each
other, so close. So close, and
running around in the rain,
laughing that we would dry

——Shush!

——Albie'll 'ear you!

——Not 'im—'e's miles away.

——'E's got that dozy look.

——Dreamy Albie.

——Ma family? You bin sayin' fings about ma famly?

——I'll get you, just you wait!

——Watch it, cocker, or you'll be 'avin' a visit from the Corps.

——I'm terrified.

——Read it out to 'er.

——No, shush, Albert'll see it.

——I don't care. 'E wouldn't get it off me anyway.

——The Corps . . .

——Go on, read it, ent it funny . . .

What the hell d'you

ourselves, and seeing, needing, once more, and making love again, this time on that just-yielding bed of grass, this time laughing where the other was serious, this time lingering and drawn where the first was swift and compulsive, this time so conscious, civilised, where the first was natural, uncontrolled, this time so lastingly satisfying where the first was immediately fulfilling. Ah, Jenny, oh god, god, god! My love, that's it, my love, you can never go back, that high, yet how I miss it! The love! Singular, only, only one, the love, the love. Not so much her, Jenny, but the love, for there were— were there?—bad things— weren't there?—about her I don't miss. But do I, were they part of the love? They must have been, yes, all part of the love, part of the pain and the pleasure and the joy, the joyous in the rain. and the suffering . . . Bloody noise!

mean by making so much noise! Silence! You, there, what's on that piece of paper that you find so irresistibly funny?

Up, get it. Up, certainly, got a stand on, no bloody wonder . . .

——Oh, Albie's got lead in 'is pencil.

Give it to me!

Girl, my grip is a hundred times yours so don't struggle. Give it to—give me that piece of paper!

Thank you.

"Jeanette Parsons, 3C. When I was young I had no sence I took a girl behind the frence I gave her a shilling she was willing I gave her a pound she laid on the ground. I gave her a spack she open her prat and there I planted my union Jack."
Not even funny. Except about the flag. Very few spelling errors, though.

Kind of you to put your name on it, Jeanette Parsons. I suppose you're proud of it, are you? Stand up.

⌐Bottle-red, good teeth, not wearing bra.↲ Not the same girl I took it from.

And the girl who was reading this? What's your name?
——Lily Stanley.

⤳Hooked nose, thin hair, eyes watering.⤙ Don't know how some parents can name so badly. Repeating terminal sounds.

Well, Jeanette Parsons and Lily Stanley, I shall report this affair to the Headmaster.
——Ooooh, I'm frightened!

Who will do fuck-all about it.

Just SHUT UP!
Now, has everyone looked at the piece of gneiss, the stone I sent round? Who's got . . . who has it at the moment?

Here! I was a silly bastard to let these thieving sods get their hands on it.

I asked a question! Who has the stone I sent round?

Not bloody funny, that stone is practically the only thing I have tangible of Jenny, she hardly ever wrote me letters, there was no occasion to, we saw each other so often.

Please don't let's play games like little children,

children's games. Who's got
my stone?
——Albert's got 'is 'ard up.
——Just for 'is bleedin'
stone.
Right! I'm just not
messing about with chil-
dren. And I certainly don't
want to punish the infant
who is playing games. I'm
going outside the door for
just long enough for someone to bring out the stone
and put it my desk. If it's
not there when I come back,
then we're in for a long session tonight. I doubt if any
of you will get home before
dark. You'll miss a lovely
summer's evening. Unless
my stone is on that desk
within one minute from
now!

Not fucking much.

*Cold, just as they say, anger.
Jenny's stone, my stone,
from Balgy, nice gneiss she
kept on calling it, gnice
neiss, so sweetly the words
became a poem, for me, a
love-poem, and the piece
broken for the two of us,
one part each, for her, for
me, a mistake to break it, a*

mistake, a symbol, a symbolic mistake, like so many others. All the others.

What will I do if they don't give it back? They'll certainly be kept in. But I want to get off myself very smartly tonight to see Terry. I could search them all. Not the girls. That means I would have to call in a woman teacher. No. Oh, the bastards!

Give them twenty seconds more.

Right!

The repetitious right or wrong. Thank the christ, it's there, covered in ink, but there. Wipe it carefully with blotting-paper, I must wash it when I get home, salve it, though wash off her touch, kiss, on my stone, our stone, the only stone, the only thing I have left, my Jennystone.
They're all expecting me to make some comment. The bastards,   the . . . waste. Waste. Snap.

Igneous rocks in Great Britain are mainly found in the Highlands of Scotland, the Lake District, North Wales, and in the moorland areas of Devon and Cornwall. Thus these areas represent geologically the oldest parts of the country, as far as we can tell. But long after the formation of these rocks the world became very cold—why, we don't really know—and large parts of it were covered with ice, great icesheets and huge glaciers. Glaciers are great masses of ice which fill whole valleys and move slowly towards the sea. Now, all except the southern part of Britain was covered in this ice at this time—it was about a million years ago, and is called the Pleistocene Age—but not London, that is, the ice . . .

——The Plasticine age?

. . . stopped some miles north of London, and has thus not affected the nature of the country as it has in the areas which were . . .

——Ooooh! You . . .

I shall belt that bastard as hard as I can round the ear. Enjoyably.

... covered with ice. Yes?
You were going to call me
something? To address me?
——What you got such a
temper for, then? Ooooh!　　*Two of them.*

All you have to do at
the moment is to listen.
Then you don't get hurt.

This ice had several
effects. For one, it was of
such enormous weight that
it ground down everything
beneath it; and there were
often mountains covered by
it, that is, it was often so
deep that it covered even
mountains. And it carried
south with it all sorts of
rocks from the northern
parts from which it came.
In this way, you will find
igneous rock, often large
boulders, in areas where
the underlying rock is not
igneous at all. In some areas,
these boulders have often
been used for building—in
Wiltshire, for instance,
which is mainly chalk,
though there the boulders
are of sandstone and are not
igneous. They are called
'sarsens', or, sometimes,

'greywethers', and Stonehenge, for instance, is made of them. The word 'sarsen' means, is the same as, 'Saracen', and was used for many sorts of stranger or foreigner: thus 'sarsens' are strange boulders, ones which are out of place, are not at home, in the place where they are found, having been brought there, as I told you, by the action of glaciers.

Myself, a sarsen amongst dirt and stuff like that.

Right, then, write down these further notes just as I put them on the board.

Got them at last. At last. Not even talking while my back's turned. And my stone comfortingly in my pocket, back again, hell, I don't know what ... But I got it back.

——Thank god for that!

Soddit, there goes the bell! Just as I'd got them.

——Aaah!

——Raaah!

——Fffffh!

——Rah! Rah!

All right, that's enough. Quiet! You can't be more glad than I am that the lesson's over. Put your books away—after finishing the

Wrong order.

sentence you're writing, of course. I'll finish putting up the notes next week.

——Next week's half-term.

I also intend next time to talk about the other classes of rock: sandstone, which is made up of very tiny ... Look, if you want to get home before midnight, you'd better keep quiet!

——You won't keep me in, Albert, boy!

Too tired to fight any more. Ignore.

Sandstone, which is closely compressed grains of sand cemented together naturally, and limestone, which is made up of the shells of millions of former sea-creatures, again highly compressed.

——Huh!

I don't know how far we shall be able to get in Geology. It rather depends on how long Mr. Burroughs is away. But with what ...

——Bunny'll be away a long time, mate, don't you worry about that!

——Yeah.

——A long time.

That's enough for one day

for me, for crissake. Get rid.

Right! That girl there can go. She's been sitting quietly ready to go.

Right. You can all go.
——Rah! Rah!
——Albie'll defenly 'ave t' go, y'know, defenly, just like Bunny.
——Stuffit, stuffit!
——'E's kep' us three minutes more'n 'e should 'ave.
——'Is 'ead is made of gneiss but it ent nice.
——No, but I will do!
——Granny and basil ent nice.
——All that fuss for a bit of stone!
——Up the Corps!
——Stuffit!
——'e's bin sayin' fings about ma famly?
——Rahh!
——If 'e's bin sayin' fings about the Corps 'e'll get one up 'is jacksie.
——Sir, could I ask you a question, please?

Certainly. I'm sorry, I forget your name?

Always makes the others sit up and shut up.
Mistake! Mistake! Soon as I said it! The bastards! Too late to bring them back now. Get them right under from the beginning next time. Try.

And only let them go one at a time, too.

Now where's my pen?

⌐Indian, thin, intelligent eyes.⌐

——Navin Bhatia, sir.

Don't think he's getting at me.

Yes, I'm sorry, Bhatia, yes. What is it you want to ask?

Only one to show some interest. The one they say makes it all worth while. Yes, yet at the same time feel disappointed that I can't dismiss the whole class as bastards.

——I was very interested in this Geology, sir, and I am wondering whether you can recommend any books for further perusal?

Speaks well, and oh so politely.

Yes, certainly I can, Navin, and I'm glad that you're interested. I'll give you a list of some books which you can borrow from the library—the school library may have some of them—is there a school library? Have you seen a pen? A Parker fountain pen, black . . .

Where's my pen?

Using it when this class came in. Making notes from Frankl. Oh, christ, went out of the room! Some bastard has knocked off my pen! Oh, oooorh! Makes me feel ill, ill.

Look, Bhatia, d'you mind if we leave this until tomorrow? I'll give you a list then. Or if your usual teacher comes back then I'll post it to you. I really will.
——I think Mr. Burroughs is likely to be away for some time, sir.
Why?
——He seemed very . . . ill, sir, the last day he was here.
Oh? Well, in that case I may be here a week or more then. Anyway, I'll see you tomorrow or the next time you're due to have me.
——Yes, sir. Thank you, Mr. Albert, sir.

Oh, god, the thought!

Now, make sure my pen's not on the floor. Or any-where else. No. One final look on the table. I didn't leave it in the book, did I— Oh! Fuck! No, fuck the bas-tards, they've spattered it with ink! They've befouled my Frankl! Oh, no, no, no! NO!

*   *   *   *   *

229 SHEPHERDESS WALK
LONDON N.1.

ATTENTION! MR. ALBERT!
   I UNDERSTAND FROM MY DAUGHTER ROBERTA
THAT SHE ASKED PERMISSION TO LEAVE CLASS
ROOM TO GO TO TOILET AND WAS REFUSED.
   PLEASE SEE THAT THIS DOES NOT OCCUR
AGAIN——
   I DONT APPRECIATE THIS ATTITUDE——WAIT-
ING FIVE MINUTES CAN CAUSE UNPLEASANT-
NESS THAT EVEN YOU SHOULD UNDERSTAND.

YOURS FAITHFULLY
J. PROBBIT (MRS).

"Since none but the human ſpecies are properly ſubject to this
menſtrual flux of blood (although there are ſome animals who, at
the time of their vernal copulation, diſtil a ſmall quantity of blood
from their genitals), and ſince the body of the male is always free
from the like diſcharge, it has been a great inquiry in all ages,
what ſhould be the cauſe of this ſanguine excretion peculiar to the
fair ſex? To this effect the attraction of the moon, which is known
to raiſe the tides of the ſea, has been accuſed in all ages; others
have referred it to a ſharp ſtimulating humour, ſecreted in the
genital parts themſelves, the ſame which is the cauſe of venereal
diſeaſe. But if the moon was the parent of this effect, it would
appear in all women at the ſame time; which is contrary to experience, ſince there is never a day in which there are not many
women ſeized with this flux; nor are there fewer in the decreaſe
than the increaſe of the moon. As to any ſharp ferment ſeated in

the uterus or its parts, it will be always inquired for in vain; where there are none but mild mucous juices, and where venery, which expels all thoſe juices, neither increaſes nor leſſens the menſtrual flux; and women deny that, during the time of their menſes, they have any increaſed deſire of venery; ſeeing at that time moſt of the parts are rather pained and languid; and the ſeat of venereal pleaſure is rather in the entrance of the pudendum than in the uterus, from which laſt the menſes flow."

from: *A Syſtem of Anatomy and Phyſio-logy from the Lateſt and Beſt Authors. Arranged as nearly as the nature of the work would admit in the Order of the Lectures delivered by the Profeſſor of Anatomy in the Univerſity of Edinburgh.* 1787. *Volume III, page* 11.

* * * * *

...where she wanted it, she wanted it, and I underneath holding her, and holding her, and holding her, and wanting her, and enormous, and o – o – o – o – o, turning, o – o – o, and it won't, won't, won't, she will, she will, she wants, it, won't, enormous, enormous, again, again, again, again, again, again, again, again, again, o – o – o....
...o – o – o – o – o. White, white. Then blueyellow-white. Pattern, lamp, greenwhite shade, Pollard, Astrophel and Stella, The White Goddess, the sovereign of my,

the white, the suspicious chair, greywhite trousers mine, the cupboard, oh! Damn! Another day! Another white day to waste on school, oh, the day, another until the day to be got through, to be suffered—no! No! Whitsun! No school! Half-term for Whitsun, three heartfelt cheers for the descent of the Holy Ghost on the day of Pentecost! Ah, rest, rest, relax, sleep until two, if I like, courtesy of my mate the Holy Apparition. Whitsun, and no bleeding kids! For this relief much thanks, much thanks!

So: waking again with this enormous tonk on, it ought to be relieved, too tired to last night, but anyway it seems to happen every night, every morning I wake with the most almighty jack. This is not good, I can think of better uses, still it's at least reassuring of my continued potence, no need to resort to Damaroids yet, remember after Jenny smashed me, for three weeks I didn't have a stand, it hits very hard, very deeply, very basically, sexual betrayal does, strikes at the manroot, at the very integrity of a man's self. Aah! There, the first thought of her, of Jenny, for today, no day goes by but that I think of her in some way or another, even though it's four and a half years since, now, four and a half long years of my selfmade hell, though what the hell is hell, it's another of those meaningless words like sin or evil or god. Nor am I out of it.

But just displace her image with the nearest thing, as usual, the nearest thing, long practice over four and a half years makes adequate.

When you drum on the bottom sheet with your tensely arched finger it booms hollow, amplified, to your ear pressed against the pillow. Cavity mattress, resonance, reverberation: drum delicate and interesting rhythms made complex by time-interval, due to the irregular cavity, weight disposition, the interstices between the whatnots,

Johnson, ah, cavity-walls, two skins of brick, rubble-filled, ties.

Today I can spend at my board, working, how marvellous, a whole day free to work, to do real work, my work, real work, vocation. I can put in a really hard day on the arts centre design. Ought really to go in for more competitions. It's the only way to become known, to break out of this destructive teaching, but I'm too lazy: perhaps too afraid, as well, too afraid of failing, of not . . .

. . . but the real satisfaction, even with success, whatever that means, would be in the work itself, as it is now, the real satisfaction, in the work. When I've done something, hewn it from my mind, then when it's actually built does not seem to matter, really, it's an accident, a commercial or economic accident, quite beyond my control.

But first enjoy lying here—what time? twenty past nine —lying this free morning, courtesy of the H.G., all morning if I like, to think as I choose, all the time in the world, time to use, misuse, abuse, self-abuse, time. Time. The great . . . wouldn't it be . . . yes, if you became dissatisfied with time, you'd go mad. Think—yes—if you wanted to catch the 9.31 and the 7.15 trains at the same time, that nothing could satisfy you but doing just that—yes, mad, they'd call you mad, that would be thought to be madness. But quite understandable. Like that old woman last week in Woolworths who asked some teenagers what day it was, and they just laughed at her, they must have thought she was mad, but she was asking, in all seriousness, what day it was, that day, so I told her, yes, it was Sunday, I thought. I was more sure at the time, now I forget what day it was: it might have been Monday, it rhymes with Sunday, I always have been prone to confuse things which rhyme, it's my nature. I choose not to change it. But today I forget what day it was, then, when the old woman had forgotten what day it was: I forget now, she forgot then, the same day, too, and what's the essential difference? Is she mad, was she mad, am I mad now, for forgetting, mad for telling her then, it was Sunday, I thought, on such scanty evidence, and subject to my known proneness? I just think the kids were stupid.

At least she was human in asking help of other humans: sometimes I think Marlene doesn't need other human beings at all. She needs something from me, though. But it's one of those . . . oh, christ, the bloody mess Marlene and that lot made last night still has to be cleared up. Don't want even to look. Still, soon I'll have the strength to get up, ha. Oooooh, last night, teachers are just, mistake to ask them round, I'm just not one of them, nor they one of me.

What do they do on their holidays, other teachers? What are they doing this morning, what's Marlene doing this morning? What's anyone doing this morning, for that matter? There are all these people, out there, in London, say, millions of them, this morning, all doing things, doing things—and I resent them doing things, for mine is the only way to live, mine are the only things worth doing, my doingthings.

Marlene is sleeping, I'm sure, she must have been late home. What a cow she is, staying after the others to make it look as though she was sleeping with me, and then not having any. But she didn't reckon on the last tube. I will not be stuffed in lifts! she says. Where will you be stuffed then, love? I says. Must tell Terry that. But a cow: I don't mind anyone suspecting I have women here, but it must be with absolute cause. Ah, why do I lust after Marlene? This is our Miss Crossthwaite, P.E. mistress, comes from

Yorkshire, y'know. It's her big tits, her lovely big tits, that's what I lust after, in the first place, anyway, oh let me rest my weary hands on your lovely big tits, Miss Crossthwaite, P.E. mistress, ours from Yorkshire, y'know.

Scott is a big tit, too, a big tit, though I've no wish to rest anything on him. I buy pop records, he says, for sociological reasons. And I listen to them because I like them, I says. Shocking, I think they found that, slightly. But they do too, really, only they won't admit it. Fascinating sociological study—balls! A load of old balls.

And Davison, too, the free liver. And I'm a floating kidney.

How do I get myself into these situations? Lust for the Marlenes of this world. Don't feed 'er, Mrs. Crossthwaite, you're overdoing it. And after last night lust isn't worth it. I shall continue to admire, my dear Miss Crossthwaite, your astonishingly big tits, but from well out of armsreach, the while frustrating myself with phantasies.

I hate these women who only want bits of me. I offer her the enormous totality of me, and she says, yes, I'll have the conversation bit, and the company bit, but not the bed bit, nor even the handsonmybigtits bit. I hate the partial livers. I'm an allornothinger. And it's usually nothing. Still. I shall allow her to spend her half-term on her own. So, have at thee with my codpiece, and farewell, Miss Crossthwaite of the monumental mammaries, other hands shall know thee, never these.

That's the thing with me, my thing with them, my way with women, I can always remove myself from them, absent myself, and stay away. Very good at it. When they won't be to me what I want them to be, then I am nothing to them. No crawling back, no being drawn, even if infatuated, fascinated by them. It's the one weapon I'm proud to have, almost the only one I do have, the ability to absent myself, and to stay absented: the ultimate in weapons.

Oh, I know very well the way to have is by the way of ignoring: but I want nothing of this deceit. By the way of waiting and allowing and showing: but I want nothing of these mortgages on the future.

Why don't you get up, you lazy sod? Today's the day you've been longing for, today you can work at your board, the one thing you really want to do, the one thing you really can do. Right then: arise and change. To live is to change. Put some jazz on. To wake up to. And then crap.

Where did all that lot come from? I didn't eat that much. unearned excrement, that's what it is. But perhaps it was all those compressed sawdust savouries that Marlene brought. At enormous expense and loss of life. Yes, I must have been champing away at those as sort of compensation, as a sort of substitute. Joseph's turn to buy the toilet-roll: only one eighth of an inch left (plus or minus point one) on the cylinder. Today—ah—I need not shave. I shall not shave. Nor need I wash. I shall not wash. I shall do or not do just as I like. Within my terms.

Jazz was, when I think of it, the first understanding I had of what art meant, what it was all about. Those incredibly subtle voices from the worn surfaces—Bessie and Ma and Ida—such dedicated sounds, the blues, poetry, feeling expressed which coincided so completely with what I was feeling or needed to feel. Used to play them over so many times, when I was living at home. I suppose it subjects an art form to a special condition, repeating it so many times, so that ever since I have been able to re-create many of the sounds in my head, as I chose. And even the special quality of the recordings—archaic and limited in

range—which added distancing, special, mine, mysterious.
Joe Oliver was always the greatest for me, King Joe, some
thought Louis, but I was always a King Oliver man, and
no one could touch him, for sure, with a mute, he could
make that cornet talk almost, with a mute, and you always
felt he was a leader of an ensemble, not a soloist with sidemen, riding, relaxed, yet still driving, leading. Yes, the
first understanding of what it was all about.

This kitchen needs cleaning. I'll do it later on. If I feel
like it. I shall have nothing but coffee for breakfast—a
big jug, real coffee, my only luxury, water, water, boil
quickly. Can hardly smell the coffee. Must be affected by
their smoking last night—open windows as soon as. Texture of irregular grains, rich foaming brown immediately
after water poured on. Now I can smell it. Makes me feel
hungry. Have a piece of cheese then. Stirred brown, milkwhite hot, table by my board, my workplace, shrine, altar,
do me a favour.

Firstfloor arches, the poor stucco imitation of channelled jointing, the semicircular fanlights, the thin cills:
all this is now so firmly impressed upon my mind, upon my
consciousness, that I wonder if I can ever design anything
uninfluenced by it. The outline against the sky is now so
moving, endearing to me. It has such rightness, even when
it is not trying to be right, or there are things like eco-
nomics against its being right, such grace, taste, good
manners. All clichés about Georgian. But right, so right.

Of course, I would really like to be designing a Gothic
cathedral, all crockets and finials and flying buttresses, but
I must be of my time, ahead of my time, rather, using the
materials of my time, the unacknowledged legislators, and
so on, in accord with, of, my age, my time, my generation,
my life.

But now: an arts centre for a town of half a million. The theatre should be fairly small, seating say five to seven hundred, yet the stage must be capable of mounting large-scale productions of opera and ballet—besides intimate chamber plays of the Strindbergian type. One solution is to use movable proscenium wings, together with a boom which can be raised or lowered, so that the pros. opening can be varied over a wide range. But when it's used in the smaller sizes then there is a vast booming stage area behind it which requires special acoustic treatment. Still, I don't think there's anything else I can do, so must assume this for the moment. Unless there was some cunning way of enabling the whole building to be reassembled for a particular type of stage—theatre-in-the-round, apron stage, opera, straight C19th picture frame—yes. But how? First of all, the weights to be moved would be so great as to involve machinery, definitely, too great for manual labour. And that means great cost, too. Still, expense is no object in Albert designs. So, if I had non-loadbearing party walls which could be moved through various angles to enclose a variable space—yes—and banked seat units which could also be grouped to suit each of several shapes. And a ceiling which could be raised or lowered. Yes. So how many shapes would I need? Large auditorium with proscenium, smaller intimate theatre, theatre-in-the-round, apron: four at least. The excess seat units would present a storage problem when the smaller auditoria were being used. The in-the-round would be the most awkward to arrange: it means cutting off the area of the pros. used in the other forms, except for an actors' entrance. And how adapt the ceiling to suit the differing forms? Ah, that's . . .

My father made this board for me, and a nice job he made of it, too. He's a clever old stick, my mother said,

cheap, cheap. Aeromodels—remember making them my-self: they never used to fly, and somehow this taught me to expect disappointment, very valuable.

And always in a crowd like this I am searching faces, all the time I am looking for Jenny, consciously or uncon-sciously, market faces, in tubetrains, in the crowds on tele-vision over at my parents, I look down the cast lists, too, of programmes because she once said she might take up acting seriously, and she could have done.

Stupid, this looking, stupid, this preoccupation with her and anything connected with her, or even things I arbi-trarily connect with her, stupid, yes, but that's no answer, that's not the point, that's not removing the why, any of the whys. Why do I feel as I do in spite of agreeing it's stupid, why did I ever make such an issue about being an architect, about my career, vocation, that she must have resented taking second place to it? That must have helped to ruin it, to destroy it, our love, and she must have won-dered why if I was so keen I just didn't go and do it. But it's not like that at all, not as easy as that, at all, it's . . . stop thinking.

A meat ticket pin. Pick up. Not so compulsive as with paperclips, of paperclips I am a compulsive pickerup. The question then arises, am I to consider myself bound to give a good home to every piece of wire left fortuitously (or so it seems) lying around? Already I admit market meat ticket pins, their shape pleases me, yet not hairpins, a dead end, hairpins, oh, the deadness, yes, the deadness of that sort of end has long been apparent to me, long since, of hairpins. But paperclips, now, yes.

Pop from the record stall, she never plays anything through to the end, constant musical titillation, she ought to be done for aural soliciting.

Please take a basket. I'll have that blonde dolly over there, I don't care if her parents weren't married, wrap her up. Rather have a trolley any day, it panders to my suppressed father instincts, even though I do only want to buy six eggs and some frankfurters. Whip round then, fast, rearwheel steering, drunk in charge of a supermarket trolley, three months and licence endorsed for running into old lady at coldmeat counter. Hit and run, out, out, 4/7d., here then, fivepence change and so farewell to the scene of the crime, the superdupermarket, out into the real Market.

Fruit, oranges, lots of veg., no strawberries yet, or peaches, then they come in with a wallop and you get sick of them, so many.

The Chapel House, good beer, comic tile murals in passage, Death of Cleopatra, Antony and Cleopatra, Act V, Sc. II, the muse of Music, smearedflesh children playing fairly underneath, waiting for their parents drinking inside.

The pub with the flowers, pots and pots on the tables, flowers, the Red House some call it, because of its long name, The Agricultural, which was too long for semiliterates to cope with, so they called it the Red House, the guvnor says, because of the facing brick, which is fairly unusual in a predominance of stocks.

A good guvnor, he is, one cannot choose too carefully the guvnor of one's pub.

Anyone I know here? Yes, several by sight, one by name, that's how it is. Ah, you know you're a regular when they pull your usual without your having to ask.

THANKS, SID.

A pro in the public, at lunchtime, too. I thought they would sleep all day. A bourgeois concept, no doubt.

Perhaps she's on days this week. Teeth like child's milk teeth, small, parallel edges, gap in middle. Is it possible to retain milkteeth undeveloped? No good you smiling at me, anyway, dolly, I'm not a potential customer. Why aren't I?

Because Jenny was so good, so what I wanted, anyway, that I can't bring myself to, for money, nor can I love anyone else, either, so I can't get it that way. But Jenny wasn't that good, really, at making love, when I think about it, not subtle at all, keen on just getting it in. You can make love with eyes and touching fingertips, I said to her once, when I was very angry, and it hurt her, and she tried, after that, but only when she chose to, when she wasn't feeling aggressive towards me. I think we both had different ideas about making love, perhaps we all do, sex means very different things to each of us, what it's about. And always lovemaking with Jenny was dependent upon circumstance rather than desire, upon opportunity rather than need or whim. One afternoon, in the summer vac, we had been out playing tennis, near her house, and the others had left, and I had been wanting her all day, Jenny, so I held her suddenly and took her up to her bedroom, and made love to her quickly, seriously, almost violently, and I remember she was particularly firm and tight that day, and afterwards she said, Always make love like that, darling, always just like that. Which was not normally my way at all, liking as I do the formalities, the preliminaries, the tendernesses, the innocencies, but for her the impromptu made it good for her. Memorable for her?

———GOT A HORSE FOR THIS AFTERNOON, SID?

———I GOT A FILLY FOR WEDNESDAY NIGHT.

Ah—he knocked and nearly dropped it. Old as he is, he still knows how a glass will behave when pushed, gravity is a constant, he remembers still knowledge he learnt as a child, painfully learnt, that glasses break when they fall after being pushed off a table, this is the constant of experience.

Pity Georgie isn't here lunchtimes, for the piano. Great he is, so in control, found his way in this way, playing the songs of forty years ago with such dedication, interest, sheer interest. That's the thing about the Angel, all the pubs have something going on in them, singing and dancing, life, you need never feel alone, in one sense, compared with the insufferable suburbs like Worcester Park or Sutton, where the pubs are like mausoleums, museums with stuffed people and not a sound but the cash register and the slurping of gargle.

———BOTH HE AND HIS WIFE WERE MARRIED, Y'KNOW.

That forerib of beef looks marvellous. And the ham.

SID, I'LL HAVE A BEEF ROLL, PLEASE.

———ONION?

Do I want onion? Yes, lovely raw crisp onion, with lovely raw underdone forerib of beef.

YES PLEASE, SID. HEARD ANY GOOD STORIES LATELY?

———I'M ALWAYS HEARING GOOD STORIES. DID YOU HEAR ABOUT THE TRAMP WHO WAS WALKING ALONG OXFORD STREET AND FOUND A DUMMY WITH FIVE QUID IN IT, SO HE THOUGHT HE'D INVEST IT IN A BIT OF THE OTHER AND WENT TO THIS OLD SCRUBBER. SHE DIDN'T WANT TO KNOW UNTIL HE SHOWED HER THE LOOT, BUT THEN SHE TOLD HIM TO GO AND HAVE A BATH, SO HE DID, AND WHEN HE CAME BACK SHE SAW HE HADN'T WASHED HIS JOHN THOMAS, SO SHE SAID, YOU DIRTY OLD MAN, GO AND WASH IT, SO HE DID, AND WHEN HE CAME BACK SHE SAID, THAT'S BETTER, NOW HAVE YOU GOT THE LETTER? AND HE SAID, CHRIST, DO I HAVE TO HAVE REFERENCES FOR IT AS WELL?

YES, SID, YES!

Fairly funny, yes, I could work on it.

There should be thicker filling towards the centre to compensate for the thicker bread part; each roll should contain protein and fat to balance the carbohydrate, and it might also be considered useful to include some essential roughage, like onion in the present case; certainly there should be protein in every roll; no butter, but beef dripping, for the purist. A dissertation upon the roll. Upon the beef roll.

———YOU PULL IT, THEN. AGAIN.

———CUT IT.

———NO, IT'LL JUST GROW AGAIN.

———NO, IT'LL GROW AGAIN. PULL. PULL! DON'T MIND ABOUT HURTING ME, JUST PULL IT OUT.

That's just what life is like, when you're old, I suppose, suddenly a bloody great long hair will grow out of your face, just grow, for no reason, well I suppose not really just like that, but that's how you notice it, that's how it seems to happen.

———WHAT YOU HAVING, JOHN?

THAT'S NICE OF YOU. BITTER PLEASE.

My name's not John, but it'll do, it's okay, for a pub name, John. Yes. I could have a different name for each pub round here, or a different identity, and a different identity too. But I should always want to be known as an architect, to preserve this essential myself, my identity, my character.

———SEEN YOU DOWN CHAP REGULAR LIKE, AND IN HERE, TOO.

YES, I LIVE NEAR, DOWN PERCY CIRCUS.

———DO YOU, THEN? WANTS DOING UP, DUNNIT, BUT THEY'LL GET ROUND TO IT SOONER OR LATER, I SPOSE.

No use saying I enjoy it decadent and decaying, decrepit,

like my state, London's state, England's state, man's state, the human condition.

YES, I SUPPOSE THEY WILL. YOU HAVE A STALL, DON'T YOU?

Expertise of Sid, the way he slices lengthwise along french loaf, spreads marge on both halves.

——YES, FRUITSTALL.

Play the identities game? Who am I? What am I? I must be taken for nothing but an architect, to preserve myself. So not to play with him, he's the sort who'd end up by saying, I know what you are, mate, you're a bleeding stupid twat.

Another drink then, for us. Yes.

Another drink.

The customers are nearly all old, here, in this pub, predominantly the old are customers here.

Another, yet another drink, then.

You ought to get back and work. You know you'll feel guilty. Another drink, then, just one.

THREE ALREADY, THEN SID? YOU MUST BE JOKING!

Out into—it's full, of people, stalls, cabbage, boxes, purple packingpaper, bruised fruit—my Chap.

That brisket looks good. Buy some. Yes. Protein to do something to the beer.

QUARTER OF SCOTCH BRISKET, PLEASE.

Lovely, lean, can't wait to eat it. Go down by canal then, yes.

Across the High Street, down Duncan Street, Clerkenwell County Court, to Vincent Terrace: British Waterways Regent's Canal, London Anglers Association PRIVATE FISHERY. Coarse grass on fortyfive degree slope straight to edge. Oil on water. Tunnel entrance, through trees, no barges, sun, sun, how unexpectedly quiet here, kids fishing, railings, sun, brisket.

That's the trouble with being a teacher, you're always afraid someone's going to catch you doing something unteacherly. Didn't I see you in Vincent Terrace by the canal railings, eating a quarter of Scotch brisket? Do it surreptitiously, then, guiltily, quickly, bolt it. But it's great, all the same, succulent, yes, succulent is the word I was wanting.

Swan. The proud swan. Yet how do I know it is proud? I the observer place on it the quality of proudness myself. The swan itself may or may not feel proud: of having feathered three lady swans, for instance, or of having fathered fourteen cygnets over the years. But only the swan knows that. Everything is subjective.

Something nasty in that bush. That even I should understand. A mother superior writes.

Back down Colebrooke Row, then, must start working, work right through now until bed, to make up for it. A ceiling of variable shape and capable of being raised and lowered. Wonder who designed Sadler's Wells Theatre then? Thirties? Yes. His problem was fairly straightforward, large theatre for one kind of staging, I would have thought. As was his solution. Possibly an oddly-shaped site, though.

Every time I pass round the back of Sadler's Wells there's an awful café smell blasted out at noselevel. All opera-singers live on when they are engaged here is toast and tea and stickybuns. That's what it smells like, anyway. To build them up. Perhaps that's what Miss Crossthwaite nourishes her bosom on, too, and savoury knickknacks, and when women like her reach her age then they start to smell, too, women's smell, which can be nasty, yes, from Miss Crossthwaite certainly, it puts one off, me off, for one. Women's smell. Perhaps I do, too, smell, or stink, there is no doubt a man's smell that puts women off. But I just think I don't, find it strange to think I could, just as I still find it strange to think of myself as a man, as a boy no longer, even at twenty-eight; as when some kid at school says That man, and I think Who? And then realise he means me, and am still surprised. As I am too when I make involuntary snufflings, noises through my mouth, or nose, or when I spit slightly in the middle of a sentence, and the kids notice, and some laugh, and I realise that as I am getting older I am less in control of my body, though more and more in control of my mind, and I fear, I fear for the future. But I am glad that I have had the chance to observe myself growing older, carefully, that I can do so, as I feel I should not have done had I married early, had become a husband with a proper job instead of wanting to . . .

The Shakespeare's Head. New pub. Old one fell down. Ten minutes after closing time one night, just as all the operalovers were wending their uplifted ways homeward, the front of the pub fell out. Just fell out into the road. Wallop. An act of god, they concluded, a most irresponsible sort of a god, evidently.

Myddelton Passage. And these uncomely flats. How the same company that owns Myddelton Square and Claremont Square could put up these, even a century and a quarter later, I just don't understand. Anyone who does less than his best, even unconsciously, must create guilt within himself, severer in proportion to the lesser-than-best that he has done. Whoever designed the rubbish at places like Sutton, Worcester Park and St. Helier, for instance, must bear, have borne, an enormous burden of guilt, probably quite unaware of its origin, of its cause.

Through the wide wicket, the space through which there is a Georgian prospect of St. Paul's. Myddelton

Square, with its prospect, and subtly-pitched dormers, and finely-beaded fanlights. To Claremont—no, to Amwell, Great Percy Street, and my Circus.

And they've cut what grass there was in the centre, and at the window I can smell it, fresh, glad I opened it before I left, the room full of the freshness of newcut summer grass.

I feel tired. Breathe deeply, good, yes, sleep for half an hour, then awake refreshed, work like hell, yes.

Pollard, The White Goddess, Mies, my books, aaah . . .

Hell! What time is it? Seven! You bloody fool! Guilt.

Guilt.

Close the window. Specks of smut on my drawing, hell, London smut. Smuts. Still.

Another day just frittered, as far as ever, farther because nearer death, from success, whatever that is, whatever that may mean, frittered, the worst crime, against myself, guilt.

Smuts, flecks of soot, coal. Damn. Won't clean off, ruined drawing, not that there was much to ruin, three lines of a . . .

Three lines. It's not nothing, exactly. Not exactly nothing.

Perhaps Terry will call this evening. Then that will take care of another day, send another lousy frittered day about its miserable business. Yes, I'll phone him, in a minute, yes.

Yes.

Guilt.

Three lines. . . .

*   *   *   *   *

SPECIAL HALF PRICE READING WITH THIS CARD

MADAM MAE

SPIRITUALIST READER & DEVINE HEALER

SHE HAS THE POWER FROM GOD TO HELP THOSE IN NEED OF HELP

ARE YOU UNLUCKY?

Sick, Blue and Discontented! If so, here is a Message of hope! Read it and then Act at Once!

FROM THE FOUR CORNERS OF THE EARTH THEY COME TO HER!

Rich and Poor, White and Colored, Men and Women of All Races and All Walks of Life!

MADAME MAE of Psychism, stands aloof and alone, far in advance of the ordinary readers you meet. For years SHE has been consulted by those in Trouble, who needing a wise adviser, have found in her THE ONE THEY SOUGHT!

DO YOU NEED HELP? The most private and personal matters successfully handled.

ARE YOU IN TROUBLE? Perhaps you are? If so, this has a meaning for you.

Through her knowledge, endless experience and rare perceptive powers, she can help you as no one else can! You make no mistake in consulting her! She enjoys the enviable reputation of telling the truth! Do you wish to know it. If you are pursued by enemies under a shadow, take advice before it is TOO LATE! Delays are always dangerous! Does everything go wrong? If so, there is a cause! DO YOU wish to continue on the downward trail, or do you desire to change and claim what God intended you to have? If you would rise to your natural sphere and enjoy life as others do! SEE HER TODAY!

(BE SURE TO READ OTHER SIDE)

*   *   *   *   *

The weding of our beloved Mr Alburt he was going to get marred to miss Croswait on the night befor he got parerlatick drunk to buck up inogth corag to say Yes. On the day they got marred he was sick twic

On thire honemoon they went to south End they had a lovly time at south End he spent a lote of money he spent about 6 penc

They had a bundol and got dievorsed

The death of Mr Albert He died of Bulgarian flue He was walking along and tript over his long bloand Hair.

We smash the school up because the teachers are not stricht and revolting it should be more stricht and we should be compeled to wire uniform insted of comeing a school in X Army Jackets and Jeans and X Army Boots and lever Jackets

The teachers are not stricht they let you do what you like Mr Alburt is one of them

*   *   *   *   *

Albert picked up his cup, scraped its unglazed base on the thick white edge of the saucer, and drank tea. The tea had a trembling encrustation of tannin, and had been made with sterilised milk. Albert minded neither of these things, on this occasion; on other occasions he might well have minded, might even have entered upon a complaint to the management, but on this occasion he did not mind.

Heat was transmitted through the coarse china to burn the middle joint of his index finger; when this became unbearable he put the cup down and gripped it again with bunched fingertips. What did they do before they put handles on cups, he thought. Who first thought of handles? Perhaps it was the Beaker Folk. Yes, let it be the Beaker Folk. One member of the Beaker Folk was constantly burning his stubby fingers on hot beakers of bedtime maresmilk, and always dropping and breaking them. Yes, thought Albert, and this would convincingly account for the enormous quantity of beaker fragments available to be excavated by archaeologists. Then one bedtime this otherwise simple, even obtuse, man (it could not have been a woman, Albert felt sure) had the concept of the Handle come upon him in a moment of high apocalyptic inspiration. The Handle. Perhaps he made the first one from a twig sprung into appropriate holes formed before the beaker was baked. Later, he had improved on this by pinching the beaker into a convenient shape. Then he had thought himself eminent enough to break away and found a tribal sub-dynasty of his own: the Pinched Beaker Folk.

Terry watched three Somalis at the next table. Small brown paper packets passed from hand to hand. The men looked normal enough, Terry thought, not at all like dope fiends as featured in *The People*. Perhaps they were only pedlars and not actual addicts. Drugtakers are the absolute example, he thought, of those who live only in the present, for the present, the only way to live: they see no farther than the next fix, they are willing to sacrifice everything for it, abandon all lien on the future whatsoever. Perhaps he should try drugs? To help him forget Janine? Drink was no use, it made him morose and it distended his stomach. But which drugs?

Two prostitutes sat talking and smoking at another table. ⌐Half-caste, straight hair, yellowing teeth, doglipped, long graceful hands, thin.⌐   ⌐Dyed daffodil-yellow hair, blenched skin, cast in left eye, short, odd effect of physical breaking-up.⌐

"I met this blind man on the bus coming home tonight," said Albert, quietly, to Terry. "He'd been waiting ten minutes for a 19, he said, and people in the queue kept on getting on other buses. He went on and on about them. Said you've got to be black today: you're better thought of. Blind prejudice if you like. Anyway, I told him when a 19 came and the conductor helped him on to the bus, but he still went on and on. 'Christmas Day and they're all over you,' he said, 'asking you all the time Are you sure you don't want to cross the road? The rest of the year they don't want to know.' Then he just sat there and whistled a fragment of a tune over and over again, as if to keep himself company."

"He ought to think himself lucky," said Terry, "that he's got such a good excuse to demand help of people, to demand their sympathy. If healthy people do it then they automatically get kicked in the balls."

Both Albert and Terry thought of Jenny and Janine, their respective betrayers, respective ballskickers, they, the betrayed, thought that this was the particular conflict in society in which they were inextricably involved: that there was now no reason for fidelity, that there had seemed to be one when they were young, but that there was now no reason, and they could not quite blame the women for it; now the only reason for fidelity was itself, faith in a concept, in a particular virtue which must of absolute necessity be its own reward. Sin and evil they could understand the passing of, these were now mere archaisms, words at best synonymous with wrong: but there was still somewhere pure within them the concept of fidelity.

The blonde one reminded Terry, oh so very faintly, in the way she held her head, of Janine.

"Let's go," he said.

Albert followed.

Between the highlevel Fenchurch Street line to the north, and the tall bricked-window façades of the London Western Dock warehouses to the south; cut horizontally by Cable Street in the north and the Ratcliffe Highway in the south; an area of two-storey Georgian cottages, savaged by the war, slums before it, largely derelict now, all condemned, still awaiting razing. And centrally there is Wellclose Square, warehouses and tall second-ratings, lovely of its nature, quiet and dark and serene in its decrepitude. But in the centre there are a school, a playground, and a house, that are excrescences, that are not fitting.

Albert kept close by the wall through Grace's Alley into Wellclose Square. Two-thirds of the way down someone had recently relieved himself against a blanked-off shopfront. The flakeworn paving was marked like a delta, like a chaotic candelabra, like a fistful of snakes. Albert paused, fascinated, then turned his head to look at the patterns in reverse. Never content to leave well alone, he unzipped his fly and attempted to impose the pattern of art on nature. Terry joined in, laughing, and made the whole area into a sea, the paving awash over the patterns, ruining the subtle tracery under the lamp's light.

"Bastard! Bastard!" shouted Albert. The façades on

one side reflected the sound, the gaptoothed bombsite on the other sucked in the sound:

"Baa! Baa!" gave back the façades, more gently, and the gaptoothed bombsite took the echoes as greedily and as gratefully as it had taken the original sounds.

Albert moved quickly into Wellclose Square. Terry followed, laughing at Albert's anger. Albert was further offended by the clutter of buildings and wirenetting in the centre of the Square: seeing empty milkbottles on a doorstep, he picked one up, looked quickly around, and, seeing no one to rat, he threw it as hard as he could, overarm, as if it were a grenade, towards the playground. It burst with a deeply satisfying splintering sound. Terry tried to look as though he were not with Albert. Albert tried to look as though he were not with Terry, laughing delightedly.

In a Nigerian café a negro came to their table with an electric razor to sell.

"Two pun," he kept demanding. Albert could not think of two quickly enough to tell him. The shaver looked new. Albert decided he would buy it. Searching, he found five and ninepence. He borrowed a pound from Terry, and offered the total to the man. Albert did not care whether he accepted it or not; he had no more money, nor had Terry; it was up to the negro. He tried for five minutes to extract more, coming finally down to asking for a cup of tea, for this too to be refused. It was not that Albert, or that Terry, sought to deprive him of a cup of tea, but that they just had no more money with them on this occasion. Suddenly the negro gave in, picked up the twenty-five and ninepence, and went out through the hardboard-shuttered door.

Albert inspected his new acquisition. There was no indication that it worked, he realised: he should have tested it before buying it. He asked the man behind the counter whether he could plug it into a light socket, but was refused.

Albert put the shaver in its box, carefully, put it in his pocket, and spoke for some time:

"So I went back after the holiday, quite refreshed as I usually am, and my form were giggling about over bits of newspaper, two or three groups of them, and making it bloody obvious they wanted me to come and see what they were up to. So I didn't. Then when I began to call the register one of the girls brought out a clipping and put it on my desk without a word. 'Teaching at Tough School Contributes to Teacher's Suicide', it said, and it was only a report of my predecessor's suicide over Whitsun, Burroughs, Bunny they called him. I just took no notice—after all, I didn't know him, did I, and if they thought they could break me, then they'd misjudged me. Gas, it was, just turned on the gasring in his digs and sat in the armchair. I just went on calling the register, but later the Head sent for me, and asked me if I'd stay until the end of the term. Don't worry about Burroughs, he said to me, he had many reasons for suicide outside school. Yes, I thought, and he had forty-three inside school, as well, and they're kicking up hell in my classroom at this moment. I can't stand this Head: he's so bloody weak, and he doesn't back up his teachers. In my first week I took a boy to him who'd been grossly impertinent to me, and when I'd told him of this he turned to the boy and said, Now let's hear your side of it. I ask you! And when he's talking to you he looks at a spot midway between your chin and your collar, never in your eyes."

"So you're going to leave?" Terry asked.

"No, it looks as if I'm stuck there until the end of term

anyway. Just the way he put it made me pretty sure he'd fix it with the Office."

"The bastard."

"The kids seem half scared by Burroughs' suicide, and yet pleased. They really hated him, I know. Yesterday, this was, and at the end of school one of them came up to me, Sweetman his name is, and said, We're going to have a meeting tonight to decide about you. And this morning, as soon as he saw me, he said, We've decided, and we're all chipping in for a gasring for you. They're half-serious, too, that's what's so interesting, half-serious. And then there was this kid Weir, who was never in class. I used to call the register, and his name was last, 'Jackie Weir', and the class at first used to chorus, 'He's not here', and then when they'd got to know me after a couple of days, it was 'Jackie Weir—He's a queer', mingled with the 'He's not here'. And the Head this morning tells me to take him off roll: he is indeed queer, and has been picked up flogging it around the more classy W.1 conveniences, and sent to an approved school—to finish his education, of course. The girls are at least normal: there's one who waits behind purposely so that I shall watch her wiggle her sweet little bum at me as she goes out of the door. I've been warned to watch the girls in the afternoons: some of them are apparently in the habit of coming to school, getting their marks, and then going off to tea-dances up west. Girls are always being brought back by attendance officers. There's this sort of uneasy balance, with the boys as well, between the police outside school and the teachers within. They know they're less likely to get into real trouble inside school, yet it's so boring for them, so bloody boring. And that's a failure in the teaching, of course: but the situation at this school is so extreme that any teacher coming into it from outside is beaten before he starts. You can see the staff are beaten, from the look in their eyes, from the way they go about the corridors. And I'm beaten, too, at this school. When I came up here I used to think I was at least a fairly competent teacher, even if I was certainly not a dedicated or inspired one. But the frightening thing here is that any sort of punishment has failed as a deterrent: whatever you do to them doesn't stop them doing what they want to, again and again. I hit them on the head with my knuckles as much to relieve my feelings as to try to stop them shouting or to make them pay attention. And they know all the rules—that you're not supposed to hit them on the head, or hit them at all if you're on supply, for that matter, and that they're not to be kept in for more than half an hour. I know that the standard answer is to treat them with lovingkindness, but you try it, mate, I've not got that much lovingkindness. And they'd think you soft. The Assistant Head—a right Amazon of a woman who doesn't seem aware of about eighty percent of what goes on in the school—said the kids would listen and behave if my lessons were sufficiently interesting. I told her that since they'd been interesting enough for every class I'd ever taken before, it might just possibly be the general standard of this particular school that was at fault. I was beaten before I ever got there. The timetable she worked out for me doesn't help any, either: about half of it is English, but I also do music, a couple of maths lessons, games on Wednesdays and several general periods which I naturally use for architecture or geology."

But Albert paused! A tap dripped in the sink behind the counter. Albert thought with awe of the vast resources behind that tap: the miles of pipes, of mains, the reservoirs, the rivers, the rain. He imagined with what wonder an African immigrant must regard the water supply: "It comes in pipes, you just have to turn a tap thing, man. And that same water is the same as the Queen drinks. When I turn that tap thing, man, I'm connected with the same water she uses. And the sewers, man, they connect, too, she don't use no special sewer, they all connect up and side by side hers and mine come out at Barking Creek. That's a democratic country for you, man."

⌐Eyes the brown of dead bracken, lips of similar thickness threequarters of their length, dyedblack hair, glinting skin.⌐ Up the stairs. A negro padlocked the door behind her. But Albert continued!

"I told you the sods pinched my pen a couple of weeks ago? I was reading this novel recently about a teacher in the east end who won over the kids by love and kindness, morality and honesty, against tremendous odds—talk about sentiment and wish-fulfilment! I can just see my lot coming to me at the end of term with a present—or even my pen back—addressed to sir, with their love! These things just don't mean anything to these kids in this school: that's what's so frightening, and I've not been frightened in a school before. Not frightened by their violence, though that's bad enough, but just by these unknown forces of character. These kids will just go on knocking off my pens for as long as I have pens to knock off. I'm sure that even if I chained a pen to the desk then next day they'd bring a pair of stillsons and have it away."

"Did you tell the Head?" Terry asked.

"Of course, but he seemed to think I was stupid for leaving things around anyway. Always lock things up, Mr. Albert, he said. He's always smiling, in a sort of slitfaced way, the Head: I'm sure he'd have that same smile on his face as he eased a knife into your back, quite sure. And I'll tell you a funny thing: the men's bog is opposite his room, across a lightwell, and there's this long window which whenever I go in there is open a few inches just at fly-level. But it may be the women—theirs is just opposite, too, for that matter. Nearly all of them are married but look frustrated—no, not frustrated, exactly, but as though their husbands had been neglecting the foreplay. But of course I was stupid to leave my pen lying there: it won't happen again. Here, today I was playing them some Carl Orff in a music lesson—a record of his setting of Catullus, good, simple, thumping stuff, and when we got to the phrase 'Da mi basia' repeated several times with increasing passion, this little Greek Cypriot girl suddenly sat up, said 'Oh!' and smiled all over her face. I suppose the Latin is similar to the Greek; so at least I pleased one of them that day, though god knows if she understood any of the rest. She's quite a nice little girl, actually, long black hair—how real black hair shows up against dyedblack— and skin like Pentelic marble. But there's a Greek Cyp bastard called Erotokritou who whenever he sees me, several times a day often, comes up to me and says, 'Have you bin sayin' fings about ma famly?' Sometimes he says 'What you bin sayin' about ma famly?' Or 'You bin sayin' fings about ma famly!' For no reason. And he's violent, he has this reaction of violence to practically every situation. I've watched him with other kids in the playground, and he—not exactly scares me, but disturbs me, makes me uneasy, apprehensive. There is latent aggression in everything he does, in every movement he makes. He's a member of the Corps, too, which is a gang of about five who wear ex-army boots and who drill each break in the playground. They're quite disciplined in their way, and they terrorise the other kids. The Head ought to insist that they come to school in ordinary shoes, of course, but I don't think he's even interested. The Corps practises kicking-in in unison—my god! Unless you came to this school you just wouldn't believe half the things that go on. You'd hardly see it as a school at all as you know schools: there's no set of rules, or even habits, to which the kids will conform or that they will even acknowledge. I've never been anywhere before, for instance, where they do not even accept that they must not talk in class: when I shut them up they resent it as though I am curtailing an inalienable freedom. And I see their point, in a way, too. But no one can teach under such conditions. You have to establish your own set of rules, let alone your own obedience of those rules, your own discipline. Which takes all the time, and an incredible amount of nervous energy. It's like I'm working at the frontier of civilisation all the time."

Albert went over to the jukebox and put a shilling in it. He spent a long time choosing three records: he found two he wanted to hear, and set the ingenious mechanism working to bring this about, but the third choice was not easy. Eventually he just pressed the button corresponding to his favourite number, twenty-nine, and then returned to sit with Terry. The two women looked at him contemptuously as soon as they heard his first record begin.

"Some classes have so many Cypriots in them that the register reads like the *dramatis personæ* of a Greek tragedy," Albert offered. "They form a conclave within the school, too, eating at exclusively Cyp tables, in gangs, and in class one smart one will catch and understand what I say and pass it on to the others. Yet I can begin to sympathise with why the older ones are restless and unmanageable: in Cyprus at fourteen they'd be accepted as men, and be doing men's jobs."

Albert thought: a block of wood, a plank of wood. When does a block become a plank? When does a plank become a block? At what point do you see that a block has become a plank, at what stage a plank a block? Plank. Block. He thought about them until the words became meaningless to him, then ludicrous to him, then nothing to him. And he was left with wood. Wood is wood is wood, he said to himself, pleased.

"If we go on half-educating these kids any more," he said suddenly to Terry, "then the violence will out. I'm sure they know they're being cheated, that they're being treated as subhuman beings. And the school *is* a microcosm of society as a whole."

There was this tremendous need for man to impose a pattern on life, Albert thought, to turn wood into planks or blocks or whatever. Inanimate life is always moving towards disintegration, towards chaos, and man is moving in the opposite direction, towards the imposition of order: as the animals are, too, but to a far lesser extent. This was the paradox: for the fundamental rhythm of life was the alternating disintegration-reintegration of matter. Perhaps five hundred million years ago matter became capable of maintaining itself by reactions to stimuli: that is to say, it became life.

The past of a man's life could always be controlled in this way, be seen to have a fixed order because it was passed, had passed: almost always, that is, for when it could not be controlled then madness was not far away. When something was passed, it was fixed, one could come to terms with it; always the process of imposing the pattern, of holding back the chaos. Like antiques, collecting them, a manifestation of the security of a pattern, harking back to the safeness of things passed. His father, he had seen, often preferred the less good, if known, to the possibly better, if unknown: and Albert felt himself always to be liable to do the same and consciously fought against it, trying to see everything freshly, trying to realise in practice his theoretically absolute freedom of will, freedom from the passed. In most things he succeeded: but for Jenny, with the memory and grief of whom he had not come to terms, upon which he had not imposed a pattern.

As an example, too: Albert walking from Balls Pond Road into Mildmay Park, buying a peach on the way, the third time realising he had done the same thing twice before, who was free to buy grapes, or an orange, or an apple, and to wander along Newington Green Road, for one alternative, had imposed a pattern unconsciously, in such a simple matter, had formed a habit, shoring what up against what decay, against what chaos?

"But what if he were to do me in?" enquired one of the women, more loudly than she had been speaking before. Albert remarked upon and commended, to himself, her pretty employment of the Subjunctive: in this tense's struggle with the Indicative in the constant levelling tendencies of language, this usage by this woman, whatever her moral standards, was indeed encouraging, a blow struck back for precision and subtlety.

Terry thought that that was one of the things that hurt most about Janine leaving him, the being forced back into this sort of world, this seeking company in pubs and cafés, without the special warmth and kindness of the company of a woman. That was perhaps the best reason he had to hate her, for withdrawing these things from him, and somehow making it impossible at the same time for him to ask them of any other woman. It had destroyed the confidence he needed to ask them of any other woman. That hurt, as well as the other things. And she made him feel like a youth again, immature: he remembered her saying to him that the ability to make painful but firm decisions was one of the chief signs of maturity. Which was why he was here, in a Cable Street café, acting immaturely, listening to music he despised and to conversation which bored him.

Albert thought of others' solutions to the sexual problem: the for-instance heavily-beringed women of about thirty-five to be seen in many Angel pubs: a half-inch of wedding and engagement rings on their finger, a sign of pride, of aggressive non-availability. Yet they must see sex as in many ways condemning them to drudgery through children, and dread it because of this. He needed someone who realised instinctively about the necessity of the illusion of love: which had taken him so long even to begin to understand. And the boy of fourteen who had talked more sense to him about sex than ever he had been able to command himself, and who accepted, accepted reversals in the same spirit if not with the same pleasure as conquests.

Albert stood up.

"I'm feeling in the mood for horrors," he said. "Let's drive round Worcester Park and St. Helier."

Terry stood up in agreement; he did not mind where they drove.

They walked through North East Passage into Well-close Square, kicking an empty beercan with considerable satisfaction, passing and re-passing to one another. In the Square an old man came out of one of the houses.

"Why don't you make more noise?" he suggested, without irony in his voice. "Just like a couple of kids."

The rebuke was so mild that Albert laughed with relief.

"We are just a couple of kids," he said.

They walked away from the Fiat, to avoid identifying it with themselves, once round the Square, and then came back to it.

"The theatre," said Terry, "is dead. Dead."

"I could give you a building that would make it live again," said Albert.

"It's nothing to do with buildings, that the theatre is dead, but because of the audience. You won't get good, living theatre until you get an audience with good and valid reasons for going, for being an audience."

Along the Ratcliffe, through the Rotherhithe, Bermond-sey, Camberwell, Streatham: the bye-law streets and tunnel-back dwellings of nineteenth-century housing legislation: Mitcham: Morden: Sutton:

Deliberately, Albert caused Terry's random direction-taking to bring them past the house of Jenny's parents. Deliberately, too, he did not tell Terry.

Albert's full contempt was reserved for Worcester Park: St. Helier was bad but unpretentious, but Worcester Park was both very bad and pretentious at the same time. Street upon street of semi-detached mock-timbered gables, Norman arches on the porches, Gothic windows in the halls, bakelite door furniture throughout, intensely un-imaginative front garden layouts, identical wroughtiron gates, twee lanterns to light the porches. William Morris was responsible for having started the movement which led to all this, Albert thought, but surely he could not have approved of Worcester Park?

Albert felt something large and hard in his pocket: it was the electric shaver. An idea came to him, and he asked Terry to stop outside the next house with a porchlight on. He opened the door and went through the gate up a shingle path. In the porch he carefully removed the bulb from the mock-renascence lantern with his fingers wrapped in a handkerchief, placed it in his pocket, and replaced it with the adaptor of the shaver. The shaver began to throb in his hand at once and he started to shave: it worked well, and he was particularly pleased with the way it cleaned the hard stubble above his top lip.

The hall light went on, the door opened, and a little fat man stood on the step. He had pulled on a dressing-gown over his pyjamas, but it was open at the fly to disclose a shadow of pubic hair.

"What the hell d'you think you're doing?" he demanded.

"Shaving," said Albert, not to be outdone.

The man reached inside the door and switched off the porchlight supply. Albert heard the telephone ping at the same time, and assumed someone was ringing for the police. Quickly he unplugged the shaver and, thrusting it into his pocket, he walked away down the path. The man followed: Albert realised he might take the Fiat's number if he reached the gate, so he turned and shouted melodramatically:

"I'm a desperate man, and I'll shoot if you come any nearer!"

The man laughed briefly, nastily and disbelievingly, and still came on. Albert took the bulb from his pocket and quietly dropped it behind him. It burst with a noise similar to a pistol shot. The man turned and Albert heard the door slam behind him.

"Heigho for Georgiou's, I think, mate," he said to Terry. "When I was a kid we used to call that poshing lightbulbs, poshing, poshing, it's a fine word."

*   *   *   *   *

Proposition: That These Children's Speech is Bad.
For the Proposition: Miss Crossthwaite.
Against the Proposition: Mr. Albert.

✗ *Miss Crossthwaite* said that they all knew the speech of children at this school to be bad: every time one of them opened his or her mouth to speak the result was almost invariably hideous, an offence to the ears. Their speech was slovenly, like their personal habits.

✗ *Mr. Albert* said that 'bad', 'hideous', and 'slovenly', were not words that could be meaningfully used about speech: a child saying *prize* for *praise* was using the same sound as in the word *prize.* The sound itself was not 'wrong', therefore, but its context was not that of so-called standard speech: accurately, it was only in a social context that sounds could be described as misplaced. Often the different sound produced by these children required more phonetic effort to produce (for example, the glottal stop) than the one it replaced: how then could such speech be described as 'slovenly'? The offence to Miss Crossthwaite's lovely ears, Mr. Albert suggested, came about because these children were not speaking as she spoke herself, these children were not imposing the same pattern on their worlds as she imposed on hers: for who approves, Mr. Albert quoted Petronius without attribution, of conduct unlike his own? For communication within their own social context, the speech of these children was perfectly suited. As a teacher, he would point out to children that if they chose to move into other social contexts then they would probably not find acceptance unless they conformed to the speech conventions of the new one, accent being generally the easiest way of determining class origin: but he would never attempt to 'correct' children's speech provided they were making themselves clear to him; that is, provided they did not speak indistinctly.

✄ *Miss Crossthwaite* was nevertheless convinced that she would still object when any child said 'ain't' in her hearing.

✄ *Mr. Albert* said that while in his childhood 'ain't' was common, this usage had now shifted to 'ent' in London. This was an example of the continual progression of sound changes in speech, in the face of which any standardisation was quite wasted, even ludicrous. And the working-class always led in such speech changes, and the upper classes were farthest behind: the Queen, for instance, always *lanches* a ship, and uses *lorst* for *lost*.

✄ *Miss Crossthwaite* said that the speech of the children of this school was bad and slovenly.

The bell went before a vote could be taken.

*   *   *   *   *

An Eye for Place

Of places most of all remembering comes.

Of Hungerford Lane that first tense evening,
for instance, where shadows, stacks and iron

escapes above us segmented the night
in a parody of a clerestory;
where I refrained in the obvious place,
choosing anti-romantically to wait
until we had reached the high limewashed vault
of the bridge; and where, while the savage trains
gunned behind their netting cage, I kissed you.

And this from one who always found more
in places than in people to love before.

My masculine room suddenly made a home
by the careful discard of un-needed clothes;
my austere room tender with your warmth,
made holy by the ritual of our loving;
its certain books you held gaining almost
the character of relics with your leaving;
and the sweet residual reminder of its bed
as I entered it again at night alone.

London that summer seemed full of tall cranes,
strutted and frail and busy in our way.

Your windhammered hair in the spring wind
on the breast of Nottingham Castle:
and the company of friends to whom we seemed
like lovers in a ballad:

the skewed house in which we stayed
for three sacred nights;
the room with its barely-yielding bed
and absurdly-patterned walls:

your chaste pain, although we must
have joined a hundred times
before, making you for this once
my pure and childlike virgin:

my terror of loss, as, dead in sleep,
you spurned my tenderness:
yet, waking, made sweet recompense
in reassurances:

And last, *The Trip to Jerusalem*,
another consummation:
a kind of voyage to a holy land
to help us understand.

And oh but how this sweet remembering numbs!

But most of all at
Balgy, where
the plump seatrout leapt
from our pool,
and ochre seashells
fell from rocks
tinkling when the tide
had left them:

You and I
by our fire leaning
against rock
rough as a catstongue,
while the moon
hung caught in a wire

fence on the
cliff above the stream:

And our free bathing
by the fault,
like pure animals
who never
knew and hated man,
to make *and why do I run my mind up
and down the honed edge of memory so constantly hold
my brain to the while these shoes did not know her since
then I have worn out two and partially a third pair of
shoes....*

*   *   *   *   *

Albert said: Joseph, mate, you're a native: what the hell
am I supposed to do with the kids round
here? I don't give a damn if they screw each
other without my knowing, but when they
drop frenchie packets in my wastepaper
basket in the middle of a lesson, what am I
supposed to do?

Joseph said: Ignore it.

Albert said: I blush, that's my trouble, I blush.

Joseph said: Don't kid me you lead the sheltered life, mate,
what with all these birds I see fluttering in
and out of here. Who was that one night
before last, for instance? She your regular
bird then?

Albert said: No, but she's someone else's. I mean, I
wouldn't have you think she was being

wasted, or anything. I'll tell you a funny story about her, mate, though, at least, you'll think it's funny. This is a dolly I had about three years ago, very keen on her, I was, very keen indeed. Then I pushed it too hard, as I always do, it's a sort of defence, a sort of need to be hurt so I push me luck—so didn't see her for a couple of years, then something happened that's never happened before—I sort of got friendly with her again—only there was never anything sexual about it—don't laugh—and I could take her to parties and things and enjoy myself—that is, not worry who the hell she was talking to or who was trying to make her —and this was all very fine, and I know the bloke she's going to marry—she's getting married in three weeks—and I like him a lot, too. So it's a nice clean friendship: but the night before last she turns up shortly after I got back from school—you know I'm bloody dead when I get back and can't think for about an hour. Anyway, I make her some tea and feed her a biscuit and we natter and it's all very domestic and she goes and washes her hair and I say how domestic this is and isn't she taking a bleeding liberty as though I was Mike her bloody intended. And she says No, she thinks she looks very sexy like this. At which I can only laugh, in my way. Anyhow, so when I can think I suggest we go to the theatre, not just wanting to talk to her all the evening, and knowing already there isn't a chance of it going the way it should if she was any other dolly, and she's dead unenthusiastic about going out at all. But only afterwards do I really notice this, and finally we go off to the bloody theatre, and d'you know what? She falls asleep—not once, but twice, once in each act. Now, I know the play was bleeding awful —the theatre's dead, mate, quite dead, you know, especially the intellectual theatre, but these bloody critics mislead you with their small change—but I ask you! But now, here at last I get to the point, last night she rings me up and asks me how I enjoyed the play. Not much, says I. Nor did I, says she, I wish we hadn't gone. What would you rather have done, then, I ask her. Stayed in and made love, she says. Jesus Christ! And she's getting married in three weeks, too!

Joseph said: Birds are like that.

Albert said: But you notice she didn't bloody say it when I could have done something about it—if she'd really wanted it, then she would have said so at the time, wouldn't she?

Joseph said: Not necessarily. Birds are like that.

Albert said: Honest, Joseph, I just can't justify women's ways to men. The lot of them beat me. Like these birds at school, that I was telling you about just now, before I got sidetracked. They come up to me after lunch—they seem to run a lunchtime brothel somewhere—and I can smell it, mate, smell it. They've just had it off somewhere. And they come and stand at my desk as close as possible, probably thinking I know nothing about it or something. Or seeing

if I do, and have got the guts to say something. It's enough to drive you round the twist.

Joseph said: Ignore it.

Albert said: That's the last thing I can do.

Joseph said: You got sexual problems, mate, sexual problems, that's your trouble.

Albert said: Of course I have, but not simple ones. It's
nothing like as simple as going out and screwing some old scrubber for a few bob.

Joseph said: You make it difficult for yourself, mate. Why
isn't it as simple as that?

Albert said: It's all connected with Jenny, and therefore
with the whole of myself, everything I am.

Joseph said: You're just using her as an excuse. You could
forget these things easily enough if you didn't
bloody think so much about them. Look, they
either do or they don't. Otherwise you're on
your tod, mate, strictly on your tod.

Albert said: I think I had more, once.

Joseph said: Then you were bloody mistaken. You were
kidding yourself. All this soul-mate stuff you
mean?

Albert said: Something like that.

Joseph said: You were mistaken, then, and you're just off
your squiff if you think you'll ever have it
again.

Albert said: You see, in one way I'd just like to go up to
some bird round here, for a try, and say 'Give
with the reechy kisses, babe', just to see what
she'd say. Of course, I know what she'd say if
she was a workingclass character in a book—
'Coo!' or 'Get you' or 'Are you off your
chump?' But what would she actually say?

Joseph said: Get stuffed?

Albert said: Perhaps. I can only find out by trying it, of course. Here, you know what they did to one teacher today? One of the girls just took out her lighter in the middle of a lesson and set fire to the curtains. Killing, isn't it? I've had the curtains in my classroom taken down.

Joseph said: Kids today don't seem to have much imagination.

*   *   *   *   *

Justin, Erotokritou, Fleming, Sweetman, Mee. They drill most precisely. They have practised for hours. Single file. Their marching an unmilitary compromise: short step, short swing. Heeling. A practice kick: double, triple, in unison, the five of them. Unison. Precision.

They knock down a boy who is in their way. They surround him. They make dangerous kicks at him. Erotokritou perhaps inadvertently kicks his elbow. The boy is in great pain.

"What d'you lot think you're doing?" Albert says.

"Practisin'."

"We're the Corps."

"You'll all be corpses right enough if you carry on like this," Albert says, failing to resist the chance of the pun provided by the pronunciation.

"Yeah, yeah?"

"You and who?"

"You watch it, Albie!"

"What did you say?" Albert says.

"Nothing!"

"He din't say nothin'!"

"You bin sayin' fings about ma famly?"

"You say 'sir' if you've anything to say to me," Albert says.

"Since when was you knighted by the Queen, then?"

"All right, then, that's your break. All of you, upstairs and stand outside the Headmaster's room," Albert says.

"After break, Albie."

"When we finished practisin'."

"You'll get yours, Albert, just you wait."

* * * * *

Terry was enjoying a *galatopoureko*: the membrane-thin flakes of pastry were crisp contrast to the yielding density of the centre, the honey ran with each bite.

Albert sat, within himself, quite alone. His shattered state after each school day seemed to last longer and longer: soon it would be permanent, he felt, in spite of the end of term being near.

"They tell me," he said to Terry, who did not listen, "that the kids take breaking up rather literally. Violently. Especially the kids who are leaving. Last term windows were broken and a couple of doors kicked in, and a lot of them brought booze in the afternoon. And the teachers had to go home in groups. Not that the kids couldn't tackle groups, though, for they could, easily enough. Did I tell you about this street fight with the Hoxton boys the other afternoon? They finish fifteen minutes before us, so that just gives them nice time to get up to us. One of the senior teachers heard there was going to be trouble, so he told the Head. You know what the old sod did? He said as it was going to be outside the school it was none of his business! None of his business! Eventually he was persuaded to phone the police about it, however, and they had a car outside at four-ten. But they couldn't do anything. The fight still happened. The police just aren't a deterrent to these kids, there's no deterrent that I know of. Anything they want to do, they do. And somehow I've got to admire them for it, even though I seem to be on the other side. Somehow they're behaving more like human beings than we are. It's the authority which is wrong, not those it's forced upon. People like the bloody Head and this inspector who came yesterday. She came into my class just as I'd got them under, which takes about ten minutes, and after a bit she asked me if she could take over. I was only too pleased to be shown how to deal with them, of course. 'You're too tense, all of you,' she says. 'Relax, look, go floppy, like this, go floppy.' My class went floppy all right, all over the place, and the noise! She just walked out after a few minutes, the cow, and I had to go round calming them down with my special foreknuckle headrap. That's the sort of authority I mean, hers, that's all wrong. It must be all wrong. Or I'm mad, which is after all not impossible."

Georgiou's latest waitress came to stack and pick up the cups and plates.

"Give with the reechy kisses, babe," said Albert.

"Kindly get stuffed," said the waitress.

"Only time I did touch them, hurt them," Albert resumed, "was today, for the first time. I was giving a bloody brilliant lesson on architecture—it was brilliant, too—and the bastards still weren't paying attention and still mucked about, and I lost my temper and said they were a lot of peasants. That they resented, being called peasants, that touched them, that hurt them. They copied chunks out of the Bible for the rest of the lesson, and I could feel the resentment in the room. It wasn't the copying out of the Bible, I'm sure, they probably hated that less than me rabbeting on about architecture, but being called peasants. Perhaps it has country bumpkin associations for London kids. Strange that it should be the only thing to touch them. But you know what I've decided to do in the last few days of term? I'm going to give them time and paper to write down exactly what they feel about me, with a guarantee that there will be no complaints or recriminations from me, whatever they say. This I hope will work out their hatred of me without it actually needing to come to violence. How about that for an idea, then?"

*   *   *   *   *

Cablestrasse

The Blue Angel had changed. I noticed the door was set differently as soon as I went through it. But the football machine was the same, the room was the same. The barman was different. He sat on two tables, stretched, and did not seem inclined to serve. Got stickybun for self, coffee for all, including mate from very posh bank (Coutts? Higginson?) just picked up in pub. Played football with him. Drunken negro kept saying fuck; reproved him for it. Beat posh mate twice. Then stood aside, inviting Terry to play with him. Terry kept popping outside, would not play. Giant negro gets up, offers to play posh mate; does so. I stand eating me stickybun, one foot on a chair, as is my wont. Older negro comes up and asks me to put me foot down. D'you own the joint then? I ask. Don't ask no questions, he says. Don' ask no questions! says giant negro. I'll ask what fucking questions I fucking like, I says, with which he hits me on chest, half-caught blow on hand, did not hurt, but I knocked my right shin on the chair and my head against the wall. Luckily his mates held him back after that—but he kept on saying things like Let me cut him down to size. I put me foot up again and went on eating me bun. Older mate again said Put it down! And Giant seemed about to get loose, so I glared at the lot, threw me bun down violently and exited.

Outside found by Terry. Walked down NE Passage. Told him about it. Gave me benefit of his fighting experience. Went back, to another, cellar, one. Giant came in after we had been there a few minutes and Terry making up to girl, dancing. Decided to leave after a couple of nother minutes. Walked, came back, telling Terry man who hit me was down there. Were standing at cellar door, packed, too to go in. Saw Giant negro other side of room. Narrowed me eyes at him. He came storming across room shouting I'll kill the bastard! I belted up stairs, waited at top to see if he was coming. He was, screaming something I don't remember. I screamed something back that included fuck and indicated he wouldn't be able to do it; and ran through passage into street. Stood outside, feeling fairly safe, but elated, shitscared, waiting for Terry. He came out after a couple of minutes, saying he had held negro at bottom of stairs so's he couldn't get up, blocking way up. He and others. Thanked him.

While we stood outside, pro passed and was in a scuffle. Police van immediately drew up, six or eight coppers got out and shoved someone in; negro. Pro shouting He tried to roll me! Take him in! I won't let any one roll me! Saw Terry and me and warned us against trying to roll her, as well. Another pro came up and talked with us about her—said she was a horrible woman. Gathered first pro was trying to muscle in on the Strasse.

Stood there a long time. Man who hit me came out, looked at us both, and went other way. Terry had meanwhile talked me into feeling safe and not running farther. Not that I didn't feel shitscared all the time, but that I accepted it and would have fought, I think, if occasion had arisen. Pro who had been rolled came back past us, on own. Terry just stepped out in front of her, and looked down at her. She apologised! Terry stepped back. Terry really rather magnificent the whole evening. Told to move on by two highup police in car.

Went down by bombed buildings, following quarrelling pro and ponce. (Earlier had thrown two milk bottles, one each, into playground in middle of Wellclose Square; Terry's broke, mine did not; can't even rely on laws of physics, now, I said bitterly.) Saw whole row of milk bottles. Did not pick them up—luckily, for policeman just farther on talking to drunk leaning over wall. Went on. Suddenly had an epiphany on sight of the roofline (*it hit me, it hit me: someone, some people, humankind, had thought about that roofline, had conceived it; it wasn't brilliant, or graceful, it was just of humankind, man's, sweated from his conscious*) and stopped to write it down. Policeman caught up with us, asked what I had in my hand, what my address was. Questioned his right to ask me anything. Terry warning me not to be awkward. Young copper, not a Londoner—Yorkshire? Showed him piece of paper—much good would it do him. Satisfied. Went up towards Wellclose Square again—Terry pissed through wire fence opposite spaghetti works. Just as I was following him, copper on bike came by. Went past, but somehow we knew he'd stopped. So we played with him up towards the Sq., dodging in and out of doorways, he following very slowly on his bike. I found a paperclip in my doorway. Did not follow us right into sq. Leaned against lampost in sq, saw copper move on couple of women and man, drunk, laughing. Copper came up to us. What were we doing. I was just standing quietly talking to my mate about the architecture, I says, they're very nice late eighteenth-century houses over there. Very reasonable copper. Not narked. Just said not the time to appreciate architecture, as this was Stepney and any minute a drunken man might rush out of a house with a knife in his hand and stick it into the first person he saw; who might well be me.

*   *   *   *   *

On the thirtieth of May, he was at Eleanour Bull's on Deptford Strand, with three men: Poley, Skeres, and Frizer. Poley was in the service of Elizabeth's government as a courier; Skeres was a government spy; little is known of Frizer. It was Frizer who had invited him to Deptford.

They met at about ten in the morning, and after lunch talked quietly together and walked in the garden of the place until about six in the evening. They then returned to the same room to dine.

After the meal he began a quarrel with Frizer over the reckoning. He was lying on a bed, and Frizer was sitting on a chair with his back to him, between Poley and Skeres. From malice and what Kyd called "his rashnes in attempting soden pryuie iniuries to men", he drew Frizer's knife and gave him two scalp wounds. Frizer, in defending himself, struggled to take back his knife, and inflicted on him a mortal wound above his right eye (the blade penetrating to a depth of two inches) from which he died instantly. Christopher Marlowe, Poet, February 1564 to May 1593.

*   *   *   *   *

What I think of flabby Chops Albert

Sir you get on any ones nerrves. with all you'r rules. regala-
tions. you say you are not allowed to talk in class but you
are not allowed to canne you you have canned me and
others You like to take the mick out of people yet if we
take the mick out of you you start being a bully. you enjoy
hiting us you don't care if we don't do any thing you still
hit us, like yesterday when you hit us for cheering you did
not know who cheered and who didn't. I myself saw a girl
cheer. In taking the mick you couldn't touch your Hair
with a pair of garden Shears with out a lot of trouble you'r
and proper pleasent your' self

English
Composition
on
What I think of Albert

I think Albert is a very nice teacher, but I dont like the
way he shout at the students and clout the boys on their
head. He is a teacher of great knowledge and very polite.
I know some times the children gets on his nerves. But I
think two boys, he should clout is Franco and Turk. I am
very clad he hasen hit the girls, because his hands might
mist and hit them in the wrong place, Albert has fair hair
hanging over his face, he is kind of fatish has blue eyes. I
think he teaches very good and I know he tries his best
that all about you
                    Albert   the end.

English

I think Mr Albert on the whole is a good teacher and I have learned a lot with him. But at times he runs round the classroom like a <u>manaic</u>, and clumps anyone in range of his hand, when he hits some boys around the head it give them a head-ache. He I think is trying to get thinner because he bealts around classroom. He should at the end of the week have a hair-cut, he is always pushing his hair back.

My Definition of Mr Albert

MR ALBERT HAS A POOR OUTLOOK TOWARDS US, CALLING US PEASANTS AND OTHER INSULTING NAMES OF WHICH WE WOULD LIKE TO CONTRADICT, IN OTHER WORDS TO CALL HIM A LIAR!

MR ALBERT ON THE WHOLE ALTHOUGH HE ISN'T ALL THERE IS A ROTTON TEACHER BUT NOT PROFFESSIONALLY FOR HE TEACHES WELL AND I AM GLAD HE IS IN MY GROUP OR SHOULD IT BE VICE VERSA. IN SCHOOL MR ALBERT IS AN AUTHENTIC NIT.

Yours sincerely
AN ADMIRER

Mr Albert

Is not to bad for teaching English and for haveing a little lark. but he is a big fat nits how is hiting Franco and Turky he is a bit hive on his fee Mr Albert wigha about 17 st 6 lb, when Mr Albert gets on a speaking wight mankin the mankin say get off you will break me in three

Mr Albert

Mr Albert is alright sometimes, but he gets very anoyed at us and shouts and calls us peasants and he goes round hitting people for nothing he only hits the boys so I'm glad I am not a boy.

He is very morbid and gross and he thinks that everybody is seducing him.

Mr Albert

I think mr Albert is Very Good teacher sod
I like him everybody does he is Very nice and fat he is
Very

I think mr Albert is a very spiteful teacher and he always moaaning. He always shout at the Student and clout the boys and the head. I think he is very polite any way. Any way think mr Alburt is nice other wise but only think he must not keep on punching the boys on the head for nothing some time the girls need one as well as the boys to Bring back there head to gether. Mr Albert always tell you off you cannot say nothing un less he tell you off or move from your seat and put you be side the Boys and I dont like that be cause I dont like Boys and I dos'nt sit be side my Brother. Franco is playing campion in class he want to Beat the Boys and girl in the class room But he cant do that to me be cause I am not a fraid of him he walk all about and hit Turce and hold him a his throat and I dont like that so could you please tell him not to do it for me please sir thank you very much. Mr Albert is like to clout he people to much.

How I think of Mr. Albert

I think Mr. Albert is horrible sometimes because he is allways morneing you can never say any think without get told of or getting moved somewhere elese. Mr Albert is fat and has fair hair, he allways has a joke with the boys but never with the girls because he's to morney. He is not a bit moden he wears old fashion round toe shoes baggy trouser and a dirty looking tie. His hair is always over the place, any body would think he has't got a comb. I think he is bit spitefull to the boys just because they say something silly but some do need hiting but not on the head. He is not very strice, when he its a boy and the boy startes sobbing or answering him back he gets scared and starts being nice to the boy. if a person stays away the next time he or she comes back he asked what they away for and that is being nosey and its nun of his bisness he to nosey. He's always got some one to shout at and when he does shout you would think the building was caveing in. it is not feare the he should only split the girls up but not the boys.

Mr ALBERT. I like mr Albert sometimes when he is in a good mood But when he isint I don't like him and I don't like him when he tells us to writh or Read, and I don't like him when he hits me and when he calls me nams his all fat and no bone he has a Bannor nose, and we know he can't play the Panio, sometimes he says he 7000 years <u>old</u> and sometimes he says he 1400 years <u>old</u>. I feel sorry for Mr Albert because we all knows he is Round the Bend and a Bit rusty Still nevery midd a, and and he in love with Gloria Haper and Jean Tig and he has been married ten times and he is quite small, and he is not very strick. and he is a Bossy no Good lay about nut case, I bet he Perms his hair Everynight and I say him do the v sign and he is a holargan and he says things about our family and our Grandmars.

Our Techerer
Mr ALBERT

He is rather a nice person to talk too he lets you do what you wante if hes in a good mood he rams his gob like he is soposed two and ceeps his place don get out of hand he is nown by som of the Boy's Mick Norm Anglei and mayself <u>CHAS</u> as poulong the pourden i think he trise his hardest But i think he has a bit more go in him but he dont want to yuse it on us he is quite tall and on the plup side But i cant tallk somtimes when we all sit down to work and he sets us the Boy's including me just fuk about in class and take the mike out of him we also somtimes just take no notis and just carey on withe what we are dowing somtimes i think he must fell like just droping avver thing and give up but he just perseyveres,

MR Albert

MR Albert is a very good sports because he can take a joke. He is allways separation me and Gloria and none of the boys. he is allways jokeing with the boys and not with the girl he think we are a bitter of dirty. I think he is

What I think of Mr. Alburt (SNOTY-NOSE)

I think Mr Alburt is a big fat over fed fool, and he dosn't teach us anything. But he can be alright when he wants to. When he calls us pesants I feel like booting him in the ear-hole. And when he hits us I feel like calling him dirty name and swearing at him. Also when he starts shouting his head of I feel like saying "Shut up you big fat lolop, and you fat barrel of compost. When we read that book I feel like raming it down his throat. Somtimes he says we are suducing him, but I would not like to suduce him for a start. When we go out the front and lean on hes piano he says, "Get off my piano," and ef he wasn't a teacher I would say Shut up Alburt and stick your piano right up your Kyber Pars. And what makes me wild is that he always picks on Turk the littlest boy in the class, one day I wish Turkey would turn round and gob in his eye. And yesterday when he was going out of the door a number of us started cheering, so he imeadiately hit all the boys, <u>but I saw two girls cheering also.</u> But if you told him he would say shut up and go away. I also don't like his type of music he favorite composer is Back and he is a right berk to. The other day we had Beethoven and we started calling he pieces of music Beethoven blues and Snoty Olivers' Symphony in Z+. And when he plays other sort of music he goes all funny and starts whistling, and makes out he's a conductor, LIKE A BIG FAT OVER-FED NITT.

He is orable for one thing for a nother he is a nosens
His face is like a back of a bus.
His to big for his boots
He is a bit of a film Star he acted the part of Garula.
He walks like a firy elephant.
We all call him puw long of the elephant.
He has got hire like a goly-wog
All the clouth he wers are from the rag shop
I wouldnot say wot I think of him in publick.
But he is a good OLD?
His diner is to big for his stomoc
he is related to a elephant I think.
But relly he is a ?
Evry time he gets on the scals the scals say one at a time.
or no elephant alowd.
        THAT IS THE END OF GOLDY-LOX

What I think of Mr. Albert

I think Mr. Albert is a peasant. For I beilieve it takes a peasant to know another peasant. Mr Albert is a great big muscle-bound bully. I put him in the same catogary as Hitler and Mussilinea. Mr. Albert looks posativly stupid having his hair long and bushy and having it over his eyes.

So that every so often he has to push his hiar out of his eyes. This is very distracting when reading a look. But his choice of books are terrible, borring, unexciting and when Mr. Albert reads the noise, is borring and at least five times while Mr. Albert was reading I nearly fell asleep.

9 lessons out of ten he gives writting.

I think he is a fat, porky selfish drip.

AND HOW ! ! ! ! ! ! ! !

MR. Alburt

I think that mr. Alburt is the worse teacher in the school. He is a bully and he think's he is Mr. Alburt 1963. He also could do with a lawn mower over his head, in other words he has got enough hair on his head to stuff a suite of furniture, in simple words he needs an hair-cut. He is the most unsuting teacher you could ever get, he calls us peasents beacuse he thinks we are like himself. Myself I think his a bit gone in his head. And my finale words are I wish he would go and decay.

P.S.

I think he's a big Nancy.

What I think of mr Alburt

I think that you are horrible you always go round the class hitting us and also shout at us as if we were fools like you. you're a big fat lolop and you also are mad. You never give us hard work We are always writing essays and reading you are the fattest teacher in the school but you can also be good at times and could be the best teacher in the school you big fat nit. Slobbery Jew you fat fomf you soppy rabbi. you are a dog. ON THE WHOLE YOUR STUPID AND YOU ARE A FAT FOMF OXEN NIT LOLOP RABBI FART-FACE.

Mr. Albert

I think you are a man who likes hitting children and kicking there behinds. You calls us 'peasants I say you are a big fat peasant and a fatty lamb chop, You goe in public houses nearly every night. You ought to hang yourself or Commit suicide in the River Thames Your a bloody nuisance a big Head. Its a wonder your still alive or otherwise you would be dead and buried, like many of us wish you to be. You look like mussllinea and goldy laks. Your a great big fat kick donkey, you talk of us you haven't looked at your self properly. Your hair is all over the place and like a poodle who hasn't had hes hair clipped. Your like a Ape or a fully grown chimpanzee like in the book, when he gave him a bottle of beer to drink he got drunk and it took ages to Sober him up, I should think it takes more than a few hours to sober you up after finishing with the pubs.

What I think of mr Albert

I think mr Albert is a good teacher sometimes what i like about him is he gives a lot of work sometimes he gets to big for his boots he jumps on kids for nothing. Someday good old mr Albert will come a cross someone his own Size who will splatter him to bits and pices he gives us good lessons sometimes i feel like swearing at him but still he's a good English teacher. There's on thing wrong with him he needs a haricut. And one thing more he rekcons his self to much he gose round the class punching us for nothing and on Friday night I am going to break his Stick. And I next term he better not go round the class hiting us for nothing like he dos'e NOW for his sake. I admitt me Chas, Mick, Norm, are troble makers but a least we don't do it for troble we do it for fun as a lot of other kids do i be glad when we brake up for summer hoildays to get away from all the teachers.

* * * * *

After fifteen hours of rain, in the late afternoon the sun slashed through, lightening first over the south-westward houses of the Circus, glinting silver on the wet courses of the chimneys and throwing the dormers into shadowed mystery. A patterned flight of sparrows was scattered in reflection from the polished roof of a car outside.

Albert lazed at his drawingboard before the great window. Nearly seven weeks' summer holiday lay ahead of him in which to work; and he could not work today, always tomorrow was the day he was going to work. Part of the trouble, he thought, was that he lived and loved to live in an area of absolute architectural rightness, which inhibited his own originality, and resulted in him being—— OH, FUCK ALL THIS LYING!

FOUR: Disintegration

——fuck all this lying look what im really trying to write about is writing not all this stuff about architecture trying to say something about writing about my writing im my hero though what a useless appellation my first character then im trying to say something about me through him albert an architect when whats the point in covering up covering up covering over pretending pretending i can say anything through him that is anything that I would be interested in saying

——so an almighty aposiopesis

——Im trying to say something not tell a story telling stories is telling lies and I want to tell the truth about me about my experience about my truth about my truth to reality about sitting here writing looking out across Claremont Square trying to say something about the writing

and nothing being an answer to the loneliness to the lack
of loving

———look then I'm

———again for what is writing if not truth my truthtelling
truth to experience to my experience and if I start falsify-
ing in telling stories then I move away from the truth of
my truth which is not good oh certainly not good by any
manner of

———so it's nothing

———look, I'm trying to tell you something of what I feel
about being a poet in a world where only poets care anything real about poetry, through the objective correlative
of an architect who has to earn his living as a teacher.
this device you cannot have failed to see creaking, ill-
fitting at many places, many places, for architects *manqués*
can earn livings very nearly connected with their art, and
no poet has ever lived by his poetry, and architecture has
a functional aspect quite lacking in poetry, and, simply,
architecture is just not poetry.

———In a world which offers nothing but hardly-con-
nected substitutes to keep me being a poet tomorrow; not
that I am complaining, you should understand this, being
a poet today is the only reason necessary to want to be a
poet tomorrow; but I am concerned to tell you something
of what this means, of what I think it means, in the living,
as well as I can, I have to write, I have to tell the truth, it's
compulsive, yet at the same time agonising, to write to pass
the time I have too much of, of which I have too much, the

end can't come quickly enough for me, as long as I don't actually have to do anything about it, but meanwhile I have to write something, to pass the time, being interested in so much, everything really, everything, compulsively, *nihil humanum a me alienum puto* and all that jazz.

——So it's nothing to you that I am rabbeting on about being a poet and having to earn a living in other ways: but what about your own sector of the human condition then? Eh? Eh? Eh eh eh!

——It is about frustration.

——The poetry comes from the suffering. The poetry is the only thing to make me face the further suffering. For the poetry any suffering is endurable. Even years for a single line.

——Is too

——Is about the fragmentariness of life, too, attempts to reproduce the moment-to-moment fragmentariness of life, my life, and to echo it in technique, the fragmentariness, a collage made of the fragments of my own life, the poor odds and sods, the bric-à-brac, a thing composed of, then.

——Tell me a story, tell me a story. The infants.

——Not that I am not fond of Albert, for I am, very; Albert, a slightly comic association with the name, offset today, as a name, and Albert Albert, to emphasize his Albertness, hisness, itness, uniqueness, yes, fond of him, I am, very, even though I have hardly provided you with a description of him, a corporate being, I know, but he stands for me, I don't need one: Albert, who stands for me, poor fool.

——And also to echo the complexity of life, reproduce some of the complexity of selves which I contain within me, contradictory and gross as they are: childish, some will call it, peeing in the rainfall gauge, yes, but sometimes I am childish, very, so are we all, it's part of the complexity I'm trying to reproduce, exorcise.

——Faced with the enormous detail, vitality, size, of this complexity, of life, there is a great temptation for a writer to impose his own pattern, an arbitrary pattern which must falsify, cannot do anything other than falsify; or he invents, which is pure lying. Looking back and imposing a pattern to come to terms with the past must be avoided. Lies, lies, lies. Secondbest at best, for other writers, to do them a favour, to give them the benefit of innumerable doubts.

——Faced with the enormity of life, all I can do is to present a paradigm of truth to reality as I see it: and there's the difficulty: for Albert defecates for instance only once during the whole of this book: what sort of a paradigm of the truth is that?

——Further, since each reader brings to each word his own however slightly different idiosyncratic meaning, how can I be expected to make my own—but you must be tired.

——On then to talk of Jenny, Jenny, a name I like even though originally I intended it to be involved in a rather

coarse pun, Jenny Taylor, Jenny Taylor, I've had no girl
called Jenny, whereas hers was Muriel, which even before
I knew her I thought comic, now I hate it, you can't call
a girl in a book Muriel, now can you? And not a cripple but
an epileptic, he was, her earlier lover, with whom I could
not compete, being whole. But Balgy, Balgy, the name I
kept, from some oddness, though it is in Scotland, not Ireland, on the southern shore of Loch Torridon; not that I
could remember much about what it looked like, I had to
pinch the scenery, such as it is, for that section, from North
Wales, which I know much better.

——That's the trouble, I don't remember anything like
everything, or even enough, so in writing about it I'm at a
disadvantage straight away, really, trying to put down
what is true. In asking Frank, for instance, what he could
remember of what I had said to him when I came back
from Balgy, he said the only thing I mentioned was that
I had noticed that she did not wash as often as I had felt
was consonant with my own surely not excessive practice.

——But an effect, salutary, yes, it has had, this working
out things with her under the name of Jenny, of release, a
definite effect of release, though I think it may be coinci-
dental, really, or at best only contributory. But welcome,
nevertheless, having been held in this memory's thrall
these four and a half years, to be released, being by the
end of this book not under the influence of her memory,
suffering the pain of her betrayal, as I was at its beginning.

——Not that most of it was not fantasy, in the first place,
of course, for it was: if I had really wanted her all those
years I should have gone out and found her again, have

made her mine, have made her want me. It was the fantasy that had to be broken. Fantasy on my part, deception on hers. For it was I who actually broke from her, wanting too much, and her not giving, or being unable to give, she put me in a position where I had to break away, to nurse my fantasy without its being broken by her reality, and in this I was grievously wrong, to myself, and to her, self-delusion is the worst crime.

――So that's another shifting of reality, in the course of the book I've come to see differently events I believed to be fixed, changed my mind about Muriel, I have this other girl, Virginia, now, at the time of writing, very happy too, but who knows what else will have shifted by galleyproof stage, or pageproof stage, or by publication day, or by the time you are reading this? Between writing and galleys, they've cut down some of the trees in Percy Circus, for another instance, taken down the railings, you'll just have to take my word for the description, now, now all I can say is That's how it was, then, that's the truth.

――But it is good that I am rid of the ghost of Muriel, have laid her ghost, difficult to lay, a ghost, good to be rid of the using her as an excuse for not loving, for not giving to, anyone else, good to be able to try now to build a new relationship on truth, no fantasy as to the kind of person . . . enough of this emotional sewerage.

――A few instances of the lies. It was Jim Wales not Wells kept the greyhounds; my parents used to live in Hammersmith but now live in Barnes; the Little Heathens I pinched from my father but gave the whippety player his name in payment, in slight recompense; and my parents have two cats, not one dog, who eat nourishing Fidomeat, not Felixmeat, which I made up, yes, I'm guilty, I made that word up; and I am unjust to my parents; and she had a broken not a hooked nose; and it is a Morris Minor not a Fiat we park in Wellclose Square; and at Balgy I drank loch water, not her, and we read poems, not designed a house, and she sketched but not me, who could never sketch, nor draw, nor paint; and only once we bathed in the pool, and it was very cold, I only went in to the waist, and she hardly more, and it was very cold, and we dressed again as quickly as possible, and sat and shivered; even Littlewoods I changed to Woolworths; and . . . I could go on and on, through each page, page after page, pointing out the lies, the lies, but it would be so tedious, so tedious.

——And even old Charlie, had to change his name to Georgie, dreadful name, as well, for god knows why, to say nothing of his wife: I went into the pub the other day, and Bert said, Remember Charlie's wife? Yes, I said. Dead and buried, he said, dead and buried. So there you are: let her epitaph be 𝔇𝔦𝔢𝔡 𝔟𝔢𝔣𝔬𝔯𝔢 𝔍𝔫𝔠𝔬𝔯𝔭𝔬𝔯𝔞𝔱𝔦𝔬𝔫. You just can't keep up with it, life.

——The one I feel sorry for is little Linda Taylor, made an epileptic, to suit my ends, the poor little figment.

——And oh but what other material is not now to be worked in! The visit to Zulf, for instance, who lives overlooking a cemetery and diverts Albert with detailed descriptions of the Week's Burials; the teacher who sleeps in the woodwork shed and cooks over the gluepot gasring; Albert playing the identities game at St. Pancras Station to first the bewilderment and then the anger of a rozzer;

the story of the child who cooked her newborn and un-
wanted baby in her publican father's salmon kettle, the
better to cut up and dispose of it: the Quixotian Adventure
of the Coloured Bird.

——And what of the projected scene in which Miss
Crossthwaite was to have been set upon by a group of
ruffianly and sensually-intent schoolboys? Left undone,
undone, Marlene left unmauled.

——But here's another story, to help to make up for
your disappointment, one story for another. There was this
man, see (there's always this man), there was this man, an
Arab, if you like, driving a coachload of bints through the
desert, for days and days—five days, if you like, and every
time one of the bints—they were wearing yashmaks and
whatevers, and were all pure and holy, undefiled and
virgin, if you like, every time one of the bints heard a call
of nature they'd make him, this driver, stop, and they'd all
form a ring around her so's she couldn't be seen, in the
desert, except for a couple who would keep an eye on this
driver, like. So I mean, he stuck the first day out with mere
fortitude, and the second day with the blessing of a
bladder of quite unique and hitherto unsuspected capacity.
But on the third day, still driving across the desert, still
unable to relieve himself as a result of the undefiled nature
of his charges, for the third day unable—when suddenly,
suddenly: he sees a lone Arab approaching on a camel. In
the middle of the desert, this is, you remember. So, our
driver, unable to contain himself any longer, and taking
the bints by surprise for the first time, stops the coach,
leaps out, locks the door behind him, runs to the man on
the camel and says, panting: Allah be with you, o fortu-

nately encountered one, can you tell me where I may purchase a score of white horses? And the man on the camel
replies, Indeed, this is a fortunate meeting, o driver of
innumerable bints, for only three miles to the south dwells
my brother Fazeem, who has a hundred of the whitest
horses in the whole of Arabia, horses of such pure breeding
that men seek them from all parts of the world, and when
the moon shines on their flanks then they gleam white like
newdrawn milk. Thank you, said the bintdriver, and tell
me, o rarely mounted one, if you can, where I may find
twenty black horses that I might purchase? Allah must
indeed, said the cameldriver, have contrived this en-
counter, o driver of a handsome vehicle, for only some nine
miles to the east dwells my cousin Hamid, who has a stable
of such black horses the equal of those white horses of
my brother Fazeem, black horses of such rarity and come-
liness that when the allseeing moon shines on their flanks
it is as though it glinted on the finest Damascus steel. Allah
be praised, said the driver, o one dressed in comely rai-
ment, and can you tell me where I can buy piebald horses?
This day Allah has indeed excelled himself in felicity, o
preoccupied one, indeed, for only five miles to the east is
the house of my second cousin Abdul, who has taken the
milkwhite stallions of my brother Fazeem and the steel-
black mares of my cousin Hamid and has produced piebald
horses of such quality to be seen nowhere else in all the
world, and when the—— Here, mate, what's that you're
doing up against my camel's leg?

——And another of my aims is didactic: the novel must
be a vehicle for conveying truth, and to this end every
device and technique of the printer's art should be at the
command of the writer: hence the future-seeing holes, for

instance, as much to draw attention to the possibilites as to make my point about death and poetry.

——A page is an area on which I may place any signs I consider to communicate most nearly what I have to convey: therefore I employ, within the pocket of my publisher and the patience of my printer, typographical techniques beyond the arbitrary and constricting limits of the conventional novel. To dismiss such techniques as gimmicks, or to refuse to take them seriously, is crassly to miss the point.

——Didactic, too, social comment on teaching, to draw attention, too, to improve: but with less hope, for if the government wanted better education it could be provided easily enough, so I must conclude, again, that they specifically want the majority of children to be only partially-educated.

——Oh, and there were some pretty parallels to be drawn between built-on-the-skew, tatty, half-complete, comically-called Percy Circus, and Albert, and London, and England, and the human condition.

——"I, yeoman and churchwarden of this parish these thirty years, have seen and had a hand in some doings hereabouts, and if anybody cares to read a simple tale simply told then they can. . . ."

——Go elsewhere for their lies. Life is not like that, is just not like that.

——But even I (even I!) would not leave such a mess, such a mess, so many loose ends, clear up the mess, bury the loose ends, the lot. . . .

FIVE: Coda

Night. A group of five marched west up Vincent Terrace along by the canal. Albert walked south along Colebrooke Row across and above the canal tunnel entrance.

"It's Albie."

"From the Angel. Well, well."

"Yeah yeah!"

"Albert Angelo."

"Ma famly?"

"Right!—One! Two!   Three!"

"Ma! Fam! Leeeeeee!"

"Ouuuugh!"

"United by the Queen, the bastard!"

"Sir! Sir!   Sir!"

"Right!—Up!"

"And over!"
" 'E'll roll, all right, fatarse Albert."

Hardly a splash.

*   *   *   *   *

A funeral is rather a nastey thing it allways makes me come out in goospimples and all cold when i herd my big sisters friends mama pastaway She said to us whould you like to see the body at first my mother would not let us then she went and see it buy urself when she come home she sade it was a nastey sight to see she said that the bodey was all painted up gust like somone on the stage thay panted the lips more red and the face hes pink and yellow thaye say it proseves it bus i think its Just plan stupid two spend and wast all that money on a thing like that it was Just a gerate wast of time and all that work fore relley nothing Just a shocking display of funeralization on behaf of the furm that was calld in.

TRAWL

α   My name is . . .
       β   What does it matter?
α   My country is . . .
       β   And what does that matter either?
α   I am of noble birth . . .
       β   What if you came from the
           working-class?
α   When I died my reputation was high . . .
       β   What if it had been low?
α   And I now lie here.
       β   Who are you and to whom are you
           telling this?

Sepulchral Epigram
attributed to Paulus Silentiarius

for my parents

I · · always with I · · one starts from · ·
one and I share the same character · · are one ·
· · · · one always starts with I · · one · ·
· · · alone · · · · · · sole · · · ·
· · · · · · single · · · · · · · ·
· · I

I have no means of telling, here, down here, when

they will shoot, but I do know, the sound reaches me down here, it is one of the few sounds that do reach me down here, when they are going to haul. *CRAANGK!* It has just gone, once, against the side: they release the towing block aft, it whangs hard against the side, and I know they have started to haul. · · · · · Sometimes it wakes me, sometimes more than once during the sixteen hours a day I spend asleep, or spend in my bunk, rather, for the towing block craangks against the stern just above my head: the towing block is just above, up, and outside, of course, right near my head: that is probably why this bunk was free, why the others were not using it, did not want to use it, that I could have it. · · · · · So every two hours or so, or two and a half, or sometimes longer, at the intuition of the skipper, *CRAANGK!* the towing block goes against my head, it seems, even inside my head, sometimes, it seems; and I am awoken often, if I am asleep, or disturbed in my thinking, if I have thoughts, perhaps as often, as rarely am I able to sleep through it: though last night I awoke, and it was five hours since the last time I looked, so I must have slept through at least one haul, which was good, which was welcome: when I am asleep I cannot feel sick, or at least do not feel sick, am anaesthetised, the pills I have do nothing for me, do not work, for me, themselves make me slightly sick, the taste of them, perhaps now by association, but I took them, at first, because they ought to work, the doctor said they would work, Best thing known for *mal de mer*, he said, pompously. Seasickness, same number of syllables, what does he save, or gain, calling it pompously? I shall upbraid him with his tablets' uselessness when I return, if I return, oh, oh, in relieving my condition, this all too human condition. · · · · · · · While they are hauling the ship wallows, and the motion is worse, I feel sickest at such points, when they are hauling: but lying down helps: I could not stand it on deck, my stomach feels as though it is trying to unseat itself, impel itself upwards, eject itself free of my shuddering body. Sometimes I wonder what stops

8

it, at which point the body forces itself not to be seasick in order that it may survive, that the stomach may be still. · · · She wallows, wallows, slops from side to side irregularly, at the sea's whim, force five only this morning, but oh she wallows when there is no way on her, when we haul! · · · · But soon they will have shot again, they do not like it to be up out of the water long, the trawl, not useful, not earning for them, for long, though exactly when, I do not know, I cannot tell, down here, when they will shoot, but it will be soon, I hope, the sooner the, twenty minutes perhaps, between hauling and shooting again, it cannot come soon enough, perhaps I can think again then, or sleep, better to sleep, of course, but to think would be welcome, for which I am here, to shoot the narrow trawl of my mind into the vasty sea of my past.

There, something to start me, from nowhere: · · Joan, her name was, Joan, it's not a name I like, Joan, no, plain, untimely, out of its times, not a name I at all cared for, no: but then I was not at that time in a position to reject women, any women, because of their names, no, nor for many other reasons, either, so, when she said, in this pub, it was just off Sussex Gardens, church property, or it used to be, near Paddington station, anyway, that her name was Joan, I did not mind, I did not notice, or hardly, that her name was not one I would have chosen, if I could have chosen, which of course I could not. She was with her friend Renee when we met, in this pub, and Jerry and I both wanted Joan: I do not know what it was about her, perhaps Renee looked too disappointed, too thin, too small-minded, too unlikely to come across with it, perhaps: anyway, luckily Joan chose me, I do not know why, perhaps because I was noticeably younger than Jerry was, though he was not old exactly, not past it, or anything, certainly. · · Neither do I know why I wanted Joan: later I wished I had chosen Renee, or been chosen by her,

9

or not chosen by Joan: but anyway, we went off to a new sort of coffee bar club place I had just found, by accident almost the night before, and I made out to the other three that I was very familiar with such places, lived in them almost, carried it off rather well, I thought, at the time, though now it seems pitiful, rather, deceitful, as well, however: Jerry felt out of place, felt up Renee to disembarrass himself, and so on, and she being mean about it, and we left as soon as we had finished our Danish open sandwiches and thick coffee: now I think how wrong we must have looked there, so out of place, so unaware of it, that is the worst part of it, now, the way it really hurts me, I feel all the embarrassment now that I should have felt then: odd.
· ·   And back to their place, which was on the first floor in Sussex Gardens, the best floor, the piano nobile, as I know now: then I did not know, was ignorant of architecture, did not even realise it was an art, thought poetry could be the only art, in my ignorance, in my smallness, just thought it then a rather scruffy area, did not see the virtues of the houses, of the variations which broke the monotony of the long terraces without destroying their unity, coud not have put a name to the ionic capitals on the porticoes, for instances: really saw only the interior, the carpet and scuffed balustrade, the yellowed cream paint and dust-holding panelled doors, remember most of all the cupboards in which were fitted the kitchen and bathroom of this one-room complete conversion. Do not remember what preliminaries, what we said when this kitchen and bathroom had been wondered at, what happened before I remember being on the bed with Joan, and it must have been dark, the light must have been put off, I am sure, because Jerry and Renee were on the other bed, or was it on the sofa, Renee would not have the bed, yes, that was it, I could hear he was not getting very far, but I was luckier, I was trying to put my hand down the neck of her blouse, a red blouse it was, of silk or nylon or some such stuff, and not succeeding, the gap was very small, I almost tore it, or did I tear it? ·
· Then she said suddenly, Here, and she had
10

pulled it up, the blouse, from the waist and there was her breast, her left one, I cannot remember whether she had no brassiere on or whether she had undone that, as well, but I felt the left breast, and it was flaccid: I was lying on the right of her, it was the one naturally to hand, her left breast, and she said, Try the other one, the children haven't made that one all soft, and I thought Christ! · · And did not let myself think any further, but felt the right one, and it was much firmer, and the nipple stood already, all ready for me, and I thought, How is it that the children suckled only one, unless for such an eventuality? And she led the next step, put her hands down and unzipped, no, they were buttons then, unbuttoned my flies and weaved her hand through the thicket, the wicket gate, of my y-fronts, and sighed enormously as she felt the hardness of my penis and then ran my foreskin back and the soreness of it as it rubbed over the roughness of my cellular pants was exciting and painful at the same time and her great mouth stopped working on mine and she said, Have you got a rubber? And I said no, and she said Please don't, then, another time when you have, but I mustn't have a baby, I mustn't have another baby, you mustn't give me a baby. And I thought she sounded serious, about letting me have it another time, that is, so I said, Okay, almost at once, and did not press her further, and we just lay there a little while, and I had my hand on it, a handful of sprats, as Jerry would call it, soft and warm and sticky and unusual to my fingers, until Renee called out she was going to put the light on and did so just before I had myself buttoned up: and Renee laughed, the first time I had seen her so much as smile, and I noticed Joan had dirty cheese between her toes, under her nylons, and I told her I would take her out on Friday: that was Tuesday, and Jerry and I went to where we had left his motorbike, a 500 AJS it was, and went back home, to the suburbs, not talking, me euphoric, him sullen because Renee had apparently insisted that her sprats went unhandled. · · · · · · · The film we went to see was a Swedish one about unmarried

11

mothers, which Joan chose, and another one with
it about palmology, or palmistry, rather, chiromancy in any case, and they claimed that they
could have told Hitler was a power maniac and
murderers were murderers beforehand, because of
their hands, because of the lines on their palms,
and they said writers had two crossed lines at the
base of one of the fingers, I forget which one it was
now, but I could not see my own palm in the dark
and kept trying to remind myself to look when I
was outside, but Joan was very clinging, in this
film, not in the other, she was engrossed in Swedish
unmarried mothers, yes, engrossed is the word, and
she somehow entwined her leg over mine in a most
lascivious way, distracting me from whether I
might be or not, and she fondling John Thomas, as
well, the while, and me remembering which was
the better breast. · · · · ·   When we came
out, I looked, and I was, though who can believe in
chiromancy, and I thought, I'd better talk to her,
and said, Did you enjoy the film? And she said, I'm
always interested in anything to do with mothers,
so I said, carefully, Are you an unmarried mother,
then? And she said, No, not unmarried. So I
thought, again, Sod it, what's so mysterious about
all this, then? · · · · ·   She took a shilling
off me for the gas and we had the gasfire on and
from the worn chintz sofa progressed on to the carpet and I got up to put the rubber on, and nearly
tossed myself off doing it, not being at all used
to it, then back and she was lying there half her
length bright from the gasfirelight and the other
shadowed, and she said, rather cynically, in the circumstances, I thought, Ah I see you came expecting it: and I did not know what to say, in reply, but
got on with it, instead, and she said, It's rather big,
I've had three babies, you know: and I thought
Christ! again, but what the hell, and when I was
in, not really knowing whether it was big or not,
not having had very much experience, at that time,
then suddenly she said, Here, I'll make it better for
you, and she closed her legs, and then took it in
again somehow, and it was much better, and shortly
a great relief to me: though nevertheless I went
12

and washed in the cupboard bathroom afterwards in case of the pox, very cramped in that cupboard, and we sat again on the sofa and she made some cocoa, half milk and half water, and then Renee came in and wanted to go to bed so I went and caught a late bus, luckily. · · · · · · ·
That was the Friday I had left a job as an accounts clerk, unbearable it was, because of this girl, Laura —no, take them one at a time. · · On the Sunday after that Friday I said I would see Joan. She wanted to go to see her children, or two of them at least, who were together in a council home somewhere up in Mill Hill, I think it was, north London anyway, and would I go with her, and I did, yes, and took the kids some sweets, and fruit, I think, yes, and it was painful, the kids in this great old Edwardian building, an institution painted in institution colours, milk chocolate and pastel green, and all the children dressed alike in well-washed, faded uniforms, denim were they? · · Yet I could not feel much, a lack in me, at that time, that I had no capacity for pity, no real capacity for that feeling, I could feel only in certain areas, and this was not one of them, compassion, nor pity, either, though I could make the right outward responses, say something like the right words, though it was easy to see through these, I think, for others. Mostly now I felt embarrassed. · · There were a girl of about eight and a boy of about five, and the other one, a younger one, was in a different sort of institution somewhere else, and I gave these two the sweets and stuff, and she gave them stuff she had brought, not much, that was, and we were talking, and suddenly she turned the girl round to me, and said to me, Look at this, and ruffled back the child's hair, and there was a great white patch of scalp, white, bare of hair. He did that, she said, He hated the kiddies, yet aren't they lovely kiddies? Yes, I said, and smiled rightly at them, their new uncle. · ·
Later she told me the girl had said, We won't be seeing this uncle again, will we? And she had said No. This was when we had come back from the home, and we were eating in some place in the Edgware Road, a distressing atmosphere to be in

13

because the place opened on Sundays, no one likes working on Sundays, but the welsh rarebit was good, I remember that was good. · · I can remember a time when food was good, strange, · · not now. · · I do not remember what she had, what I bought her to eat. The conversation was not much, after the uncle bit. She complained Renee had twice brought men in that week, who had stayed all night, which she thought was not fair on her, she had not felt it was fair to expect her to sleep in the same room, and I did not know what to say, but asked her when Renee would be in that evening, and she said after six, she finished at six, so I thought to myself, That gives us over an hour. Then back, I suppose it was about five, quite warm, still, without the gasfire on, and I undressed her, she said she had never had it in the nude before, oddly, she liked it though, and I was quickly come, and we lay there a little while playing with each other's, and I stood again very soon, and she crawled over me, haunched up, and put it in, and said, Just let it rest there, just rest, but I could not keep it still, of course, and she winced a little, and I had to hold her hips to get proper friction, she was so big, but it came, long and ever mounting, the best I had ever, and we lay there panting together for a long while, and I could think of nothing but how I could do it twice within twenty minutes. ·
· · · · · · What then? I must think of it all, remember it all, it must be everything, otherwise I shall certainly not understand, shall have no chance of understanding, that I most desire, that I am here for. · · I sat up, did not look at her, went to the bath, discovered I had lost the rubber, turned to her, told her, panicking. Forget what she said, all I could do was turn back and try to wash in that awkward space. · · This is all very painful, painful. · · Then suddenly she said I've found it, dismayed, and I pushed back the cupboard door (for I was modest) and she was standing by the bed and pulling out the sheath from between her legs and the emission was sliding down the inside of her left thigh, and I was relieved, and laughed, and she made a face but did not laugh. ·
14

· · · · Renee came in as we were having some tea, Joan had bought a quarter of brawn for our tea: Renee had been on Sunday shift, she was a telephonist, and she shared our brawn and we toasted bread, and Renee made joky references to what she knew we had been at, and it was all friendly and almost domestic, and soon a man named John arrived, unexpectedly, a friend of Renee's, who just completed the four, who was very welcome, as it happened, and he told me he was a motoring journalist and he was on his way back from seeing his mother for the weekend, and Renee explained that he did not get on with his wife, and she looked very sad about it, and John looked very sad about it, and took Renee's hand in his and then we all cheered up again and went and had a drink over the road at the Marquis, which had all kinds of hunting scenes painted on its walls, badly, and there was a shortstrung piano, or whatever it is called, low, anyway, so that the player could look over it, and we all had a perhaps overfriendly evening and took some back to the girls' room, or flat, and there John took a packet from his overnight bag, and there were sandwiches in it, I can still remember how welcome they were, beef and thickly buttered and thin white bread: delicious. ·
· I can still think of food as delicious. · ·
And John talked about the car he was then running, and told me my transport home that night was assured: and something he said about cars set Joan laughing, and she said she had had a good rebore today, from which I took it she had not had it for some time before meeting me, and we all laughed and laughed, knowingly, and rebore has never meant the same to me since. · · · · ·
The idea of going to bed with a woman, with somebody else, another couple, in the same room, would have appalled me, but now it was so natural, the four of us had been together all evening, it was natural: the light was out, and I heard Renee quietly ask What about protection? And John reply, I'm all the protection you need, darling: and Renee seemed to accept this, which I took to be whipping it out just before, *coitus interruptus*, the

15

Latin came to me suddenly, in fact, from the books, and also that it was thought to be bad for the woman, and I began to think I would like to try that, I began to long for it without the intercession of the rubber, just her next to me, ah, yes, but that night I still used a sheath, and this time it was a long while before I came, and she became rather tired of it, but it was great for me, when I did make it, and she was all right then, stopped her complainings, perhaps she had been dry, unlubricated: then she chattered a lot, I forget about what · · I should remember, everything would help, if I could, but I cannot, no matter, I cannot recall what I cannot recall, so: · · I think she had her hand on it all the time we were chattering, but it did not come up again as it had in the afternoon, not hard, but as she fondled it, it was sort of partly distended, half and half, and suddenly she said, I bet I can get it in backwards, and I was suddenly surprised, and said, Up your...., groping for a euphemism, but before I could find one she understood, and said, No, you can get put in prison for that, here, I'll show you. And she wriggled round, her back to me, and bent and manipulated until she had it part way in her vagina, and then she said, Leave it there, just leave it there, and I think we fell asleep then—no, there was one other thing, she said, it must have been before she put it in backwards, yes, she said, When I get to know you better, I'll do it with my mouth, and I thought a minute, and said, You know me well enough by now, and she thought a minute, and did take it in her mouth, but not for long, and only the head, and I hardly remember what it was like, I mean, there was very little to feel, as she did it, as far as I can remember. · · · · · John took me home, and I was worried that they should see where I lived, the girls, that is, they came too, but I wanted to get home, it was about four in the morning, as I remember, and I was to start a new job next morning, with an oil company in High Holborn: and I was still first at that office next morning, and the first time I went to their gents I stood there in the stall and John Thomas was·
16

slightly sore, and I thought towards him, This lot
don't know what we've been up to, do they, mate?
And I thought again of *interruptus* and of a time
when a sheath would not be necessary, not with
Joan, but with someone.... · · no, why think
of that again, I am going over it again, shirking the
real thing I must think about, the end, the why? ·
· It lasted I suppose a couple of weeks, certainly
less than a month, the time is not important, the
end is, I remember · · —hard, but I remember, work at it, force it, the mind tries hard,
does its best, to forget what hurts it, has hurt it,
has threatened it to any point, let alone to destruction. · · We were in the Marquis of Whatever
one night, a Saturday night, yes, and now I was
with Barry, a friend from my old firm, before I
went to the oil company, an asbestos belting firm
in Hammersmith, vicious nineteenth-century type
capitalists: Barry was a salesman and had a car and
I was an accounts clerk and did not: I had rung
him up and said, You know we were always looking for enthusiastic amateurs? Well, I've found a
couple! And he had taken to Renee, though Renee
did not much take to Barry, for later she would not
let him have it, but did give him a shine, for his
trouble, but · · that's irrelevant, what happened in the pub is relevant, that evening, careful
· · Now: I do not know whether Joan knew him
from before, or not, but this man—tall, bulky,
awkward-looking, stubbled hair going grey about
the ears and round to the back of the neck, I can
see him still—this man talked to her briefly, perhaps he was only excusing some clumsiness towards
her, or something: but he spoke to her, certainly,
and I was suddenly jealous, and when she came
back to where the other three of us were sitting I
said, Who was that oaf? · · Yes, oaf was the
word I remember, I remember distinctly using it,
for it is not a word I use often, oaf, it has too many
borrowed class overtones, for me: but oaf, then, a
word of limited use, but I used it on this occasion
hurriedly, just to hurt Joan, just to express my
jealousy: and it did hurt her, I see now, and
probably saw then, she did not speak, drank her

17

Dubonnet and lemon, she always drank Dubonnet and lemon, or did she? And did not speak, and Barry must have brought us into some other kind of conversation, he had a great line in chatter with women, suave fitted him, suave, another word I do not use often, but there are some words which fit some people exactly, better than any other words, and suave fitted Barry just right, so right. ·
· · · ·   The other thing was, when we were back in their room and had had coffee, yes, the dutiful coffee made by Joan, the little in return for our largesse, the slight domestic token recognising that no economic prostitution was involved, for all our consciences: then an atmosphere which I recollect with some surprise, for its freedom: Barry had taken off his shirt and was lying on Renee's bed, and Joan was in her bed, she could not have been naked, no, that's right, how funny now, she got into bed with most of her clothes on, and undressed under the bedclothes, so that the others would not see, and urging me to put the light out: but I was relishing a power, delighting in my control, and made a task out of washing up cups, and at length turned, and Renee had taken her blouse off, and stood leaning her bare arm against the mantelpiece, I can see that posture still, and in my sureness I went up to her and put my arm around her shoulders and said, quietly into her ear, just touching her ear with my lips, Look at them both lying there, wanting it, but we're in control, aren't we? She smiled, and I felt then, I'd rather have Renee tonight, I liked Renee much better since I had seen her with John, but some sort of loyalty told me I should not, and so I switched off the light, and went to Joan's bed, and as soon as I was undressed and in beside her she said, What did you say to Renee? And I said, Nothing. And I could tell she was hurt, but she did not press me as we got down to it: I kissed her hard, anyway, and fondled the slack dug as well as the firm one, and tried to please; but she did not respond very well, and then when I was in I could not obtain a proper purchase, she felt loose, not gripping me, so I asked her to come down on to the floor, which she grumbled at,

18

but did, and it was better with the hard floor under my knees than the flabby bed, much better: and afterwards she got back into bed, I behind her, and from the far side I saw that Renee was still standing whitely at the mantelpiece and that Barry was with her, trying to pull her down on to the bed, this seen in the light from the streetlamps out in Sussex Gardens. · · Joan just lay there, usually she liked to hold me, but now I had to put her hand on it, and she just let it stay there, not working me up, so that it was half an hour before I stood again, the while not saying anything, my left hand between her thighs, listening to the sounds, movements, from Renee's bed: and when I did stand and turned to Joan for it, she grumbled again, complained, and did not want it another time, but my cock rampant would bear no denying, so to the floor we went again and with no help at all from her I mounted and laboured long until I came in a great burst, and she breathed or sighed long and hard and I took the rubber off into a handkerchief and left it near my trousers, or did I leave it under the pillow and did she find it there in the morning? · · · · · Perhaps I fell asleep then, perhaps she did, too, anyway, I remember next asking Barry if he was ready to go and he said Yes, so he and I dressed and then put on the light, and Renee still in her bra and panties got up to see us away, quite friendly to Barry now, and to me, but Joan still slept, or pretended to, and I woke her and said I would see her on the Sunday, and then, realising I ought to try to make it up, solely to secure my immediate future sex, I said I would come about two and go with her to see the kids again, and she murmured Yes and I kissed her forehead and went. · · · · · And in the car going back, this little Anglia the asbestos kings allowed Barry the use of, he said Renee would not let him have it but he had shot his load God knows where, and he did not seem disappointed, and I asked him if he was going to see her again and—.
· this is irrelevant! · · I certainly felt, feeling that sick awareness which comes with almost everything I have to do with women, that it was virtually

all over with Joan: but I expected her to be there that Sunday afternoon, and she was not there, nor was Renee, so I went down to her landlady, who told me Joan had gone away for the weekend, and I was shocked, bewildered, and went to a café until four, the one with the good welsh rarebit, and then to a cinema until the Marquis opened at seven, where the girl behind the bar said she had last seen Joan on Friday night when she was in with a man whom I recognised from her description as probably being the oaf. · · It was just the betrayal at first, I call it a betrayal, dignify it by such a name, but it was that which hurt me in the beginning, only that, but later all that hurt was missing the sexual release. I did ring her up a day or two later, perhaps, and she said she had been down to South Wales to see her aunt, who had given her her dead mother's wedding ring, or was it she saw her dying mother and she had given her the ring as the only thing she could give? Anyway, something about her mother's wedding ring—yet wait, I saw the ring at some point, yet I did not see her after that Sunday, no, how could—I cannot remember. The point is, she went off to Wales for the weekend with this thick from the Marquis, and she said on the phone to me, He's not an oaf, you know, he's not. · · · · · · · And I left it there. · · · · · Except that Barry and I a couple of weeks later took two other girls we had picked up in Richmond to the Marquis, one's mother owned a hairdressers' in Kensington and the other worked there, and as we came in through the door Joan and Renee were there with the oaf and Joan said, Oh, here come the boys: but otherwise they took no notice of us, and we did not tell the girls now with us. When we took these two home all my one gave me, the hairdresser's assistant, was a slobbery kiss and an allowed hand on a tit half in and half under a bra, watched from the Anglia's front seat by her employer's daughter: then I thought of Joan, and missed having the release, at least, and thought of the oaf probably having her that minute, and was very sad and desolate and very bitter and wondered what I had done to make her just desert me

20

like that, was baffled by her giving me up and I still ask, Why? Why?

Why do I trawl the delicate mesh of my mind over the snagged and broken floor of my past? · · ·
· · In order to live, the question does not need to be asked, for me. · · · · · · · So this incident, squalid as it now seems, certainly is not as I would now behave these eight years later: but is this because doing it would bore me, because I know it would not give me release, would not be of any use that I would call use? So, this painful incident, what should I learn from its painful recall? ·
· · · · · · It is now easy to see and to understand that I was too selfish: that is, I did not know at that time about enlightened self-interest, that everyone gives in order to receive, that all actions are invariably for selfish motives however much self-delusion there may be about them: and that the enlightenment is all. I took from Joan, and gave little in return. And I did not see at the time —how I could not see it is now difficult to understand—that obviously what she was looking for was security, economic and emotional security, and that I offered her nothing that she wanted, being to her only someone who came from an address he was unwilling to have known, took her for a few drinks, and then screwed her, sometimes when she did not particularly want to be screwed. · ·
That is clear. And that she went off with the first man who looked like providing some security, even a possibility of a home for the children to be with her. Or is that too obvious, too simple, too naïve? ·
· What was I looking for? Regular sex, for one thing, probably the main thing. But I did not want other women at the same time: I have never wanted more than one woman at a time, never. So I must have expected from her some sort of closeness, and I must have felt I had it to have believed myself betrayed or let down afterwards: mustn't I?
· · · · · Analyse systematically, then. · ·
ONE I was too demanding? Yes, probably, but she liked and wanted it, at least at first, apparently
21

even needed it, as well. · · TWO I was too young? Yes, in the sense I was too inexperienced about relationships, and also that she must have been twenty-eight or nine, or even more, while I was twenty-two, just, then. · · THREE I brought her no security? Yes, in the nature of what I wanted, needed, I could not, did not want to marry her, as a woman, let alone a mother of three children, already, and I had little money with which to be generous, earning no more than eight pounds a week at the time, barely supporting myself, eight pounds a week at twenty-two, for this vicious asbestos firm, though I did spend money on drinks for her, and things for the children, and I did take her for one meal at least in that place in the Edgware Road · · the Edgware Road . . . can't remember her name, from college, though, Peggy, Pauline? · · No, something odder, can't remember, but from college, some years later, I must have been twenty-four or five by then, older than her, going later to college than most was better for me in many ways, bad in others? · · Prudence or Perdita? · · Her I shall just call her, her, she lived in a women's hostel, students' dosshouse, off the Edgware Road, towards the park, wonder if I thought of Joan then, doubt it, that was a different existence, oh so? Forget what brought us together, Priscilla, was it, some college activity, extramural, certainly, beyond other sorts of walls, bounds, too, ah? Aah Aah! · · No, no! Whatever it was brought us together, not so much me, I was never so keen, but it meant going to this hostel, to her little room, formal, a study-bedroom, they called it, whatever it was brought us together, ha! · · But I remember lying on a deep red, coverlet would one call it, on the bed, anyway, and fingering her, and she loved it, but she would not let me have it, and I lay on her, in situ, so to speak, and I said, Look, that's where it goes, it's made for you. But no, she would not, and we went out, to cool down my ardour, as I think she meant, in her middleclass way, laughable really, and had chicken liver sandwiches sprinkled with chopped egg, or perhaps saltbeef
22

sandwiches slapped all over with mustard, or perhaps one of each, each, or both, but certainly at this Jewish nosh bar or sandwich house, on a corner in Edgware Road, it's not there now, had gone the last time I looked, at least. · · Food again. · · I wonder I did not take her to the Marquis, Perpetua, we might have met Joan, or Renee, and that would have pleased me, the irony, at that time, I was very interested in irony, perhaps inordinately, irony, not dramatic irony, which I studied, but irony in life, I was a very ironical person, then. But She, Paula, Pegeen, what the hell, she I was sorry for, that I had to hurt her, who was not used to hurting, usually it was I who was hurt: but I saw something else, knew something else: Gwen: pursued where I would be hurt, hurt in so pursuing, in order to pursue, to be free to pursue. On purpose, that is, who knows, so that I deliberately chose to hurt her, Phoebe, Phyllis, who could not hurt me, in order that I might pursue her who could hurt me, Gwen: · · This amateur psychology. · · Ah. She said, Yes, when I said Sorry, Portia, Poppy, walking again, across Barnes Common it was, this time, that if I did not find someone else she would marry me · · · · · No, that was not it, it's difficult to remember, here, try harder. · · We walked across the common, the sandy lane or path with the white posts beside Mill Hill, I can't remember what I said to start with, but later it was that I did not want to marry her though I realised I might be giving up the only chance I would ever have. She said the same or similar either out of pique or truthfully, and then said jokily, We'll meet again when we're thirty or something and if we haven't married others by then, we'll marry each other. But she need not have worried, Polly, Primrose, she married a Vicar, yes, though he was only a theolog at the time, not licensed to perform births, marriages, churchings, exorcisms, and the like, not on official terms with God, so to speak, an amiable fellow, words which fit him, not like a cleric at all, really admirable for her, she need not have worried, So. · · · · · I knew something else, knew someone else, Gwen, but later, of which there is

23

little left, of which there will soon be nothing left, that is not me, that does not, little is left of anything, for that matter, for any matter, no, all tends towards disintegration, towards chaos, I repeat myself....

· · When it was over I saw Petronella again, just once to talk to, really, though I often saw her at college, regretted of course when it was over with Gwen not having Perpetua, Pearl, now yes, then, rather, no, · · This grows tedious, what am I trying to think of? · · The last time I saw Psyche it was at the hostel again, I called one afternoon to collect a guitar I wanted to buy from her, very cheaply she let me have it, in the public lower hall of the hostel, the guitar that is, waiting like a visitor, as indeed I was now a visitor, and I recalled the fingering on the bed, yes, regretted I would not be lying there this afternoon, that she would not invite me to her formal study-bedroom this afternoon: she said she was busy working, but she might have someone else up there, the Vicar for a very good instance, the theolog, rather, the one she was to marry: but perhaps not, perhaps she was working, yes, she did well in Finals, better than me, yes, 2.1 to my 2.2, Phillippa, Prunella did, was perhaps working hard at that moment, and my coming for the guitar was an interruption, probably, once I had paid her, in mint tenshilling notes, I remember, but how many, I do not remember: once I had paid her, I went, was dismissed almost, without any sign of remembering the fingering, and the closeness, as though it was not meaningful, as though it had never been: and now I only regularly associate her with ingrown toenails, whenever I have one, because I had one, very painfully, when we were so close, or so close as we were, almost the whole time, with Patience, if that was her name, which it was not, and whenever I have an ingrown toenail now, or perhaps whenever I cut my toenails, I think.... · · What the hell has all this to do with Joan? Discipline, order, clarity, truth. ·

· · · · FOUR. If none of the previous three points of analysis, singly or together, completely explain Joan's betrayal, defection, whatever, (and they do not) then the only other reason must be a
24

character fault in me, which is unknown to me. And which I will allow to remain unknown for the moment, until I am forced, perhaps by similar conclusions from other analyses of memories, if they are not too tedious, to examine, later. · · · ·
· As though reasons help, in any case. · · · ·
· What had I from it, afterwards, in the end? ·
· New knowledge of my body's faculty. · · Confidence from consummation of my full intention, for however brief a time. · · · · No lesson that I learnt well enough to avoid later painfulness.

So where has all that taken me? · · · · · ·
· · Nowhere. · · · · · Where I was before? · · Perhaps. · · · · · Nowhere. ·
· · · · · · · Here.

Here, my knees jammed against the bunkside, my back braced against the sternside, rolled and pitched, dropped and bottomed, flung and held in three dimensions by the nomadic sea's subtle kinesis.· · · · · · · Time? Watch affected by falling about on the bridge yesterday? Says eleven, just after, still going, could be right, cannot see the chronometer from here, no: is Festy in the bunk underneath, up, lean, oooooh, sickwave, no, rest, head must rest, be at rest, not move. The unlit lamp, brass, in its gimbals, working like a consciousness. After discharge the extinguisher must be washed out carefully with fresh water, using at least two changes. Could call Festy? He would not like to be woken. Anyway, if he's there, what would it prove? Little: it might be any time during his off watch, any time between six and twelve in the morning, in which case he would not like my waking him. Or he might just be resting, catnapping, between hauls, at any time, which would not help me at all, which would merely mean I had woken Festy in the middle of the night, perhaps,

or at some other very inconvenient hour of the eighteen he is on watch, of which he snatches a few down here, in his bunk, a Third Hand's privilege, I suppose, very few of the deckies do anyway, they wait between gutting and hauling up in their messroom, playing dominoes sometimes, with the others, the fireman, whichever one is off watch. But Festy would tell me, if he was awake, Festy would tell me the time, for he does speak to me readily, Festy: I liked him from the first, when we first started rolling, as soon as we were out in the river, and I first felt sick, it was Festy who found a bucket and put it on the floor by the bunk under mine, and lashed it with string, very neatly, and told me everything on a ship had to be lashed, you lashed everything, and I said I wouldn't get down to it soon enough from the top bunk, couldn't I have it up here with me, I'd be sick before getting down to it, and Festy said, You'll get down to it quickly enough. And I did, yes, spewed up my hard green pear, the only thing I'd eaten recently. · · But I shall not worry Festy now, raise my head, see if any of the others are here, reading perhaps, to tell me the time, confirm that told by my suspect watch: the aluminium-painted radiator, the globular lights, down, no Scouse directly across, his bunk rumpled: further, yes Johnny asleep, back towards me, dead to the world, he has no watch: anyway. I cannot see the chronometer on the bulkhead, too far to lean out for my sickness, an inconvenience of this bunk, again, in order not to become sickened, worth it, no, all I can do is assume my watch is right, that it is after eleven. · · So: I should rise, ha, lower rather, to the floor, she seems to rock as bitchily as ever, not so much here as she did across the North Sea, perhaps, no, but badly enough. · · We eat at twelve, I could just reach the bridge by then, stay on the bridge, then eat, perhaps I'm hungry, yes, up then! · · · · · :
· · Everything takes twice as long, merely putting on trousers, easier than my sweater, though, have to hang on by one hand while trying to drag on my trousers, but at least this is possible, whereas pulling the purple over my head, with one hand on

26

the bunkside, seems for long periods impossible, so that I shall soon have to consider sleeping in my sweater, as I now sleep in my pants, and shirt, change them only when the ship is still, which is never, the ship is never still, but when it is still, comparatively, then I change, or when I can stand the stink no longer, which is oftener, change my pants once in three days, perhaps, used to change oftener, every day, on land, ah, when it could be done without thinking, now everything has to be done with so much thinking, and with taut effort, and one hand always for the ship, for her, for hanging on as she bucks, and the floor comes up and drops away again, and the matting slides from under my feet, and I thresh around to hold, tighten my fingers against the mahogany bunkside, hold like hell as she bucks, she bucks, and the floor drops away from me yet again, like a hangman's trap, no, that is too extreme, find another image, no matter, what use are images anyway? For one thing simply is not another: and this is the floor of the after crew quarters, right in the stern immediately above the screw, the transom cabin, they name it, with a sloping floor, which tilts itself to avoid the screw, to leave room for the screw, to allow the screw due freedom in its pursuit of screwing, or whatever: I do not really know why they had to make the floor of this transom cabin higher towards the stern, have a drop of perhaps a foot or nine inches from the stern some ten feet towards the bow: I know the words, I usually find the right words, it is the reasons I am lost on. But for whatever reason, the floor of this my cabin slopes, cants, careens, inclines, which makes a disorientation extra to the hazard of her movments, which are inconvenient enough, for me, and surely no little less for the others, the other four who share this space with me, allow me to share it with them, though they put up with much, with many inconveniences, are not sick, though they grumble, and swear every other word, literally, a reaction to the harsh conditions, their speech reduced to words on paper would read near to meaninglessly, would present great problems in its transcription, if anyone wanted to trans-

27

cribe it, it would be better not *CRAANGK!* Hauling, yes, I'll go up on to the bridge for this haul, that is, I'll try, try to reach the bridge, for this haul: I missed the first haul yesterday, You're the first pleasure-tripper I've known to miss the first haul, said the mate, and I said I was ill, so I was, that nothing mattered, not even the first haul of my first trip, my only voyage, and I took Duff up again on calling me a pleasuretripper, I who am here to work as hard as anyone, at my own task, and am suffering more than most, am not at any pleasure I know of, but no, they persist in calling me the pleasure-tripper. ·   ·   ·   · So up, up the companionway, the ladder, holding the handholes in the teak sides tightly, through the hatch hanging on to the vertical brass bar, right: what's this on the cream walls of the alleyway, brown, smearing the painted surface? ·   · Blood, yes, it's blood, it can't be human, can it, no, it's where they brush, from the gutting, where their bloody smocks smear against the sides, their rubber smocks all gory with the life-blood of fish, with their guts, their entrails: for which I feel no disgust, though I would not touch the walls of the alleyway, but however, I feel no repulsion against this random blood-decoration, against these gut murals, but though I would not touch them, I cannot help it, she throws me, restrains me, pitches, so my squeamishness is irrelevant. ·   · Cook and the galleyboy working hard, there must be a meal soon, yes, my watch must have been right, yes, good, on, through the bloody alleyway, to a door, a space, I'll breathe a moment, the air is good for my seasickness, almost as good as sleep, far better than pills. ·   · The sea, the land in the distance: honed to one general level by glacial action, but broken to the sea in fissures, clefts, valleys, defiles, abscissions, cracks, gorges, rifts, ravines, gullies, and crevasses: defined by snow at the highest, snow whiter than the line above it, of cloud surely, of some alteration in the atmosphere attributable to it and not to the sea: as the sea is lighter than the thin grey layer up to the snow, which merges into the sky where there is no snow, where the valleys fall, the gullies fission,

28

the firths no doubt lance into the land: the land, which does not reassure me as we trawl parallel to it, be it Norway or Russia, Finnmark or the Ribachi Peninsula, the foreign friendly land in the distance seems less real, so small in relation to the bland sky and the vehement sea: yet I would rather it were there. · · New wood, hard wood, hardwood, looks like mahogany, but surely not: handrail, new wood, new brass fittings, on the boat deck level of the bridge, one stage down from the bridge, strong, robust handrail, yet it was smashed last trip by a wave, a great wave to smash this and twist the wroughtiron stanchions, the violence of a sea that it should be capable of such damage. · · They haul, they haul, they haul! The winch groans like some great beast condemned to labour, is barely under restraint, and seen from here on the bridge only between gouts of steam, but heard, heard constantly as a great gnashing of steel dentures, the warp too heard creaking and writhing in travail as it bends itself to the winch's ferrous will. · · Below me, at the aft gallows, three men wait, at the fore gallows another two and Festy, Third Hand, all six watching, relaxed. The winch note rises and falls as the otter boards weave, weave below the surface, I imagine, great half-ton plates of oak and iron which hold the net mouth open, skid their shod heels along the ocean floor: they break the surface suddenly, the aft one just before the other, and Festy shouts: the winch slows with always surprising obedience, and the dogchains shackling the otter boards are transferred to the gallows by men's vulnerable hands. Another yell and the winch sucks and gasps steam, the grooved drum slips and then grips the warp, and up come the bridles, the dan lenos: then, with a shock that staggers the whole ship, the ground line is dropped heavily over the side, on to the deck, so suddenly, the great iron balls, bobbins they call them, with thick oak washers, as well, worn black rubber-tyred wheels two feet in diameter. I wonder this too does not wake me when I am in my bunk, the ground line thundering on the deck, I wonder why it is only the release of the towing block that wakes me:

nearness, obviously, it must be the nearness, the towing block is nearer, right above my head when I sleep, if I sleep. · · The men give no sign of eagerness, of expectation, not looking to see if the cod-end floats, too busy almost to look at the sea, the great running cables and loose fittings being all their care, for their own safety, for the protection of their hands and lives from the vicious friction of the running warp and the deadly weight of the swinging shackles. · · But she does float! The sudden sky of gulls, yawking, drop and fly to a red-pink disturbance on the surface of the sea: the deckies take no notice still. Along beneath me they haul now hand over hand at the net, eight of them doubled at the heavy brown mesh: and the head line with its tethered aluminium spheres is shortly over the low bulwark, Duff hooks at something, leaning apparently beyond his balance over the side, they stop handhauling, someone shouts, and the winch clanks slowly, not straining, to send one line vertically along, a single float attached to it, towards the fore gallows. Now they watch, now they watch! The winch takes a sudden strain, slows, makes up, and by the fore gallows the cod-end of the net appears, narrow-necked like a pear, swings inboard against a cork-protected cable, dripping, tight with fish, pinkish red, silver, black, shining, olivegreen. One redfish, eyes bursting, mouth an oval of overstrain, makes good his way through an interstice just a few seconds too late, thumps down on the deck, kicks once, and lies still. Festy steps into the pen, under the shaking wet cod-end which is lined with slimy cowskins green-blue from soaking in bluestone, with a ritual jerk undoes the one knot which keeps the catch confined, and the pens are suddenly alive with a mercury-like mass of fish, bucking and mouthing, start-eyed and helpless, sliding on top of, writhing under and over each other, Festy up to the knees of his waders in fish, fish, fish, as he now again ties the single knot in the delivered cod-end, shouts, and the net returns to the water to begin once again a descent to the sea-floor. · · · · · · · The skipper does not endorse my enthusiasm for the catch, even though
30

it is larger than the two I saw yesterday. I begin to understand him as a professional pessimist, I begin to wonder what size the cod-end would have to be to draw enthusiasm from him, to raise him from the set anxiety shown in his eyes. His dedication since we started fishing is complete. It would be too much to say he is a different man from when we were on passage, but certainly he now has little time for conversation, or anything but searching for fish. But he does come to dinner, now, when they have finished shooting, he takes his chance, the more or less coincidence of the end of shooting with dinnertime, on this one day. He does not say much at dinner, nevertheless. The mate, Duff, makes up for him, talking nearly all the time, a great stream of East Anglian composed of opinions, almost all of them intelligent, about an enormous number of things, mixed with dirty jokes and scabrous reminiscences and sea stories and fights in pubs and catches he has made. We eat thick soup, savoury flavoured, I do not know what flavour, perhaps it is pea, or oxtail, but the colour suggests neither, and I enjoy it, I hold my plate, the heavy thick white soup-plate, like the others, compensating with no little concentration for the roll of the ship, spilling only twice, as she bucks untowardly, and try to show at the same time the interest I do have in what Duff is saying. The Chief sits next to me, and says as little as the Skipper. Perhaps he is as preoccupied with his engines as the Skipper is with fishing. A onesided conversation as we start upon the dozens of thin slices of beef, the potatoes, the diced swedes in abundance. Duff sloshes soup over it all from an enamel jug, a rough, noisy feeder when he is not talking, tells me This is the life, and Wouldn't you like to do this for good, Three square meals a day which don't cost you anything, All the freshest purest air one could want, The Sea the greatest purest element, Freedom from nagging women.... · · They call him Duff, the Skipper tells me, and I learn by example as he starts into the great sultana pudding we have next, because this pudding they call duff, and they call East Anglian men Puds because they

31

eat so much of it there, in East Anglia, they don't
know why, nor do I. Duff used to fish from Lowestoft for the herring, the herring he still calls the
finest fish to be caught, but there is more money in
the distant-water haddock and cod, even in the
redfish, which some call seabream, or berghylts, or
soldiers, or just those red bastards: and so the
Lowestoft men are Puds: the mate is the only one
on board: Duff by extension. · · I slop the
enamel jug of custard inadvertently as I pick it up,
she lurches as I take the weight and I stub the rim
on the fiddle, on one of the raised wooden parti-
tions of the table which keep the food from sliding
too far about. A fair proportion of the custard
finishes in my plate, the tilt was in an appropriate
direction, I am fortunate at least in the small accidents, or is it unfortunate, to be having them at all?
Nevertheless I enjoy duff with custard on it, thick
doughy duff, crumbly towards the outside, and just
made moist by the custard enough to avoid clog-
ging the throat, and then the little bombs of sul-
tanas which explode sweetly and fruitily and unexpectedly in my mouth every so often, quite frequently, in fact, for he is no niggard with his sul-
tanas, this cook, as indeed he is not with .. oh, ouh,
ough! Out! Out, that's why I sit near the door, rush,
hold it in, through the door, into galley alleyway,
hold it in, hold, ouh! Along, bloodsmeared, hold
gut, over step, out, can't worry, ouh, she pitches,
ouh, stomach retches, hold, ah taffrail at last, over,
ouuuuuuuh! There goes my dinner, staining white
a few fluid inches of the vast sea, ah, but I did
enjoy that dinner, that I now spew up, oh, what
point, ouuuuuh, more, that must be all, my stomach
must be next up, or so it feels, and the headache
comes as well, worse, cold taffrail under my hands,
now I notice, cool my head against the pitted red
steel, stained with puke, ah, the all-cleansing sea
will wash away my, · · the blood on my
hands, the · · puke, · · · · · Lie down,
 · · should lie down. · · Yes, · · relief
at failing to stay up here. · · · · · Yes, ·
 · door, alleyway, avoid fishguts this time. ·
 · Down steps, so narrow, steep, brass-treaded,

wooden, down. · · One of the firemen waiting to come up, never talks to me, nods and
grins, perhaps at my white face · · my sickness, the firemen have their own cabin, two of
them, almost it is a cupboard, not a cabin, for
two to sleep in. · · Watch the jute on the floor,
for safety, unsteady. · · · · It hits me like
this, my gut strains towards my throat and pains
me for hours, constantly, really, at the base of the
ribs, my head beats, thunders. · · · · It
is almost beyond, now, one pull and rest, stand on
the seat, hand on the bunkside, pull, not on the
brass rail, curtain rail will pull away, aah! Yes,
beating, head, gut, and heart, aaah, no, again! Yes!
Just be, build up pillow, mattress feel as though
stuffed with hay, but comfortable, or straw, or grass.
· · Take sweater off to pillow, no, too troublous,
aaaah, turn, rest, think, sleep, think, half-sleep,
think, work out, think, perhaps sleep, think. . . .

They told me cats were put to sleep to doctor them.
I knew something of what doctoring meant. For
nights after that I was afraid to go to sleep. I kept
awake for as long as possible in case they doctored
me after I had been put to sleep. Peter was the cat
we had then. I remember Peter. They told me they
bought him not long after they were married. So
Peter was older than I was. I was there on my own
when he died, poor Peter. I must have been thirteen or fourteen, then. The war was over, I know.
I was back home after being evacuated. Peter was
skinny by then. Feeling his bones through the skin
was not pleasant. But we all loved him still. Peter
was a country cat. His hair, long black and white
hair, became matted under his tummy. Perhaps it
was our fault, that it was matted. We should have
combed and brushed him more often. And he smelt
and messed a lot, as he grew older. But I loved him.
I was glad I was the one who was with him when
he died. I had come home from school one afternoon. I was always in before they were. They
worked up in town. I was in the kitchen making
33

my tea when Peter suddenly went mad. That is, he rushed around the kitchen banging into the legs of things and knocking himself about. He ended up lying panting under the gas cooker. It was difficult to lift him gently from under there. I laid him on the carpet. He was panting, breathing hard and scratchily. I cut a piece of meat from the raw joint there was in the larder, and I gave it to him. That is, I laid it by his mouth as he lay there with his breathing so difficult. He ate it. I was pleased, and I thought he was going to be all right. He opened his eyes and looked at me and I felt sure that he was grateful to me. That is the way he looked. He and I had always loved one another. I grew up with him, he was there when I was brought home as a baby, he was there before I was. Suddenly his poor old eyes closed and his head fell just the short distance to the carpet. I felt for his heartbeat through the old ribs. There was none. Poor old Peter. I felt very sad, though I did not cry. I felt he had tried to eat for my sake, and I was grateful to him for it. · · · · · · · We had another cat at that time, as well. They gave him to me, he was mine. When I was first evacuated, it was with my mother, to a farm in the country. They came in one morning, put the kitten in bed with me and woke me up. It was a kind thing to do for a child, was it not? I said, Is he mine? And they said, Yes. All mine to keep? I said, and Yes, they said again, and I was so pleased it was true. I called him Winkie. I expect this was because he kept blinking. I could check on that. My mother would know. When I return. · · · · · Later Winkie grew away from me. He stayed in London when I was officially evacuated without my mother. When I came home after the war he did not really know me. I tried to show him I was his master. He did not like this. I think he must have hated me. He would not do as I told him. This made me angry. I pulled him about too much. He would not stand for this. Cats have limits. Not so long after Peter died Winkie brought down a stack of planks upon himself, and was injured so badly that he had to be put to sleep. That was on a Saturday morning
34

and I played football for a team in the afternoon. They shouted at me because I played so badly. I kept thinking of Winkie. He died hating me, before I had had a chance to put it right. They shouted at me. I nearly cried in the dressing room afterwards. I could not tell them about Winkie being put to sleep. · · · · Chloroform do they use to put them to sleep? Perhaps there is something cheaper for animals. Thawpit. We used to knock ourselves out with Thawpit on a blackboard duster at school. In the bogs, that was, during lunch hour. Other kids used to go to the bogs for a quiet smoke. Doug and Freeman and I used to knock ourselves out. Not all at once, one at a time, two bringing the one round with water from the lavatory pan. Once Doug nodded off in the lesson immediately after lunch and I had to keep pinching him or Gus would have seen. · · I never smoked. I do not say I was in the habit of knocking myself out with Thawpit, either, but somehow it was in the same category as smoking, but more exciting. All the other kids at school used to smoke to look big, I now say, my weak adult joke when asked by strangers why I never started, but I was big already. Not far from poor, as jokes go, but genuinely my own, which is not nothing. I wonder what the manufacturers of Thawpit would think? Or Dabitoff, for that matter, let there be no favouritism in the matter of tradenames for carbon tetrachloride. First remember smelling it when I got tar on my trousers from down by the river. There was always driftwood going up and down on the tides. I loved playing there from a very early age. Before the war. I used to think of it as my river. Very few other kids played there. But I used to get very dirty, not only from the tar. All sorts of things drifted down. My uncle once rescued a cork boat for me from amongst the drifting things. It was a flat piece of cork with a stick in it and on the stick there was another flat piece of cork which was thinner so that it could be bent to form a sail. It looked more like a raft than a boat, when I come to think about it. He went to so much trouble to fish it out of the dirty river. He was annoyed when I

35

put it back into the river. Well, I wanted to see it sail, didn't I? A boat or raft is no use unless it is in the water, sailing, is it? I did not understand why he should be so annoyed. My uncle was tall and I thought he was handsome. He had a wonderful smile and said things which made me laugh. He went in for sports and was often in car accidents. Rowing I remember him doing best. Just down at the end of our road at Hammersmith was the river, and there were many rowing clubs there. One rowing club kept an eel in their practice tank. We used to watch the Boat Race every year. I was always Oxford. They told me I was, and I accepted it. Later they explained that they had offered me two favours when I was a baby in my pram down by the river, and I had taken the dark blue one. I do not remember this myself. But they told me I was Oxford and I accepted this. It does not seem important. It was my first experience of the essential arbitrariness of university matters. · · My uncle and my mother and my father told me as well that once they were walking with me down by the river past a house bought by Henry VIII for Nell Gwynne. My mother asked why, and my uncle replied for goings-on or some such. They tell me that I then said that I had often seen them there together, Nell Gwynne and the eighth Henry. This caused them great merriment at the time. Enough for them to want to tell me of it in later years, anyway. I do not remember this pearl of wit, myself. So much of one's childhood must be taken on trust, seen refracted through others. Especially the earlier parts of a childhood. · · · · · There was a girl ... there always is a girl. There was a little girl called ... yes, Dulcie. She used to play with me down by that dirty river, sometimes. Her mother did not let her do so very often, I recall. Dulcie used to play in our garden too, sometimes. We used to play Mothers and Fathers. We would build a house at the end behind a syringa tree. Not an actual house, of course. We used to mark out rooms with stones and twigs. The plan of a house. The early times we played Mothers and Fathers were interesting. We spent a lot of time watching each other go to the lavatory. It was very interesting. I think Dulcie's mother must have thought we were doing something nasty because one day she came and saw us and took her daughter away at once. They always watched us when we played after that, and soon Dulcie did not come any more. I could not play just Fathers on my own, could I? I lost interest in that game then. Dulcie was at the same primary school as I was. We were both in a class play together. The boys had to wear triangular scarves round their necks. We lined up at the teacher's desk to receive our scarves the day before the play. I worked out two or three boys ahead that I would be given a purple scarf to wear. Purple was a colour I hated. He made me wear it. I cried. But the next day we lined up for the actual play and he gave me a yellow scarf. I was very relieved. I liked yellow. I ran across the playground to the bogs in my yellow scarf and played who-pees-highest with some other boys. My Mum and my Nan were coming across the playground and saw me go in. They stuck their heads in the bogs and saw us. I do not remember who had won. Dulcie had a yellow thing too. We matched. Now I like purple, I have a purple sweater. One changes. I cannot remember what the play was about. All recollection of it escapes me. Dulcie I liked. Perhaps she was the first girl I loved. I doubt it. The teacher I did not like. He told my parents not to give me bacon and fried egg for breakfast because I was too fat. He told them to give me fruit and cornflakes instead. I think he must have been an early social reformer. My parents gave me fruit and cornflakes for breakfast for a while. I did not like my breakfasts then. Sometimes I did not eat them all up. Later they persuaded themselves that this was not proper food for a child, and I went back to bacon and fried egg. I began to like my breakfasts again. The teacher gave some kids codliveroil and malt each day. I loved codliveroil and malt, but I was not a skinny enough kid to deserve it. Dulcie was not a skinny kid, either. Dulcie's Mum was skinny, though, and she had a square bum and one eye was different from the other one. . . . like me, like me,

37

after that . . . the green pro, with Terry, no, I was not with him at that, but it was he who pointed out to me that since the disaster of not being able to with the green pro my left eyelid had begun to droop and sometimes for days on end I would have a twitch in that eyelid, a sudden tightening of some muscle there, uncontrollable, an inexplicable twitch. But perhaps they are not connected, the twitch and the green pro, perhaps it was coincidence that Terry just happened to notice it at that point, perhaps he was unobservant until then, but he is quite observant, more so than most, I would think, and the twitch certainly started within a few hours · · sleep · · these things will · · · · · sleep.

They mislead who say the sea is savage:
Are wrong who believe the sea is friendly:
The sea is neither and both: is neutral:
Men put themselves at hazard on its face:
Attribute savageness and friendliness:
But the sea merely and mightily is.

They wear gloves and rubber smocks, long boots, thigh boots, waders, some even like rubber dungarees, if that is the name. The knife is very ordinary, a single folding blade, pointed, kept sharp on a stone in the crew messroom. They seize one of the fish lying about their feet in the pens, seize it onehanded through the gills on one side, fingers crushing the fine, blood-filled membranes for a certain grip, and cut shortly sideways from this natural opening to the centre of the throat. Without taking the blade from the flesh they rip downwards along the belly with ease and accuracy exactly to the vent, and then with a short flick they sever the anal canal. The flap of one side of intestinal wall hinges flabbily, the multicoloured guts hang down from the windpipe. The knife is deflected aside in the hand holding it as the fingers grasp at the long khaki sliminess of the liver, which, wrenched away,
38

is thrown into a basket to join many others, a conical withy basket in which the fishlivers constantly shudder together with every movement of the ship. Two more short snicks: one across the windpipe as closely as possible to the head, and the coloured guts fall: the second completes the symmetry, slicing back to the gill to leave the other wall flapping. Still with the same hold, they throw up and accurately into the washer, which is like a great opened sardine tin with a mesh guard on the far side. Considering the size of some of the fish, they are remarkably consistent in their throwing.   ·   ·

·   ·   ·   I watch the gutting from the bridge. The water in the washer surges with both the movement of the ship and the force of the seawater jet filling it. Each surge spills water over and, at one end, fish, now gutted and washed, edge gently over on to the top of an inclined roller chute down which they ripple faster and faster, to disappear down through the round hatch of the fish room. Those which come out of the washer head first have an easy passage, those which present their tails often stick them through the rollers and thus become stuck. Analogies suggest themselves. The redfish, the soldiers, which for some reason do not need to be gutted, have the easiest journey of all, plumply sliding down the chute to turn half round the circular hatch lip before falling. Occasionally there is a jam, too many tails become trapped, and one of those gutting will come round to clear the chute, and perhaps will pick up those few fish which have not been accurately thrown.   ·   ·   ·

·   ·   ·   ·   Perhaps I feel, have felt, some sympathy for the fish, as for any form of life about to die what appears to be, would be for a human, a painful death, after perhaps some not so short suffering: but once gutted, washed and sliding down they become absurd, the fish, no longer pitiable, even stupid, without their guts, the flaps of their sides hanging flabbily and unfunctionally now, already to be seen as food, no longer as fish.   ·   ·

Oh, some of them kick still, yes, there is in some of them still life, of a sort, one might say, the brain I suppose is still intact, the central nervous system

too: something of them still works despite the great shocks to which they have been subjected. But what kind of life is that, to splash about in twenty gallons, be flushed out, to arch your back twice in a sad imitation of the old way? The anthropomorphic fallacy. ·   ·   ·   · They hose the deck clear of the accumulated guts, debris, starfish, ginnies, dabs, rejectamenta. All disappears in foul surges through the scuppers, doors wide open, and then the gulls descend like white harpies, have been following us like white-winged erinnys, scream in their hundreds as they drop and fall, plunge and plummet, into the gut-lightened sea, squawk and fight over the stream of offal, flap and settle and hit the sea and air to raise themselves with some intestinal particle draped from their beaks, scavenge and hawk and eye each others' lots for chances to improve their own. The anthropomorphic fallacy. The gulls are wild, wary, no tame Thames visitors these: they will not land upon the deck to take their fill of the tumbled guts, far less will they snatch the liver from the deckie's hand as he selects it from the slimy living guts to keep it for its special value, no: but perhaps they are more daring when food is scarcer. ·   ·   ·   · A gull on the water attacking a dying redfish through its anal vent is pointed out to me by the Skipper: he tells me that the bird is interested only in the liver and that this is the quickest way to find it if no gutter has already separated it for the bird. ·   ·
·   ·   ·   I feel better today, and the Skipper must notice it and think me worthy of conversation. Now is the only time he might have time, between hauls. Even so, his dedication is still intense. He sits on a special seat, fixed by a rod in a column, which was not in place before we started fishing. From this he overlooks the deck, the pounds and the winch: his knees touch the casing of the fishfinder and he glances down every few seconds at the instrument's cathode ray tube. The fishfinder indicates by a green line-pattern at regular intervals what fish there are in a given depth of water. The Skipper's careful hand demonstrates for me how the depth of water shown can be adjusted by a knurled knob,

40

and then he re-adjusts to thirty feet above the sea-bed. He explains that the instrument is of only limited use, since it indicates that fish are directly under the ship at that point: while the trawl is perhaps half a mile astern. The Skipper nevertheless scans the fishfinder as it bleeps: it is after all his only guide to what is happening. ·   ·   ·   ·   ·

· · There is a great deal of brasswork on the bridge. Every day out this was polished, but no one has bothered while we have been fishing. The wheel has a brass boss and a brass band circling either side of the outer rim, and a brass catch for locking it: brass radiator covers are patterned with holes in simple designs. There are brass speaker tubes to the deck and engine room and other points: they are not used unless the telegraph and telephone fail. The telegraph is a brass manikin, duplicated either side of the bridge, its wedged instructions plain and unambiguous. Alternate windows in the bridge have crimping levers of brass to lock the half-inch glass into position, and even the circular all-weather window has a centre nut of brass. · · But the radar set, the fishfinder and the automatic steerage make little use of the yellow alloy, being finished in various versions of an official grey. The automatic pilot clicks away its points of error from the set course: four points this side, six back, three again, four, back seven, constantly. The radar glows orange in its hood, darkly cowled, rings round distances, to me difficult to interpret. Behind the Skipper as he sits at the fishfinder is a linked machine which tongues out a long strip of sensitized paper on which an inked needle has swung, recording fishmarks and the bottom: the former as patches of cloud, the latter as a solid mass. Next to this is the Sal log, the speed indicator, luminous pink, the arm now round about the three-and-a-half knots mark as we tow the trawl; whereas all the way out on passage it hovered between twelve and thirteen. And beneath it the long wave radio on which the Skipper calls up other ships belonging to the same owners to discuss catches and positions, its telephone handset and coiled plastic wire seeming strangely out of

41

place in this setting. As the chartroom seems a different kind of place from the bridge: it opens off, a third as wide, slightly deeper, has the feel of a study. A large flat top to a chart chest of mahogany, brass fittings, a cupboard, the spare radar set squatting in a corner covered over, and a duplicate Sal log on the wall next to the chronometer. Brass and mahogany everywhere, dark green cushions along a bench seat where I slept that first few hours before the crew came aboard. Next door, also leading off the bridge, is the radio room, about the same size as the chartroom: but appearing smaller since it is packed with equipment, with a desk elbowed into a space along one longer side for the operator. The operator on this trawler is Molloy. · ·   ·   ·   ·
·   ·   ·   Before each window is a brass leaning rail, on which it is possible to rest one's arm only at those places not encumbered by the wheel, the radar, and the fishfinder. These standing places are towards the sides of the bridge. I can look down at the deck threequarters forward in two places, left and right respectively, or I can look squarely to port or to starboard at two others. I have already become used to standing for some hours at a stretch at one or another of these windows, whichever one will keep me out of the way of the watch; it seems the easiest way to pass the time, and the fresh air alleviates my seasickness considerably: makes it more bearable, that is. When facing forwards, in either position, it is possible not only to rest the arm but also to brace the buttocks against the telegraph, which makes for the greatest weight being relieved from the feet whilst yet remaining nominally in a standing position. For the first few times I would be struck almost painfully by the telegraph brasshandle as it was rung the other side of the bridge. Indeed, catching the pleasuretripper on the arse unwares has become something of a sport with several of those on watch. But the score is decreasing steadily as I become more aware of the times the telegraph is likely to be rung. ·   ·   ·   ·
·   ·   ·   ·   Today has been a good day: I have felt less sick, the weather has been better than at any time on the trip, perhaps I am nearer to under-
42

standing something about myself: I shall sleep well tonight, or sleep and think, both: about the war, yes, and being evacuated: if any one event or section of my life can be said to be more responsible than another for my isolation, the word is not too strong, then it must be that one. · · · · ·

· · The first real sunset of the trip, as well, today: great blazing streamers bar the sky like long banners at a tourney, the light alchemizes the brass of the bridge into winedark gold: now the short northern autumn day closes quickly: the coast, of Norway is it, or of Russia, appears only as a formal change in the pattern of clouds on our port side. Down below on the deck the lights steadily illuminate no activity but the swell of the water in the washer, and the way starfish and the white bellies of dabs move unnaturally in the bilges. A fishgut hangs like a hank of hair from the iron grill in a pound board. · · The green bleep from the fishfinder now catches the Skipper's intentness as he sits over this talismanic yet scientific aid to fishing, brighter now than the sun. · · · · ·
Yes, it has been a good day. I shall sleep tonight. It is four o'clock. I shall read until tea at six, and then sleep. And think.

This must be carefully in order, as far as I can think it. · · I was six years old when the war started. The first I remember of it is connected with a haversack of light khaki material with thin brown leather facings. The thing I remember most clearly about this haversack is that it had one single pocket on the outside, facing away from me, and that this pocket was just the size to contain the square box of a Lyons' Individual Fruit Pie, and that in this pocket there was indeed placed on this occasion a Lyons' Individual Fruit Pie. The exact variety of the fruit filling escapes me. I suspect it was apple. The purpose of the haversack was to contain clothes and other things for a journey, and the Individual Fruit Pie was to sustain me on this journey. It was to be undertaken without my

43

parents and was organised by the school I was attending at that time. I remember once going to school with my haversack and lining up with many other kids in pairs in King Street, Hammersmith, near the Regal: perhaps it was outside the Town Hall. But we did not go on a journey. Indeed, I do not know by what manner of transport they intended to convey us. I slept at home that night, and was allowed to eat my Pie as some small recompense for not having been sustained by it on the posited journey. This false start, I later understood, was one of several scares in 1938–1939. Perhaps this one was at the time of Munich. It would be easy to check: but not here, and it hardly seems important enough to worry about for my purpose.
· · · · · When the war did start I was not, however, involved in the official evacuation. My father's mother lived in Westminster, in a little terraced working-class house off Horseferry Road, and there was a pub she and my parents went to a lot. Indeed, I think my grandmother worked there as a cleaner and my mother as a barmaid, at various and several times. The landlord of this pub suggested to my mother that she look after his son, who was then about four, on a farm in Surrey where he had friends who were willing to take in the three of us. That is, the boy Timmie, my mother, and myself. There we would be out of danger. Why my father and grandparents were to remain in danger I do not know. Certainly my father had to work and his work—he was stock-keeper for a bookseller—was in London. · ·
This farm was just outside the village of Chobham, and it was more a smallholding than a farm really, about six acres, a brick bungalow with extensions in asbestos sheet and lath, a barn, various shack outhouses, two old bus bodies of which one was used for living and the other as a workshop: these grouped around a yard, with another barn a quarter of a mile away up a track. · · The bungalow was I remember comfortable enough to live in. There was a long glass veranda on the west side, and the lavatory had a thunderbox which the old man used to empty very early every morning,
44

sometimes waking me. He and his wife, both over sixty, ran the place with the help of their son, some twenty-odd years younger. With his rather unwilling help, that is, for Jack was a buyer of props and scenery for a film company, and spent much of his time in London. He came down at weekends, often with a friend who ran a car business, Mister something, whose name either mad Em'ly or I mispronounced as Mitter, so he became Mitter or Mitt to me, and to others when talking of him to me. · · The yard was a good place for a child to be growing, I seem to think, now. The bungalow was on the south side, the barn on the west, and between them came the drive, through one right angle from the road a quarter of a mile away. Mitt stored several cars in the barn, at ground level, and the loft was full of film props and junk. A couple of wooden huts formed the northern side, full of small farm implements and having dusty shelves untidy with bottles and packets of Kruschen's Salts, and de-worming agents. A track led next to these in the corner to the farther barn, and on the east side were a cart with its shafts trained upwards like twin wooden gunbarrels, and several more huts and a bus without wheels, engine, and a number of windows. Here lived mad Em'ly, whom I was not allowed to see: but occasionally I heard her talking. I watched her food prepared on an enamel plate and sometimes saw it handed in to her. She mumbled only partly intelligibly: dropped certain sounds in her pronunciation. I think she must have been mentally defective. · · Parallel at the back of her bus was another bus full of farm bric à brac: I remember particularly the moletraps, the gins, and being locked in there once by Mitt: for fun to him, but distressingly to me. Behind this again was the air raid shelter, down steps into a black trench smelling of earth, with slatted seats and a too-public lavatory. · · The farther barn was a curious place: chickens picked at grey grit and defecated whitely while four stagecoaches, carriages, stood around, intended once for some film, perhaps, but now slowly rotting, their painted panels cracking,

45

their upholstery musty with the straw or hay stuffing bursting from it, their brass handles and catches bluegreen with verdigris: delicately spoked wheels, delicately lined panels, delicately curved shafts. · · · · · · · Whenever I have read *The Miller's Tale* I have set it in the courtyard of this farm, the old cuckolded carpenter, his wife, and the clerk high up in that barn amidst the dusty scenery, waiting for the Second Deluge: and the window at which the sneaky Absolon had his kiss so hilariously requited has always been for me a window of that bungalow. · · · · · · · ·

The pigsties were behind the sheds on the left of the track to the farther barn. The great pigs were feared by Timmie and me, particularly an enormous boar which slobbered with fat and whose slightest movement towards us was enough to send us dancing away from the low fletton wall over which we had been hanging. One Saturday morning they killed this boar. When the slaughterer came we children were gathered in the sitting room of the bungalow and made to sing at the tops of our voices while a lady played the piano with the loud pedal hard down. Either I knew at the time or discovered shortly afterwards that this was to drown any possible sound of the boar's death squeals reaching us. I did not hear any sound: I have a very clear memory of *There'll Always be an England* being one of the songs that were played and loudly sung. I did see the boar as meat. There was rationing, of course, then, and the part they did not have to surrender they salted down and hung to smoke in the huge fireplace of a cottage they owned some miles away. Jack did all this processing rather badly and unwillingly, and when we came to eat the bacon I remember it being almost inedibly too salty. The cottage was a place where I very much enjoyed being. It stood by a small brook in which I caught leeches as they clung to stones, and there was an old meatsafe on the outside wall where I kept them between visits. The cottage interior walls had on them many flintlock pistols, old duckguns, shotguns, carbines, perhaps an arquebus, and the like. One night some boys

46

from an orphans' institution not far away broke into the cottage when no one was there and stole many of these weapons. The police traced them easily back to their Home by the trail of footprints and discarded weapons and cartridge cases. · · · ·

· · · · It is very difficult to remember the order of any events at Chobham, but some of course I can date by outside events, not to say historically. Thus, my memories of aircraft dogfights: tiny black shapes occasionally flashing silver—but what would have been silver? They were not painted silver—sometimes followed by vapour trails as they went higher and once or twice excreting black smoke as they were hit and began a descent: these must belong to the summer of 1940, to the Battle of Britain. A Heinkel 111 crashed in a field not half a mile away, and we went to see it, all black and with a stubby transparent nose. Police would not let us collect souvenirs, but a village shopkeeper had a machine gun from it in his window, with a collecting box. Even nearer, a Hurricane came down on a piece of wasteland between the farm and some houses. When they had taken what was left, the pieces, away, I found a small flat fragment of aluminium embedded in the soil, with a nut and bolt through it. I was very pleased with this souvenir. I still have it somewhere. I do not know if it was the pilot of this particular aircraft who baled out, but one afternoon in that summer a parachute was seen coming down and people on the farm began to run to where it would land. My mother took me by the hand and we left the farm at the top end and crossed the brook in the next field. I began dragging on my mother's arm, fearful, terrified suddenly that the man would kill her. Yes, I remember that clearly: I was fearful for her, not at all for myself. We went through a hedge into a copse, and some hundred yards through we saw the man, his parachute bundled under his arm, walking away with half a dozen other men, walking quickly, in a buff flying suit, with leather helmet and boots. The men did not seem to be coercing him in any way, and though I have always believed that he was therefore a British pilot I have no other

47

means of telling how I came to this conclusion: perhaps just that he no longer seemed to threaten my mother. I find it rather strange that I can remember comparatively little about my mother at this time. Certainly she was a good mother to Timmie and me, and perhaps it is an indication of that goodness that I have little outstanding to remember about her. She worked on the farm besides looking after us, but was not I think an official Land Girl. There was an official Land Girl at one time, at least, a lumpish girl in breeches. My father I hardly remember visiting us at all, though he must have done so quite a lot, perhaps even every weekend. Nor do I remember thinking that he must have been in danger in the London that often appeared as a fireglow lighting the sky to the east. We spent some nights in the air raid shelter, and these were dreadful: there were ants' nests, and nightlights: I still associate the two. I would long for the All-clear to sound from the village, which would restore us to our proper beds. It did not occur to me that it was pointless being evacuated if we had to take shelter too, even down there in Surrey. · · · · · · · · I learnt at Chobham: not formally, for all I recall about St. Lawrence's School was trying to start a Gang similar to the one I had been in at the London school: unsuccessfully, for the local kids were just not interested. But in other ways. I learnt to read very well: so perhaps this school did do something for me. And I can still remember that afternoon when, subjected to the frustration of feeling quite recovered from an illness but still not allowed to be up, I read my first story. It was in one of that kind of comics which contains both picture strips with speech-balloons as well as stories in words with a title illustration, and I read it out of boredom, in desperation almost, after exhausting all that the picture strips had to give me. It was a spy story with a boy hero who sent messages across the Channel by means of a petrol-driven and radio-controlled model aeroplane: a highly improbable story, I see now, but that afternoon I read it over and over several times, with infinite pleasure, delighting that
48

I could now read stories. I learnt to ride a bike: Mitt used to sit me in the saddle and give me a good push off down the grass path leading to the farther barn. Every time I would crash, often hurting myself. But one time I suddenly found my balance and could ride a bicycle. · · I used to make model aeroplanes from kits, crudely, and knew the shape of many of the types then flying, both British and German. I knew quite a lot about the war in some ways: not about Fascism or the political ideas —not unlike many adults, I was later surprised by the concepts to which I had been unconsciously subscribing—but I could understand a certain amount of the adults' conversation, and someone gave me a map of the Ruhr marked with bombing targets into which I stuck little flags with bombs pictured on them: at random. · · I learnt that alcohol made me drunk. There was in the barn across the courtyard a small barrel, perhaps it was a firkin, of port, kept there by the old man to thicken his ageing blood, or for some such euphemistic reason as they give to children. It had an enamel mug kept under an untight spigot, and Timmie and I used to drink the wine which had collected in it. One morning we helped the tap to leak more than it would have done in the normal way, and at lunch Timmie kept giggling and swaying about, and finally he fell off his chair. My mother immediately demanded of me, redfaced and hardly steadier, what we had been doing and I, giggling, told her. We were sent straight to bed, where we both slept soundly until well into the next morning. I do not think I had a headache at all, but I have never liked port since. My parents thought themselves rather enlightened about drink, I feel. They would always give me a taste of whatever they were drinking when I was a child. believing that if it were denied me then I should become a drunkard later. My dislike of port may have been partly established earlier than this Chobham tasting since, when on one occasion I was disappointed that the doctor prescribed no medicine for some illness I had, they faked a bottle with water, sugar and port wine to aid my recovery,

49

psychologically, they presumably imagined. · ·
I also learned to swear at this time and in this
place, apparently, and was punished for this, too.
It was one of the times my father was at the farm
on a visit, and both he and my mother overheard
me say Fuck! as I was digging a little piece of land
allowed to me as a garden. I think the word was
addressed to a spade with which I had cause to be
annoyed, why, I cannot remember. They stopped
my shilling pocketmoney for a week. Associated in
place with this swearing is a room nearby in which
I had German measles: the places are in some way
connected. The measles, all the worse for being in
name at least attributable to the enemy, I do not
remember at all, no pain, no inconvenience even,
merely the fact of having them. But there was a
picture in that room of a lady crouching her bare
bottom over the rail of a liner whilst smiling, and
underneath the words Every Little Helps. I could
not see how this was meant to be funny, nor did
it teach me anything new: I had already found out
how ladies widdled. · · · · · · · · From
boys on the farm adjoining ours I learnt something
about the country. They took me fishing in the
brook which wound deeply across their land and
behind ours. Bullheads are all I remember catching: some people called them Miller's Thumbs. We
actually fished with bent pins on a cotton line, fixed
to a peacane of bamboo: the classic boys' tackle.
They had airguns, the two from the next farm,
though no pellets for them. But at least they made
a bang, even without pellets. Their farm had long
rows of greenhouses, and every so often sewage
tankers with flexible trunks and a pump under the
armpit would arrive to spread a foul layer of
detritus upon the land to be ploughed in. They also
tunnelled like troglodytes, these two, forming a
fine pit for a headquarters, shored up with boards
from chicken coops and lit in one case by a green-
house frame. · · · · · · · · A girl called
Sarah, of about the same age as I was, seven, at this
time, taught me something about sex. That is to
say, we learnt from each other. I learnt little more,
really, than I had from seeing Dulcie's. We used
50

to expose ourselves to each other, Sarah and I, behind the air raid shelter. It was the difference that interested me, still, at this time. I think we did it two or three times, I don't know why not more, perhaps because once my mother disturbed us when coming to the dustbins nearby, though she could have seen no more of us than our heads. Sarah would never let me touch it. I don't remember whether she touched mine. I suspect not. Sarah was the daughter of two other refugees from London who were on the farm as guests of Jack, or the old couple, whichever. They did not like my mother and the two children she looked after, Timmie and me, and I see now that this was something to do with class. We were working-class, my mother and I, and the boy Timmie, as the son of a publican, was scarcely better. The newspaper these people, Sarah's parents, read, which had a column in it called 'London Day by Day', I now know to have been the *Daily Telegraph*. Their dislike of us, their bare toleration of us, was certainly shared by Jack: my mother was in fact or virtually a servant. Let me think through that again, clearly: not a servant paid by him, not a servant to him unpaid, but just of the servant class, to him. At least, that is what my memory and my instinct insist to be the truth: to him my mother was to be treated as a servant. Perhaps I am wrong. The old couple bore us as they bore everything: our presence was merely one of the things which made life hard for them: life had always been hard for them, it seemed. Mitt was an exception: I don't think he was exactly middle-class by birth, coming of farm stock, it's difficult to say, but he was certainly so in wealth: I know him now to have been a dedicated motor engineer who worked hard and well for his financial success. Then I knew him as a kindly man who yet often took too far his jokes on Timmie and me: in locking me in the bus, thought of that, and sending the credulous two of us off to hunt rabbits with a packet of Saxa in support of his assertion that they were to be caught by sprinkling salt on their tails. But Jack and Sarah's parents: we feared their scorn, their contempt, their disre-

51

gard of us, which was far worse than Mitt's heavy handedness. Somehow Jack seemed too educated to be a farmer: and much of what he did, in his sporadic attempts to make a contribution to the War Effort, was amateurish and unsuccessful. A granary of corn was attacked by rats and went mildewed, clamps of beet and potatoes were penetrated by frost, the sows ate their farrow, chickens laid less than the national average, kohl-rabi and Indian corn were not exactly staple crops: in the top chicken run, however, Jerusalem artichokes grew tall and rooty, providing several meals for the gourmet Jack in the autumn evenings. · · · ·
· And I grew strong, and learnt, and was myself: whatever that means. · · · · · · · ·
Other memories are caught by the filter. I shall only think them, since everything must be considered, not discuss them with myself. I think I have the important thing. · · · · · · · ·
Jack taking dead and dying chicks from the light-bulb-warmed incubator, and burning them in the kitchen range · · cream and orange ferrets being slipped down rabbit burrows, and then the cries · · walking a mile along the country road into the village, the hedges all cow parsley, old man's beard and wild dogroses, the seasons mixed all into one for me now, with Timmie, our gasmask cases banging against our thighs · · the rear wheel of my bicycle being buckled by Jack's car backing over it (I had been made to believe that it was my fault for leaving it there: but see now this was an injustice done to me, that it was his carelessness that he passed off on to a child of seven) ·
· playing in one of Mitt's cars which was stored in the barn, and finding a red light come on when a key was turned · · driving a caterpillar-tracked tractor for one memorable afternoon, harrowing the sun-brown soil till it was turned-brown damp · · watching an ARP demonstration of the method of dealing with an incendiary bomb by smothering it with a sandbag, information I always wanted to employ but never had the opportunity to · · seeing the old woman stand on a chair and reveal hidden in the roof a store of rationed
52

goods, bought before the war or at least before shortages, tea and sugar and apricot jam with kernels · · the village kids, who threw stones at us, and at whom we threw stones · · the brickworks, vast landscape of smooth brickearth mountains and dusty cranes, catwalks, ladders and rectangular piles of finished bricks, amongst which it was an extreme pleasure for some reason to wander and clamber in our Sunday best until they chased us off · · clambering along the low walls and up on to the roofs of the pigsties, half thrilled and half terrified, to cockcrow on the ridge · · flying model planes from an upturned metal trough in the field, planes made by someone at Jack's studios, and given to us, his only kindly act, as I remember: except perhaps for that in having us there at all.

All that has helped me to understand perhaps just one thing in my research to trace the causes of my isolation: I now realise the point at which I became aware of class distinction, of differences between people which were nothing to do with age or size, aware in fact of the class war, which is not an outdated concept, as those of the upper classes who are not completely dim would con everyone else into believing it is. The class war is being fought as viciously and destructively of human spirit as it has ever been in England: I was born on my side, and I cannot and will not desert: I became an enlisted man consciously but not voluntarily at the age of about seven.

I have studied closely here these two pictures of myself: both are school photographs of the kind for which children are marched out in forms and lined up in fives against a neutral background. The first was taken at the school at Chobham, and shows a bright, chubby, roughly fairhaired boy, his eyes burnished with interest. The other photograph is of barely recognisably the same boy two years

53

later: anxious, narrowed, the eyes now look as though they have seen most disappointments, and expect the rest shortly, the hair is darker, combed, and haircreamed back, parted, the mouth hard, compressed: in all, the face of a human being all too aware now of the worst of the human situation.
· · · · · · · · This second photograph was taken at a primary school in Brotton, which is a village just outside High Wycombe, in Buckinghamshire, and about thirty miles from London. I do not understand why we left Chobham, but it was certainly after the blitz on London was over and there was thought to be little danger. I can remember approximately the date, too: June or July, summer certainly, of 1941. It occurs to me now that there may have been some emotional or political reason for us leaving the farm: perhaps they could not stand us any longer. This seems fairly likely, as I have not heard my mother since speak with any kindness about our nearly two years' stay there. I was not in London very long: the only memory I have is of a coalman's horse and cart outside the Hammersmith house and (some quirk of remembrance) that it showed chalked on a board the price as 3/6d. a cwt., and (I must have learnt this at school) I knew this meant a hundredweight. The stay must have been very short therefore for me to remember nothing else: presumably only long enough for the authorities to arrange to evacuate me officially instead of privately as before. For my area, some division or subdivision of West London, the point to which the children were evacuated was the town of High Wycombe. The early situation is not very clear to me. I stayed with Mrs Davies, a widow of about forty-five who lived in a terraced house backing on to the railway on the western outskirts. My schoolmates—no, the school I was due to go to, had had my name put down for but had not been quite old enough to go to when war broke out, this school was more or less together at the village of Brotton, which is to the south-west of High Wycombe. Thus I belonged to this school, being now old enough, they accepted me as one of theirs, but I knew none of the boys

54

and none of the masters. Some sort of administrative error must have arisen, I feel, yes, in billeting me so far from my school. At one point—it must have been within a few weeks of my arrival—they moved me to a suburban semi of what I now know to have been the worst type, but much nearer to the school: I would not have it. I created a fuss, and within a short while I was allowed to stay with Mrs Davies yet continue to attend the school at Brotton. It must have been an impressive fuss: I remember it involved not letting the other children at this semi read my comics, and *Film Fun* looms large in this connection. In this move or refusal to move I am now restrospectively certain my instinct was right: that is, I instinctively preferred the life which I could sense went on in these old, even obsolete, dwellings of the railway age, to life in the fletton boxes: or perhaps and more convincingly I just did not want to be unsettled yet again. Anyway, they let me be an exception to whatever rules there were, and I lived in Gordon Road and went every schoolday on the bus a twenty-minute journey across and out of the town to Brotton, to my school at Brotton. · · · · · The evacuated London school as I remember was housed in a tin hut, orginally used I think as a nonconformist meeting place, perhaps Presbyterian, yes, Presbyterian is the word that comes to mind in connection with this building, a corrugated iron shed with a tiny bell tower and bell upon its roof, crowning its ridge. · · · · · Here an old but I recall dedicated man taught us. I remember two occasions, only two. One was him teaching us *Beowulf*, in translation, of course, or re-told, more likely, the schoolboyishly gory bit about tearing off Grendel's arm. The other the occasion of my first joke, my first remarked joke, that is. A boy called Hunter came into our shed, an older boy, several classes up, and I told him we did not want him hunting in our class. He clobbered me at playtime. But I had made my first joke. Or at least the first joke I remember making. Poor, jerhaps, but certainly my own, springing naturally and organically from the occasion. · · · · · · · · This is

all very loose. Is there no other way? · · · · ·
· · ·   No other way: the other ways have all
been tried. · ·   No other way. · · · · · ·
· · We were in this tin Presbyterian shed because we overflowed the Brotton village school
buildings. My memories of the shed are so few, I
must presume, because we were there only such a
short time after I belatedly arrived to join the
school. Certainly, I know that the school was re-
patriated, dis-evacuated, whatever the word is, and
that it was probably some time late in 1941. There
was thought to be no more danger in London, I
presume. So much of this is presumption on my
part. There are ways of checking these things: but
I cannot do so here and it would be too tedious in
any case. This does not have to be a documentary.
Dates are rarely important. The question that I
must now ask may be significant, is likely to be
important: why did I not return with my school to
London? · · · · ·   The worst would be that
my mother had had enough of me and was glad I
was off her hands and did not wish to see me back
again so soon after sending me away. It is more
likely that she was simply not aware of the position, perhaps thought that.... Certainly I would
not really impute malice to her. I am quite sure
that she thought she was doing the best thing for
me in keeping me down at High Wycombe, or in
not allowing me to return to London: whichever it
was. Perhaps that would be the kindest assump-
tion: that she did not know that I could return, and
that I wished to return. What other explanations
can there be? · ·   I must think harder. · · · ·
· But surely in any case she could not have understood the corollary? That is to say, to reply to an
eight-year-old boy asking *Why am I parted from
my mother and sent away to live with strangers?*,
that it is for his own good, to protect him from
danger: not seeing that this terrifyingly implies
that the mother is exposed to that danger from
which he is being protected: and that the thought
of his mother being killed and him being left was
far greater agony of mind than the possibility of
injury or death to himself. · · · · · · · ·
56

My father was in the Army by this time, and my mother was having to go out to work to keep herself: that might be another reason for it, yes, that she would not be able to give her time (or enough time) to looking after me: though I find it strange that she should imagine any fostermother would care for me as well as she could.

Mrs Davies was a widow of about forty-five. Her husband had either been killed in the First World War or had died at some later date of wounds received in it. They had no children, but Mrs Davies had taken in several boys from Dr Barnardo's Homes and fostermothered them before the war. Boys, she did not apparently like girls. Two of these were now old enough to have been called up while still with her and were now fighting respectively in the Army and the Navy. She was a dumpy little woman, who smiled often and wore glasses with thick lenses: the smile could be deceptive, as her face tended to retain the shape of it even when she was angry, it was the shape of her mouth, now I come to think of it. She did no job that I knew of: that is to say, she did not go out to work: she must have had a pension of some sort, and I know she received something for fostering evacuees like us as well. She had enough to do looking after us, for that matter. I believe she rented the house we all lived in, though I would not be surprised to hear that she owned it. It was one of a terrace of perhaps thirty two-storey houses which backed on to the railway not far from High Wycombe station, and it was comfortable enough: Two down, two up, and a half-width extension from the back with kitchen downstairs and another small bedroom over. Next to the front door, which opened into the front room or parlour directly off the street, was a passageway, alley, or tunnel which led through between every two houses and which provided access to a small yard, the other half-width, and then to a patch of earth available for cultivation or the erection of a small shed, to name only the two most obvious of its potentialities. A fence of obso-

lete brown sleepers thickly marked off the railway embankment from this patch. From the living room trains could be seen running as though along the top of this fence: from the bedrooms on the upper floor there was no such pleasing illusion, as the track appeared in its true relation. The line carried GWR trains to Paddington, and LNER ones to Marylebone: both companies used saddle-tank locomotives, though of different designs, for this local traffic, but there were also namers which often went straight through so fast we could not catch the names. Then there were great American engines which pulled long wagonloads of war material: very alien-looking machines of great power which I later learnt were part of Lend-Lease agreements. At the station some two hundred yards from the house there were convenient walls to sit upon and collect train numbers, and it was easy enough to gain access to the station itself: at least for short periods, until some railwayman chased us off. · · · · · There were several of us during the three and a half years with Mrs Davies, all London kids. I stayed longest, saw others come and go. Alan and Harry were there when I came, George arrived shortly afterwards: he was two years younger, the other three of us were all of an age, more or less. They did not go to Brotton school as I did, but to some other, nearer, one. Not only this set me off from them, but also that I wore a uniform, a school uniform. Even when all that London school had gone back, I still wore my uniform. Alan and the others forced me into a position where I was meant to be somehow better than them just because my school wore a uniform. I did not want to be better than them, but since they forced it upon me I may have accepted it eventually out of pique or anger or something. Perhaps my arrogance dates from this point: it is worth considering: perhaps later. · · · · · We lived nearer the end of Gordon Road away from the station. Just past our house there was a tiny sweet shop and grocer—really a converted house, the front room given over to trade—and from this point the road began to drop and curve away right at the same
58

time. The houses ended, an area of allotments, then the coarse grass of the embankment narrowing and narrowing until it had swung through a right angle, as the road did, too, to pass under two railway bridges (separate lines built by different companies as a result of that maniacal nineteenth-century sense of competition): the road formed a tee-junction with the London Road a hundred yards farther on, by the cricket ground. I remember the walk down that road very well: I can still see the pram shop past the bridge, and some of the objects in the house windows opposite: a lustre-ware vase, a bright metal model aeroplane on a stand. Turning right at London Road there was a pub with a Simonds sign that had tiny arrows sticking out of it: they pleased me, those tiny arrows, and only long after the war did I come to know that they were actually spring clips for neon tubes. I still prefer to think of them as arrows. Past this Simonds pub were a few shops, and across the road from it a small garage with a petrol line on an arm which swung out over the road to deliver. Just beyond this began the interesting part, for me. The river Wye to a child suddenly appeared on his left through a railing, going backwards through a grating into an arch-opening under the shop he had just passed. It moved swiftly and darkly, that river, and god knows where it went from there: farther over was a mill and some sort of engineering works. It only took a moment to adjust to its flow, the river, but it was a weird moment, for a child. Farther on was a footbridge over the Wye into the Rye, a rectangle of meadowland used as a public park, a recreation ground with a children's playground and paddling pool. The grassed area, perhaps half a mile by a mile, seemed vast to me. It was planted at this time with wood, dead trunks and other vertical pieces, that is, embedded to stick up at regular intervals in the ground like secular totem poles awaiting the carver and decorator: they were there to make the Rye · · CRAANGK! · · Ah, they haul again, recall me again to my state, to this narrow bunk, the ventilation orifice which plays fresh air on to my face, the

59

curtain rail, which is not perhaps brass, merely brassed, I do not know, I can hardly tell, no matter, think, back again: where was I? · · The poles on the Rye, which were there for ... to prevent enemy aircraft landing, yes, that was it, if any should think of doing so. On the far side of the Rye, running parallel to the Wye on the other side, there was an artificial waterway: not exactly a canal, rather wider, but of the same sort of puddled-clay construction. At diagonally the opposite corner to the footbridge from London Road this waterway drew its water from the grounds of the Abbey, Wycombe Abbey. I now know this to be a posh girls' school, but then I knew it to be some sort of military establishment into which it was difficult to gain access from Keep Hill, though exciting once one had done so: after the war I was surprised to learn it was RAF Bomber Command Headquarters. I do not know why I should be interested, really. It is of no real interest to me, now, that. So: at this end, whence this waterway issued from the mystery of the Abbey grounds, there was a boathouse, with skiffs, punts and less easily nameable boats, no, canoes as well, for hire. We often used to hire boats, when we had the money. Once near that boathouse I found a two-shilling piece. It was far enough away from anyone or anything for me not to feel guilty about not attempting to hand it in as lost property anywhere. In any case, it made up for one I lost down a drain grating, but that was later, waiting for a bus. But I still remember that as one of the best things that happened to me at High Wycombe, finding that two bob. Lack of money was another pain, a deprivation for my simple needs: perhaps my little need for enough money, my uselessness at handling money, has dated from this moment. Perhaps. But: this waterway, canal, whatever it was: I think it had some special local name, one word, and an article, like The Dug, or The Ditch, or something, I could check, at home, but what's the point? This canal had many thick green weeds, flowed very slowly, was about four feet deep in the middle, shallowed to two feet at the banks. One bank
60

sloped on the other side down to the Rye: I think now the canal must have been formed by an embankment: obviously: and on the other side were trees, beeches mainly, a small copse between the canal and another boundary of the Abbey. This copse was sole-deep in beechmast most of the year, or part of the year, and once when we were walking there a squirrel fell to the earth some few yards ahead, bounced, and as soon as it touched again was already leaping for the nearest trunk. We were very startled: we would have grabbed it if we could, but it all happened too soon. It ruined the day for us, that we could have caught a squirrel and did not: of course, we could not have done, really, but that just made it worse. There were trees as well on the Rye side of the ornamental waterway, but only for perhaps a third of its length the opposite end to the boathouse. The embankment here was of a different composition, for some reason: it was chalk, and the bottom could be stirred kaolin-white with a stick, and then tiny fish would dart through the clouds for the deeper waters. There were wild ducks on the water, too, which we would throw stones at while little George loudly and loyally protested that they were the King's birds and that we would get hung if we were caught. I do not remember hitting a bird. Most of the time we were thinking of villainy of some sort or another, often we were actually trying to achieve some piece of villainy, of this petty kind, that sounds too melodramatic, and almost always we were simply incompetent, were frustrated in our attempts. But this canal! · ·
At the end opposite the boathouse, a distance perhaps of a mile and one third, the ornamental waterway ended in an ornamental waterfall, a fall of perhaps thirty feet, no more, but mighty and impressive to us. Even now, the word waterfall recalls that place to me, and for years of schooling afterwards an appropriately sized-up version served to make real for me Niagara, Victoria, and other Falls which were otherwise merely names. It was dark, overhung with—not beech trees, and we could clamber up it, only becoming moderately wet,

since the water force was that through a pipe of little more than eighteen inches in diameter. This pipe led from the canal above, and was embedded in a concrete walkway across the width at this point, separating the canal from the fall. At the base of the fall there was a deep pool, which, surprisingly, held crayfish—or did I dream this?—we called them crayfish, yes, or crawfish, but that sounds like an American word. I remember them distinctly, lobster-like creatures a rusty brown-red in colour, and I think we caught them by accident at first by pulling dead sunken branches from the water and later intentionally by putting branches in ourselves, to which they clung. This does not sound very likely, but it is a distinct memory, yes, a distinct memory. I think we stoned them to death when we had caught them, or threw them back. Certainly we did not take them back to Mrs Davies's, for she would not have had them in the place. All this sounds most unlikely: perhaps I dreamt it: perhaps someone else dreamt it. · · ·
· · God knows where the water went after the crayfish pool—wait, yes, it ran or some of it ran past the foot of Keep Hill, a tiny stream, very clear over a sandy, small-pebbled bed, with very bright green weeds, and I (I remember no one ever with me when I did this) I used to lie at length, bathe my face, drink the water, stare at the subtly-moving stream floor. That place came to my mind, and the waterfall, when I first learnt about geology, years later, after I had left school, the continual eroding action of water: the great rocks (though now I see them as artificially placed and arranged) of the waterfall, and the tiny pebbles and graded sands of the brook two hundred yards away. And the meadow that bridge was in, that came back too in a very different context: once while reading something about witches I placed the performance of a potent female spell (dancing three times naked round a house whilst menstruating during a full moon) in this meadow, though now I can remember no house there, nor what result the spell should achieve. · · · · · · · At the boathouse end a road backed away through a curve, the curve

62

of the Abbey grounds again, alongside the Wye for fifty yards or so, to a road bridge near the main road by the civic buildings. Over the Abbey wall at this point, fence it was, rather, were greenhouses and some great horse chestnut trees. These latter attracted us several times over the wooden fence and the barbed wire along its top, and once we were caught and shown smartly out by the main gate with an austere warning. Other times we were more successful, harvesting great burdens of milk-crowned conkers. One autumn we heard that conkers helped the War Effort, as rosehips did: the centre for collecting these was down in the High Street near the covered market place, Guildhall, or whatever it was. We found enough ripe red rosehips to half fill a jamjar, and enough conkers to fill an old pram. They gave us threepence for the rosehips and said that did not want the conkers, had, indeed, never wanted conkers. They were even somewhat rude about it, as I remember. In a fit of justified (I feel) disgust with authority we wheeled the pram in the deepest disappointment round the corner to the deserted market, tipped it briefly over on to the cobbles as a very satisfying antisocial gesture, and ran, ran, ran, pulling the pram behind, up through the town and away, not pausing until we were certain we had not been followed. I still feel something of that disappointment: here they were on at everybody to help in the War Effort, and when we did, our efforts were spurned. Now, I feel they might at least have accepted the conkers, told us no more were wanted, and thrown these away themselves when we had gone: but ... the bastards. · · · · · · ·
The playground on the Rye—swings, roundabout, slide, climbing frame—was looked after by an old man, Uncle Tom all the kids called him, a seafaring old josser with a beard and face like the sailor on a Player's packet, but wearing a peaked cap. Once he retired, but the local paper said the kids made such a fuss he had to be re-employed. I never made a fuss about Uncle Tom, though I was glad to see him back. He used to rub candlewax on the slide to make you go faster. · · · · · · · Just

where the road from the boathouse turned there was some sort of official building—yes, a clinic, I remember now, I went there to have my teeth attended to at least once, more than once. Just in front of this there was some sort of shelter, like a bus shelter, a roof and a skeletal frame. I do not think I ever knew what function it had. At one point I wanted the other boys to perform a play in this shelter, to the public. It sounds now a quite ludicrous and unpractical idea, and I do not think it ever went very far towards fruition. But it was an idea: I can still remember being elated with the romance and excitement of the idea. The play was I think some sort of dramatisation of *The Wind in the Willows*, incongruously, pathetically, I see now.

· · Farther along this side there was a mill behind a brick wall, and the river flowed under this mill, naturally, driving I do not know what machinery. The wall was perhaps four feet high and easy for us to climb: a foot in the cupped hands of Alan or Harry, back against the wall, a lift up for the last man, and we were standing on the top. We first did this to see what the river was doing after it ran behind the clinic and before it appeared at a bridge from London Road farther up: it ran against the wall immediately below where we had climbed up, and slid blackly under the mill. But what interested us more was that the garden of the mill was full of fruit bushes and trees: black and red-currants, apples, pears at least. But at the point the river left the wall a spear-pointed railing began with a vicious segment bowed spikily out into the garden. I suppose it must have been a July day when we decided we would help ourselves to fruit, for the blackcurrants were ripe. We climbed on to the wall, swung out over the segment which bore our single weights apparently safely but which needed careful negotiation if one's trousers, to say nothing of one's privates, were not to be savagely torn. Once round this, it was easy to edge along the railings standing on top of the wall and then drop off on to a wedge of land, cross a narrow wooden bridge over the river, and the fruit was ours. I do not know who saw her first, but I think I must have

64

been the last to see this old woman come running out of the house. Certainly I was last across the bridge and last up on the wall, and I had nearly reached that spiky segment when she grabbed my ankle from below with both hands and prevented me from moving farther. Harry and Alan were over and I saw them running very quickly away towards the clinic, not looking back at all. I felt sickened, wishing it had not happened, trying to shake off the old woman's hand. Perhaps she was not so old: everyone over thirty seems old to the child, this cliché is true, as so many others are. After a very short while I gave in to her repeated commands to come down. What else was there to do? I was never one for stalemate: I liked things decided, even against me. What would I have done now? I might have threatened to smash her face in with the foot she was not holding, but I doubt very much if I would actually do that even now. Then I was really a coward, or at least had a great distaste for and fear of violence of any sort. What else was there to do? She led me by the arm into a farmhouse-like kitchen, with a flagged floor and an inglenook fireplace, rather bare, that kitchen, now I think of it, where she asked me which school I went to. I would not tell her. She said it must be Scale Lane, which it was not, at that time. I said nothing at all. Then she suddenly snatched a diary from the top pocket of my cheap jacket, triumphantly, and found out all she wanted to know. It was one of those schoolboys' diaries which contain pages to be filled in with all kinds of personal particulars, amongst which was included my school and indeed the name of my headmaster, I believe. She wrote these down and handed the diary back to me, smirking and saying that my headmaster would be hearing from her in the near future: then led me to the door opening on to the bridge to London Road whilst still holding my arm in the pinching two-handed grip which she had used to bring me indoors from the garden. I have never filled in personal details in any other diary since, and indeed have always subsequently disliked pocket diaries and have very rarely carried one. · ·

This was a Saturday afternoon, I am fairly sure, which meant I had most of a weekend worrying about what was going to be done to me when the old cow's letter reached Mr Cunliffe. If she wrote before Sunday post, then it would arrive Monday morning and I would be for it some time that day. She seemed in the mood to sit down and write that minute. But Monday passed without anything being said, Tuesday too, and Wednesday. The agonies of conscience, guilt, and fear of punishment I had been in for days began to lessen, and I imagined that an almost unimaginable clemency had overtaken the old woman. Then, right at the end of school on Thursday, just as we were standing by our desks ready to be dismissed, the teacher told me to see the headmaster before I went home, and indicated I should do so now, go before the others did. I walked out, embarrassed, ashamed. Now ... this teacher ... it was in the top class of that junior school ... I do not remember her name ... but that means I must have been ten, if I was in the top class: · · I've jumped, this piece is out of order. No matter. · · The headmaster had me sit down opposite him, packed his pipe, and then said, without looking up, So you like fruit, eh? It had come at last. I felt relieved, tonight I would sleep properly, the punishment would be over. Why d'you have to steal it? he went on. I said nothing. If you want fruit, don't steal it: I'll give you some: you can come any time you like to my garden and help yourself to fruit, he said, still not looking up. I do not remember answering, or him saying any more. Surely I said something? It seems likely that I cried during this interview, very likely, for I cried easily, at this time. He did not punish me physically: the shame of the way he did punish me, by humiliation, by making me feel a pauper, an underprivileged thief to be understood, remains with me still. · · · · · · · · That same woman teacher who added her own mite to this punishment also inflicted another humiliation on me, about something different, on a separate occasion, that I also remember with pain. I had lost my Bible for one lesson: it had just disappeared from

66

my desk: someone had obviously taken it: so I did the same, took someone else's, but was caught doing so. She—it seems she was a girl—complained to the teacher, who strode up to my desk, took the book away from me and returned it to the girl and then wrote in capital letters on the board the three words THIEF and LIAR and CHEAT. She turned, looked directly at me, and said Ugly words, aren't they? And repeated, Ugly words. No more. This time added to my embarrassment, humilation, was also the injustice of it all: I had neither lied nor cheated, and the theft was only a nominal one, as schoolbooks were common property amongst children, not personal possessions like fountain pens or pencil boxes. She had no right: but she had the power, ah, the power! · · · · · · ·

Everything else at Brotton school. I might as well finish everything else I can remember at Brotton school. · · · · · · · This same teacher ... what else? A play, yes, with pirates or some species of villain, and soldiers, another species. I was chief pirate, perhaps this was typecasting on her part, had my words written out in her square hand on lined paper with just a few previous words as cues, in a different coloured ink: but I was ill for a few days, and when I came back she had given my part to another boy, a boy who I can still see in a white shirt and red sash, with a black patch over one eye, holding a stripped willow stick as a sword. Perhaps this was another way for her to hurt me: to make me play the villain and, when I had accepted this role as at least an identity, a secure place, to deprive me of even that. I was made a soldier, one of a group who came on at the end, a very small part. I do not remember a performance, but I do remember costume rehearsals: fat Burston was too big for any of the soldiers' uniforms, and I suggested that the teacher's—Miss Hearne, I've just remembered her name, Miss Hearne—I suggested that Miss Hearne's coat would do for him, which was a short red jacket with no lapels, and unexpectedly she agreed, even seemed to commend me for the suggestion. There is a photograph of the cast of that play somewhere,

at home, all of us standing on the school steps. I do not remember what I look like, but perhaps that is where I have the image from of the boy with the willow sword. · · · · · Miss Hearne's was the top class. I was a milk monitor ... yes ... fractions: I missed an important lesson on fractions one morning by being milk monitor, by taking an inordinately long while to carry round the crates to each classroom, on purpose, with another boy, and it was years before I caught up on fractions, yes, years, though I was so relieved not to have to learn them that morning, so relieved, but is that significant? A significant gratuity, yes, one of the points at which things are decided, in which life is directed, yes: for I did not lack brains, I did not lack the capacity to learn: but at this point this capacity was directed away from maths and towards nothing else in particular, went inwards upon itself, I suppose. I believe, all aptitude aside, I could have been made interested in maths, in the scientific side: was ready material to be formed in one shape or another by a sufficiently good teacher: my brain could have been made to apply itself to anything. It was generally applied to nothing: except perhaps itself, whatever that may mean. ·
· · · · · · · I first knew love in Miss Hearne's class, I think. Love, that is, as distinct from the peering at genitals with Dulcie, and Sarah, were their names? This girl I do not remember the name of, I am not good at names, so. It started with looks, as these things do, loving looks across the classroom, looks which encouraged me to believe she felt the same, or similar, love, a kind of love, a kind of burning inside the mind which left no room to think about anything else. It must have been St George's Day, Empire Day, that is, 1942 or 1943, I suppose, more likely the latter, for we were in class listening to a radio programme from round the world, and even now I associate *Waltzing Matilda* with that girl's face, pretty in a sharp, small way, and that love I felt between us. I took it that one stage further, fatally: I wrote a note declaring this love and gave it to her at playtime. This destroyed the love, I was surprised and dis-
68

appointed and pained to find: for I saw her giggling with her friends over the note, and later they were all giggling at me. Then the other boys knew from the other girls. This was a betrayal of my fine, intense emotion, and it ceased as a result. I did not worry about its loss so much as the embarrassment of having to stay in the same class with her: an embarrassment that has been repeated so many times since, oh so many times since, in classrooms and offices, rooms of all kinds and various forms of transport and, oh, so many times! · · · · ·

· · · Burston, fat Burston I had a fight with in the playground, over I remember not what. All that lunch hour we circled each other round the playground, neither landing a blow that hurt, both afraid not so much of the other as of violence, as of pain, as of blood and crying. Eventually after a long while I pretended to be hurt by a low blow of Burston's, broke into something convincingly like tears, and went round complaining that I had been beaten by a foul blow. At least it ended it, the fight, at least both of us could claim not to have lost, even both to have won, clever resolution, I feel now. I was never one for stalemate, again: I liked things decided: either way. Would force a decision against myself if necessary: how often have I done this with girls, with love relationships? Far too often.

· · · · · In the playground another lunch hour a boy cut his arm, the fleshy part midway between his elbow and his shoulder, on the pointed railings between the school and the road. It was a pyramidal sort of wound, as deep as the two cuts were long, with much blood. I did not actually see him do it, but I was near enough to realise what had happened. I volunteered when Mr Cunliffe asked for eyewitnesses and told him that the boy had been climbing the railings and had fallen backwards, cutting himself before he had had time to hold with his other hand. It seemed obvious that this was what had happened, though I had not actually seen it: perhaps I did deserve to be called a LIAR. · · · · · The playground had a great shed for us to use when it was wet, and along one of the shorter sides of this there were lined half a

69

dozen or so galvanised water-tanks with wooden lids. These contained the emergency water supply for either us, or the village, or both, in case the mains were damaged by bombing. They were green and slimy inside, and I consciously feared the occasion upon which I would need to have to drink from them. I was one of the monitors who drained these tanks every Friday afternoon and refilled them from a tap in the main building through a long black hose. I was given several menial jobs like this, I see now: having been a teacher, I recognise this as being either because it was thought absence from learning would do me harm less than anyone else in the class, or being done out of spite, out of a desire not to be put to the necessity of even looking at my face. This was Miss Hearne's class again, the top of the juniors. One other thing about her comes to mind. We read, that is two boys I knew, read in the local paper that the mayor or someone like that had visited the central kitchens where our school dinners were cooked, had plunged his hand into a sackful of school greens and had found them mushy, yes, mushy was the word, I think that was probably the time mushy first entered my vocabulary. One of the boys on my table put a cutting of this incident next to his plate as we sat eating school greens, and Miss Hearne came up and screwed up the cutting and said she wanted to see every scrap of everything cleaned up off every plate, particularly the greens. We cleared up everything, but it was brave of the boy who did it. Miss Hearne was a right all-round cow, now I come to consider it. But it was wartime: perhaps she had some justification for her impatience with us. But the meals were very poor, I do remember. · · · · · The main school buildings were an island in a sea of playground. On the side nearest the road there was a flagpole, up against which we used to play cricket with a tennis ball and an old bat with a very springy handle, all falling to bits. I can still remember the sensation of making a hit with that bat: no bat was ever the same, afterwards, they were all too stiff, had too little latent power, power of their own. I remember
70

the construction of the flagpole: two side pieces
with a bolt through the top and through the pole
itself in the middle of them: I realised they must
have bolted this one horizontally and then swung
the top up and the end down and bolted it there.
Perhaps it was through observing these things that
I was poor at cricket, could not concentrate. I was
usually out to the first straight ball, after I had won
my innings either by a catch or, very much more
rarely, had bowled someone by my all too orthodox
action. I could never make a ball spin: perhaps no
one could make a tennis ball break on asphalt:
could ask Zulf, he would know: when I return.
However. We also played football with a tennis
ball in that playground, at the other end. I was
better at football, though not by any means outstanding, and not as good at that time as I later
became. · · Right at the top end were shelters,
air raid shelters. I remember being in these only
once, as part of a drill. They were dark, cold, dank,
and again I hoped, as with the emergency water,
that I would never be called upon to use them in
earnest. Nearby was a children's drinking fountain
at which, once, having splashed my face with water
to cool myself after a hot playtime running about,
a girl asked me, astonished, if it was all sweat on
my face, and I, lying, said Yes. For some reason I
cannot at all explain, this memory is closely associated with a chromium Bosch cycle dynamo. · ·
· · · Beyond the shelters a path led up to a
patch of ground with elders beside the path. This
land, perhaps it was an allotment, belonged to the
headmaster and was cultivated, though the word
suggests something far too sophisticated, by the
children as their gardening lesson. We grew cab-
bages, sprouts, lettuces, parsnips and other vegetables for that man. Pressed labour we were, and
never tasted a green leaf for our trouble. Nor do I
remember learning anything either: I hated gardening. It was not as though we were providing
our own mushy greens, either. · · Not always
... we did not always have dinner at that school,
for we sometimes went to a secondary school, a
big-boys' school, not far away, for school dinners

71

there. They were no better, I feel, for probably that was where the primary ones were cooked before being transported half a mile up the road. But there was more to do afterwards there, on a great grassy open space with the occasional tree and a swimming pool at one end. Not that I went swimming much there. Once, I think, when a man taught us rather badly to try to swim: I did not learn from him. That was another thing about the war that caused us to miss things: in peacetime there would almost certainly have been someone around with interest and special knowledge to have taught a difficult case like me to swim. The same is true of all the other teachers who were not there, who were at war. At least the probability of there being someone there would have been greater. Perhaps I delude myself: perhaps I am what I would always have been. · · The big boys at this secondary school would make expeditions a mile away to see one train pass at a roadbridge, the lunchtime express or something, in order to collect its name and number: their dedication impressed me: so did the standard of football they played. · · Returning to our own school we passed a baker who sold good cream buns, which of course could not have been made with cream but which were still delicious. That baker's is weirdly associated with Wimbledon railway station in my mind, and with an announcement in the papers at the time that rye was going to be used in bread. That does not seem very logical, to say the least. No mind is logical, logic is not a quality of mind. At a sweetshop and stationers someone started a craze for buying flat boxes of six (was it?) Anadin tablets, dissolving them in water in a small bottle of aspirin size, and drinking the pink liquid as though it were lemonade or some other children's beverage. No one came to harm of this craze, that I knew of: it seems very fortunate and most unlikely. Next to the secondary school there was a hut, a workmen's café, an eating place where more than once—or was it only once?—I queued up at the side door, from which warm smells from the paraffin cookers blew, and bought a Slice. This was a piece of white bread about an

72

inch and a half thick, thickly in proportion covered with margarine. This was after school: I was hungry: it seemed natural to go there for something to eat: I was hungry! I had the penny it cost, the Slice, to spare: I enjoyed it, I remember enjoying it. Next morning in Assembly the headmaster, without mentioning my name, remarked adversely on a certain child from his school who had shown it up by being hungry and satisfying this hunger at such a common eating place. It was some time before I realised he was talking about me. It was humiliating to realise it. Another humiliation. I felt they all knew it was me. They probably did. These things get around. I was only hungry. I see no shame now, despise them for taking their bourgeois offence. The class war again. They made me their enemy. I am satisfied that they did. They will have cause to remember me: have had. · · · · · My clothes, too, were a source of shame, or, rather, of anxiety about shame, I felt anxious lest my clothes should bring me to feel shame, that others were looking down on me because of my clothes: I was an awkward boy, heavy, I grew quickly, my clothes were never expensive ones, often of the cheapest kind, I led them a rough life. I have never had enough clothes to change often, to give clothes the rest they are curiously said to need from time to time. I wore everything to destruction, to rags for the totter, quickly. My mother had little money, my father had only the pay of an RAOC private: clothes were rationed, on clothing coupons. I remember my parents buying me two jackets once, for thirteen coupons: they saw this as a bargain, one jacket was normally thirteen coupons and these were only six and a half each, half the usual. This was because they were made of sackcloth, that they were six-and-a-half, grey, the texture was loose, like that of sacks I had seen at Chobham. Even when they were new they looked shoddy. More than one kid commented on the slackness of the weave, embarrassingly, the coarseness of my sackcloth coat. One I wore to school, one I kept for best, ha! My shoes were always wearing out, I was heavy on shoes, I went through them,

73

through them. The toecaps would be disfigured by a transverse dent in them about a quarter of an inch from the end, then the ridge thus formed would get scuffed white, or leather colour, and a hole would form. Though before then holes would have been worn like a contour map through the soles. My body caused these things: it was painful. · · · · · · I was always short of money: obviously. But it was not exactly money I recollect being without: it was being without so many of the things bought with money: tritely. I had pocket-money from my mother, half a crown a week, or even five shillings it went up to, perhaps, I do not remember, so it could not have been important to me, money, as such, as itself. It was all the other things I lacked, I felt I had missed, felt I deserved, perhaps. Once in that school hall at Brotton I was one of those in charge of a raffle at some sort of Open Day, Fête, and I put a half-crown from the receipts into my right trouser pocket. I was sure no one had seen me: there was a great press of people round me: everyone felt excited: there was no way I knew that the money could be checked: yet nevertheless after about half an hour I put the money back. It was pure fear of being found out, not any moral decision, or one prompted by conscience. ·

· That hall is associated with another memory: one minute's silence for the first world war dead on an Armistice Day anniversary: we were told to think of the dead, and I thought of soldiers being killed: that is, I thought viciously of the killing, not the dead, no, that was what they wanted me to believe, to think, but I would not, no. · · · · · Stern and another boy called Mervyn come to mind as the only names apart from Burston I remember there. · · Once more—last—the hall. The headmaster on my last day there saying farewell at Assembly to his top class, wishing them well at the local secondary: all except me, he explained, whom he had promised to allow to go to Scale Lane. We had all taken the eleven plus, though I do not think they called it that then, and Eric and I had taken a special exam, different from the others. I realise now it must have been a London

74

eleven plus, not the Bucks one, for Eric, who was another name I remember now, and was a leftover, the only one apart from me, from the London evacuation, Eric took it at the same time as I did, and passed, or was chosen, or whatever. I did not, was not. I can remember sitting the papers in the headmaster's study, room, the two of us, three rather. Afterwards Mr Cunliffe looked over my paper, kept me back, said Couldn't you do even that one? He seemed surprised as I shook my head. · · · · · · · · Is that all about Brotton school? That is all about Brotton school. I can remember no more. It bores me, anyway, Brotton school, now. I am glad to be done with it. · · · · · · · · Scale Lane was much nearer to where I lived with Mrs Davies than the Brotton school was and I think I must have asked to be sent there, in view of what I remember the headmaster saying that last day. But I should try to keep things in order, chronological order, so what things happened outside school before I went to Scale Lane? · · · · · I tried to run a Stamp Club in the front room at Mrs Davies's. There was this book, I think it was called the XLCR Stamp Finder, a green pamphlet rather than a book, yes, which told you how to organise and run a Stamp Club. I held a Stamp Treasure Hunt, concealing stamps about Mrs Davies's formal front room, under the legs of chairs, between the keys of the piano, suchlike places. It was not a success: the others found them too easily. And I had to supply the stamps. Though it pleased me that Alan found an eightpenny British that he needed for a set. I forget the other games we played at the suggestion of the XLCR Stamp Finder, but there were others, I assume, my organising did not end there. But there was only one meeting of the Gordon Road Stamp Club. · · · · · The lavatory at Mrs Davies's was outside, out of the back door, down the yard a few paces, through the coal storage, past the wooden-rollered mangle, and sharp left. There was a pool of water once in there, and I showed it to Jim, who was home on leave from the Navy at the time, and he said it was someone who could not aim straight.

75

But I felt guilty about it, and not about my aim, either: I suspected I had slammed down the seat too hard and broken the pan: it leaked badly round the rim when it was flushed, which was how the floor became wet. I denied direct knowledge of it, truthfully, as I did not consciously do it, break it, and Mrs Davies fairly reasonably and without recrimination paid over a pound for a new pan. But for several days I was worried, very anxious: it seemed a very big thing at the time: rather ludicrously, it represents for me when I think about it now something like the very type of my anxieties.

· · Jim I think was briefly home when I arrived at High Wycombe, though he went into the Navy soon afterwards. He was small and fair, one of the Barnardo's boys, serious and not very approachable by us evacuees. He worked in the furniture trade: High Wycombe is more concerned in the woodworking industry than in any other. It was Jim who made us our sledges, from beechwood chair parts: more or less the back of a chair, the curved side-pieces forming the runners, with stretchers in between. These runners were rubbed with candle-wax and the sledge could then be used on grassy slopes in dry weather. They were enjoyable enough to use, but a burden to carry up to Keep Hill where there were some fair slopes. To reach Keep Hill we went across the Rye, past the waterfall and up a short track which ended by a chalkpit. At least, we always called it a chalkpit, though perhaps it had not been dug, was merely a natural escarpment. You could go another way, along London Road and down a lane with a closed Walls Ice Cream Depot on the corner and a cottage with a large ANTIQUES sign outside (which I would always mispronounce to myself) on a crook in the lane, which led to the track up to the chalkpit. The sledges had a rope on them by which to attempt to steer, but they were extremely inefficient in this respect. The slopes were from the side of the track, perhaps a fall of six feet in fifteen yards. I always associate the song *Old MacDonald had a Farm* with those slopes: why? The chalkpit was far too steep, sheer at the top, for us to use sledges down it. But we enjoyed
76

climbing it, and once we ran down it: this was exhilarating: I fell over perhaps a third of the way down, rolling head over arse anyhow and breaking a small mirror in my top pocket. I grimly accepted it meant seven years' bad luck and whenever I had bad luck in that period and even afterwards I thought of my breaking that mirror. My father gave me a steel mirror some time later, either chromium or stainless steel, which I could not break, an Army one. Why did I need a mirror? · · The chalkpit it seems to me had tiny blue flowers growing on it at a certain time of the year: but perhaps this was not so, perhaps it was a blue butterfly, the chalk blue or something, I could check, at home, I can check practically nothing, now, ah. · · · · ·
Blue flowers or blue butterflies, then, a most delicate shade of *CRAANGK!* · · They haul again, yet again, interrupt my thinking, no, I must not allow myself to be recalled, who am recalling, when recalling. · · · · · I remember the grassed cap of the chalkpit very well: the trees there to climb: I feel sure if I went back there now, over, yes, twenty years later, that I should be able to climb those trees, I should recall exactly how, that is: they would have grown, but so have I, more so, in proportion, I would be able to stretch easily for holds which were very difficult before. And there we went nesting, finding few, and other boys telling us they had fried blackies' and thrushes' eggs in a cocoa tin lid over a wood fire, they were just a mouthful, they said: I was repelled by the thought, they might have been addled, or had partly grown young birds in them. It did not seem cruel to me, nesting, I did not think of it as in any way cruel, no. That was a place so thick with years of beechmast that it came over the side of my shoe, into my shoes, uncomfortably, where I remember them telling us that, though we were up trees, our trees, at the time, yes, Alan and Harry and I each had a tree, and George always stayed at the bottom, sometimes crying, sometimes telling what were obviously lies about what he used to do when he was with his father, to make up for not being up the trees: he could not climb, was too afraid to

climb, being young. · · Once a Yank drove a
jeep up the easier slope beside the chalkpit, at right
angles to the precipitous part, paused, and we
wondered whether he was going to try to drive
down the scarp: we knew these jeeps were supposed to go anywhere. But he did not go over: he
saw us looking, from our trees, it was in the evening, and he reversed in an arc and shot off down
the milder slope on to the track, and down towards
the road. There were lots of Yanks about in High
Wycombe, particularly in the last years of the war,
in uniforms of smoother cloth than the English
forces, and with gaudy insignia on their shoulders:
I suppose they were something to do with the
Abbey, the base, and so on. If it was not there they
were all billeted, in the Abbey grounds, then I do
not know where they lived in High Wycombe. In
the town we kids would ask them for chewing gum,
Got any gum, chum, was our rhyming mendicant
catchphrase. Perhaps once in fifty times of asking
were we given chewing gum, in flat packets, delicately flavoured, so much more interesting than the
English kind, which came in a different shape, with
a white sugar coating. We knew they used to go
out with English girls, and we knew that there was
often trouble with English men because of this.
Once a Yank quarrelled with his girl across the
street from me, in London Road, near the Rye entrance by the garage: a fairly tubby little man, and
she turned and left him standing there, and he
shouted after her, Now look what you've done,
You've broken my heart! The woman just went on
walking away. And I was sorry for him, but I asked
myself why he did not follow her, and could not
answer. · · We could get into the Yank camp,
into the Abbey, from the top of Keep Hill. It was
a difficult climb over barbed wire on a high railing,
but we would use branches, both dead and on
nearby, almost overhanging, trees, to help ourselves. Once inside it was good: what I now know
to be a plantation of young spruce: then we just
thought of them as Xmas trees. At least once we
took food in there and made ourselves a camp and
lit a fire. But they made it very difficult for us to
78

climb in after a while, and at one point there was even a guard patrolling the top of the grounds, along the netting where the Abbey grounds were adjacent to Keep Hill. On the legal side of this fence we more than once found used sanitary towels and sheaths hung up on shrubs, decorating the spiked hawthorn bushes. We called them jam-rags and spunkbags, and I do not think we were very clear as to what they were used for: but we knew they were connected with sex, and we believed they were the work of Yanks. I do not think love touched us at this time: I am not sure. But there was a scheme we certainly talked about a lot: capturing girls and tying them up in order to do what we liked with them: though what it was we would have liked to do is very difficult to recall accurately. Certainly to look at them, yes, to investigate their genitals, to make those parts less private. One day we even took some string up to Keep Hill with us, but we were not able to bring ourselves to seize any girls even though we saw some about our age who looked to be just what we had in mind. At the last, it was simply far too embarrassing: hardly less so now. · · · · · What other places? · · · · · · · The caves at West Wycombe, and the church with the ball on top. We made expeditions out of going there, usually on a Sunday, and climbed the stairs to the tower parapet. A quadrilateral roof, its lead gouged, scrawled, initialled, supported the ball itself, which was much larger than it had seemed from below. A vertiginous set of steps with chains for handholds led into the ball. A terrifying climb: I remember making it only twice. Inside the brass-sheeted ball were four portholes, ah, through which the view was of course scarcely better than from the parapet. Wooden construction. Room for perhaps twelve disciples on benches around, a table in the middle—or was there a table? It was built in the eighteenth century, for a Dashwood, Earl or somesuch title, and was alleged to have been the scene of orgies. At least, they played cards up there in the ball. The caves under the hill were hollowed out of the chalk to provide metal for the

road that runs a straight collimation into High Wycombe. All this I think I knew at the time, all this useless history, but I may have picked it up later. A prominent sight on the road to Oxford, as the motoring handbooks say. Yes. There was and probably is a fake mausoleum up there, too, built by the same lot, rather half-heartedly, nearly derelict then, the stucco fallen in places to show the cheap brickwork underneath. The caves I remember enjoying, going in with a lighted candle bought from a man at the entrance: slimy dirty chalk walls, treacherous stepping, a chamber or hall at the end with cribs off it in which the members of the Hellfire Club, dressed as monks, were supposed to have taken their women, dressed as nuns, for purposes which even to my inexperienced eyes there seemed to be insufficient room. Did I know these things at the time? Or later? For I went back several times, yes several times, after the war. · · This is tedious, has no relevance. · · We boys used to race, scramble up that hill, up the sharp scarp side, through rough grass and tripping in places where the chalk had broken away vertically, to the top, panting like old men.... · · Yet it is compulsive: the memory has no stop, is only partly under control, bubbles on, once switched on · · Booker was another place: at Booker there was an aerodrome from which Tiger Moths drawled over Brotton school many times a day, many times. They were yellow, the Tiger Moths, trainers, and we kids were always rather contemptuous of them, who had seen Spitfires and Blenheims, Hurricanes and Beaufighters. But Booker I remember better because of walking once near there to a football match, in my football boots, for miles past the ground, because I had misunderstood the directions to the ground: miles it seemed I walked into open country until an elderly man put me right, a kindly man as I remember: I arrived just at half time, played the second half at centre-forward, badly, I could not play very well then, I must have been eleven or so, I was better later, by the time I was eighteen I was playing for the ATC team which won the Spitfire Trophy against the whole
80

of England's ᴀᴛᴄ. But that walk at Booker I remember bitterly: I was crying at least part of the way, from frustration, towards the end, before the kindly man, as I remember. · · I was mad about aeroplanes at this time, indeed at earlier times, there had not been a time when I could remember aeroplanes not engaging some considerable part of my attention. Any flying films that were on I would try very hard to see, though they were grownups' evening rather than children's Saturday morning pictures. Somehow we—for Alan or Harry would come too—would try to dodge Mrs Davies's uncanny system of knowing where we were without actually being with us, and go to the pictures: though we might have to leave early, before the film had perhaps finished. One such flying film I saw was *Target for Tonight*, guiltily lying to Mrs Davies afterwards, hurrying to bed quickly from the bad temper she fell into, she knowing we were lying but not what about. A man in a flying helmet is all I remember from that film, no face, just a head in a leather flying helmet. Perhaps there were American aircrew in that audience that night who would die in the air the next— · · ah, that is fanciful, smacks of fictional speculation. · · Another film I did not see was *The Phantom of the Opera*, which was forbidden to children, as a result of which I have always since wanted to see it, knowing nothing of it but its title: but somehow never have. Both were on at the Odeon, but did they have Odeons then? The name? An Odeon-type cinema, anyway: there were only three, and the other two were the Rex and the Palace. We did not often go to the Palace, and even less often to the Rex. Our Saturday morning pictures were at the Odeon-type, cowboys and thriller serials and soppy kids' stuff and one I remember for its enthusiastic signature-tune *Anchors Aweigh*, American that must have been, and stuff which must have been patriotic and English and sometimes boring. When it was boring the kids talked and mucked about and you would see a constant bobble of heads across the screen as kids went to and from the bogs, while when it was good no one

made a sound or moved. I saw the Belsen newsreels
at the Palace, why I do not know, that must have
been at the end of the war, even just immediately
after the war: I remember the warnings outside the
Palace about the nature of the newsreels, the insis-
tence that They believed they must be shown. I
do not remember what I thought of them. I do
know what I am supposed to have thought of them.
I was only twelve: at twelve I did not have much
judgement of these things. The Palace I also remember for the time Mrs Davies took me there, not
for her taking me, but that she gave me half a Mars
bar out of her own sweet ration, the kindest action
of hers I recall, as such, though now I am adult I
see that she must have been one of the kindest of
women to have taken in evacuees at all, for next
to nothing. Though she must have felt a need out
of her own lack of children: but having found a
motive, a reason, so what? · ·   She used to drum
her fingers rhythmically, Mrs Davies could beat
drumrolls and so on, did this even in the pictures.
She taught me a little how to do it, starting very
slowly, moving my large fingers: I preferred in the
pictures to feel the velvet pile of the seat standing
firmly against my finger pads. · · · · ·   Near
the Odeon-type was a Temperance billiard hall
where—why I can't think—they let kids like us
wander in and watch the play, and once at least I
bought there a dry cheese sandwich and I seem to
remember buying food with much of my pocket-
money at this time, whenever that time was, any
time between 1943 and 1945. Compensating—
though, again, what use are bloody reasons? · ·
And near that the grocers where we bought pearl
barley for our peashooters, to be arraigned by
teachers for our wastefulness, our filthiness, our
lack of patriotism: but there was never a sweeter
peashooter ammunition than pearl barley. It was
not as though it tasted good as food, anyway. · ·
· · · · ·   All, all? · ·   All? No, but go
on now to Scale Lane, enough of the earlier past,
this works in chronological order as far as it can,
if it works. I begin to suspect I shall wish I had
never started on this examination: I keep surprising

myself with my own nastiness, with my own limitations. · · But on. · · · · · · · Instead of the bus ride to Brotton, first of all, there was a walk to this new school, a secondary school, Scale Lane, fairly new buildings, on a hill over High Wycombe to the east, north-east-by-east, perhaps: a long walk, certainly, but an interesting one, one I really enjoyed, for the period I did it. I went down the hill from Gordon Road, across the triangular patch where three roads became one, past the barber's, and up an asphalt path with an iron handrail, very steep, glad to haul myself up by the handrail, at times, at some points, though often I would take a run at it and reach the top without needing to hold. At the top of the path, past a few houses, there were open fields and hedges, and the roof of the school could just be seen over the arc of the hill. To reach it I turned left along a hedge—hawthorn, I remember, may in spring, later, with red berries we called bread-and-cheeses though they never tasted remotely so to me, and elders, shrubs like that: which merged into a copse, or spinney, I never know the difference, of tall spindly trees, stubby bushes, undergrowth, perhaps two hundred yards long, perhaps fifteen yards wide. I remember coming across the words copse and spinney and realising with delight that the wood on my way to school was one of these: which one, it never bothered me, I liked both words, I liked the wood too. Wandering through that copse I could imagine myself into all kinds of situations, set all kinds of weird fantasies and imaginings there. · · After this copse or spinney, I would turn right up another path, of yellowish clay, up the hill beside fields to the edge of the school grounds, to a side entrance. · · This was the short way to school: there was a longer way, along roads, up Totteridge—was it?—Hill, which I used when the weather was bad. It had to be really bad, however. The only time I remember going that way was when several inches of snow had fallen, and I was snowballing up Totteridge Hill with other kids on the way: and suddenly I felt ill, faint, my heart drumming, and I had to sit down on the pavement against a sapling in a wire guard: or I would have fallen, have fainted. Many kids passed and took no notice, in the way boys do, through embarrassment, or self-interest, or whatever: but one boy, perhaps he was a prefect, enquired into my sitting in the snow, helped me up, accompanied me to school. I forget whether I was sent home or not on that occasion, as a result of that illness, shortcoming, whatever it may be called. But on another occasion I was sent home after fainting: I felt the same feeling come over me whilst standing in the hall waiting for Assembly to begin, and I turned to tell our teacher, who stood at the side against the wall. Before I reached him, I blacked out. The other told me afterwards that Mr Proffitt caught me before I fell. I was in the staffroom when I recovered and went home an hour or so later. Mrs Davies was I suppose surprised to see me. I felt well again very quickly, and went down the town to buy some fireworks. That dates this second time of fainting, for the fireworks never let off in November 1939 were available for Victory Celebrations in May 1945. · · · · · · · · The reason I remember being happy at this school was because I very quickly found myself a character I could accept, could even be pleased with. I found I enjoyed school work, and that, most surprisingly, I was very good at it. I do not think I realised at that time that I had been sorted out as not worth a grammar school education, and that I was not really competing on the same level any longer. But relatively this was unimportant. This newfound confidence was almost wholly due to my class-teacher, Mr Proffitt, a wonderful teacher, full of that kind of enthusiasm which flattered boys by appearing to assume that they were equals, by its sheer communication to them: a man who, I see now, must have overcome the liability of his physical appearance—he was small, about fifty, bald, red-beaked, dry-skinned and he wore metalrimmed spectacles and slummocky grey tweed suits: an invitation to disrespect—by outstanding teaching technique, by his character alone. My first-year class respected him completely: I do not remember him ever having even to threaten physical punishment. I still respect his memory more than that of any other teacher I ever had. Now I see it was perhaps his intelligent resentment of the educational system which had declared us to be less than first-rate and implied that therefore we were hardly worth bothering with, even at our own levels, that he tried so hard and so successfully with us: he was so good, particularly with those whom must just have missed grammar school entry: he gave so much to us, put so much into his lessons, organising them so well that they stretched the abilities of the best of us, yet still were not beyond the capacities to learn at least something of the worst of us . . . But perhaps I go too far, project an ideal teacher on to his memory: but not very far past the truth. · ·

He taught us English, besides being our form master. We did not even resent him calling us by our surnames all the time. · · At the end of that first term, Xmas 1944 it must have been, we had exams, and I came second of the whole class. It was my first evidence of something I had always hoped, had in a way known but not believed: that I was in some ways at least better than others, that though I was working-class and embarrassed by my clothes, I was yet better than some others at some things. The confidence this gave me was enormous, of acute importance, and it was given very satisfying public acknowledgement when, at the beginning of the spring term, Mr Proffitt arranged us in the order in which we had come in the December exams: there, at the back to the teacher's right, sat the boy who had come first, I forget his name, another quiet boy, and I, in one double desk. I was particularly encouraged because the two hitherto established stars of the class, Nobbs and French, to whom I had until Xmas considered myself far inferior, had come third and fourth, and were now to my right in another double desk. · · · · ·

I can remember only one of Mr Proffitt's lessons in detail, one in which he coaxed us into telling him of what wood pencils were made, and how pre-war Japanese pencils were of such poor quality that they tended to break very easily: because they

85

were not made of the best wood: cedarwood. But many elements in my basic education must have had their foundation in Mr Proffitt's classroom. ·

· While none of the other teachers commanded my respect as Mr Proffitt did, I can remember several of them very closely. The geography master, tall, sunburnt, bald, taught calmly and well. He once asked for volunteers to take a message to Spring Grove school, and, even though I did not know exactly where this was, I volunteered and was accepted. It was raining, and the way led down the hill from the other side away from my copse, or spinney, a path across a sloping field which could be seen from this teacher's classroom. I was told not to run, but did so very briefly down that path: I can see myself from that classroom, and as myself on that path: a double vision. One boy reproached me for running, when I returned, I forget who he was, pettily. · ·

There was a music teacher who kept very strict discipline: even from the piano, a specially short cross-strung one, ah, over which he could look whilst playing. We sang—I can't remember, but it has words by Pope, years later I learned at college the words were by Pope—yes, *Where'er You Walk*, that was it. And one day I heard that teacher's voice, as strict and disciplinary as ever, on a schools broadcast when I was myself a teacher and one afternoon used the BBC programme to cover up that I could not myself teach music. · · I remember the headmaster coming into my class only once, and my answering correctly his question about the name of the Bramaputra river in northern India—is it?—and him insisting that neither a forward nor a backward slant was desirable in handwriting. Oh, and a mnemonic he taught us, that I still use, as to how to tell port from starboard: With a bottle of port you can never pour it all out, there's always a drop left. · ·

The only one I remember disliking was the history teacher, a graduate I suspect, who was in his early twenties, curlyhaired, with darkrimmed glasses: and him only because he breathed rancidly over me, too often, once was too often, garlic I imagine

now, though then it seemed connected with small
black sticks like charcoal that he chewed during
lessons. He went up for the VE celebrations, on
VE Day, and told us about it, about waiting in front
of Buckingham Palace for the King and Queen and
Mr Churchill. I was not impressed even then: I just
wanted to go home, and resented him, not a Londoner, being able to go there when I was still forced
to be down at High Wycombe. He kept the library,
a dark place for some reason, in this new light
building, not a very good one, as I remember, full
of old books in tatty bindings, some without spines,
perhaps inherited from some older school. · ·
A hobby I picked up at Scale Lane was religion,
which was fostered fervently by the gym master,
ironically enough, in his lunch-hours. Every day—
it seems like every day—a group of boys would
meet in his gym and hold a bible-study session: at
least, that is what I think they were called. One
of us would select a passage from the Bible, read
it, and then expound on it, with the object of illu-
mination for all. It was a hobby, yes, now I look
back: there was involved no question of belief. I
could have done the same for any other text on any
other subject, I imagine, at that time, for I made it
all up, the interpretation. But it pleased the gym
master, I assume, that we would thus be exposed to
such as he thought good. Would it worry him that
in my case it has done me no good at all? Rather, I
hate the propaganda of such as he, of his church, of
his god. But perhaps such hatred does not have its
origins in what he tried to do: I feel no real malevo-
lence towards his memory, I still remember the
guilt I felt for some time at not corresponding with
him after I had returned to London, and I still have
the Bible he inscribed (though someone else had
given it to me) some time during that period at
High Wycombe. · · · · · The boys at that
school I remember far less well. Nobbs seems to
have been thin faced, handsome, with fairish hair,
while French was definitely roundfaced, large-
headed, with very fair hair. I went up to French's
house once, on the west side of the town, near the
Thames Valley bus station: but the only thing I

recall is that we were in the kitchen and someone told me French's granny cut his hair, ha ha: perhaps it was French's granny. And there were some girls there, French could attract girls. · · · ·
· · · · It becomes confused here. At the point! Did I find no friends at this school? Was I isolated there? Is this the point it begins, where I find the cause? Think harder! · · · · · · · · It seems I was satisfied with the friendship of the boys who lived at Mrs Davies's: perhaps we were a close group, as if a family. At the end of the war, towards the end, that is, these boys went home, one by one, until I alone was left with Mrs Davies, perhaps that was when she took me to the pictures and gave me half her Mars bar? But there was a boy at Scale Lane I had become friendly with, Bates, his name was, I called him Batesy, they all did, who offered me his friendship, and I remember him doing so on a school stairway, that sort of glitter in the composition, when I had told him the last of Mrs Davies's boys had gone or was going: and I said, No, I preferred to be a lone wolf. That was my actual cliché, I remember using it, remember the definite sense of foreboding, thrill, of the term, of the romantic loneliness I was choosing for myself. · · · · · Now that should seem important, that is as obvious a cause—no, as clear an example, an early example, of my isolation, as I have yet dredged up. But of what importance is it? Ah... · · · · · · · · But I did become friendly enough with Batesy, did with him whatever it was I had to do that involved a second, though I always kept the main part of myself within me. Remember shooting an arrow into Batesy's bare leg just above his boy scout's sock, with the two green bands on navy, and it made a just pierced round blue mark. The arrows were thin shoots of a reddish-barked shrub, ideal for the purpose, having a heart of hard white wood which sharpened well. I shot at Batesy's leg out of boredom, from about a yard, and was surprised that he did not retaliate or even appear to dislike me after the first sharp pain had passed. That was up on Keep Hill, beyond the sledge-slopes. Mrs Davies

did not like me going around with Batesy, no, and perhaps he knew this: perhaps this is why he put up with my shooting an arrow into his leg, that I was in some way superior to him, could withdraw my company from him? A bit fanciful. Was Batesy a member of an undesirable class that Mrs Davies should want me to have nothing to do with him? Were there lower classes than the one I belonged to? I had not thought so, no, I had not thought so. Perhaps Mrs Davies wanted to keep me to herself? It does not seem likely. But certainly contact with Batesy lessened, and when I left High Wycombe I do not remember saying goodbye to him. · · ·

· · As for girls: there were two as I remember, only two. The first had the same surname as myself but sent back my only note, tentatively arranging a meeting, with the most untentative repulse, listing as places we would not meet, one by one, all those I had suggested. She was several years older, but the second girl, who lived just a few doors away, at a butcher's shop, strangely enough, was more my own age, twelve, at this time, and I used to exchange abuse with her, for a period of some months, nothing more, until finally I was able to insult her by telling her I was leaving High Wycombe, and she me by saying Good riddance. · · It was difficult to meet girls while at Mrs Davies's, or perhaps it was that I grew shy with puberty. · · Two other girls I remember meeting, being keen on, in connection with some expedition made with the scouts, involving a trek cart, carting stuff of some sort or another from one part of High Wycombe to a Fête, where we gave kids rides on the trek cart and broke the shaft of it by dropping it when loaded on to the path. There were three of us, and I think we must have picked up these girls there, perhaps they were girl guides, at that Fête, two of them: yes, I felt left out, that the other two would get the girls, perhaps they even knew each other, from before, or one of them did, while I knew only the boys, neither of the girls, until the Fête, until that day. We took the trek cart back to headquarters, and one boy said he would report it to the scoutmaster next day. Then we went with the girls to the fair which was that week on the Rye. I did not feel out of it, then, five was a loose number, we all gave. But I had to leave early because my mother was coming down for the weekend, that evening: ironic, that she who came so rarely chose the evening just when I—so rarely too—had something else which might have kept me from missing her. For the missing was a constant of my life. And when I was forming a real part of some sort of group—but something would have happened, it always did, to throw me back, yet again. My mother slept in Mrs Davies's room upstairs that night. I was glad to see her. I took her a cup of tea that Sunday morning. She suddenly said Listen! I heard the drone of an aircraft. It passed us and began to fade. Then suddenly it stopped. A buzzbomb, said my mother. There was a dull explosion some way away, and then she told me about the buzzbombs or V1s they were having in London, and I was terrified for her. That bomb landed in Hughenden Manor, I believe, if that was the name of the place, harmlessly. It was the first around High Wycombe: later there were others, in some way off their set course for London. My very occasional weekends in London with my mother and grannie were now no longer allowed. Perhaps that is why on this occasion my mother had come down to see me. The scouts I joined twice: different troops, that is. At one time I was in the scouts and the cubs at the same time, shook fearfully at some singing jamboree as Akela saw me in my scouts' uniform but said nothing, to my relief. The first scouts took me under age because I was big, and pushed me through tenderfoot very easily: it was enough for them that I could repeat knots once under instruction though I certainly could not do them the day afterwards. It was this troop's trek cart that I helped to break. Later, at Scale Lane I joined another troop, more keenly run, which I enjoyed hardly more. It was not that I was not interested in what they were doing, for I was: but I wanted to be interested in my own way, I wanted to enjoy myself in my own way, which was not necessarily their way. I failed as a member of that

group as I have failed as a member of all groups I have ever joined: gangs, schools, cliques, churches, cubs, scouts, youthclubs, football teams, cricket teams, tugofwar teams, tennis doubles, all of them. · · As here, too, it is repeated: for I am on this trawler, on the crew list a supernumerary, even, but not of the ship. · · Even from Mrs Davies and the boys I became estranged, towards the end, mainly because of that eagerness for knowledge promoted by Mr Proffitt, my capacity for observing too much: so that no topic of conversation could arise from either her or the other boys, it seemed, without I would say, I know, and soon my I know became a catchphrase of ridicule and attack against me. But I did know, I would say to myself: and perhaps here my arrogance began, perhaps this surprisingly again showed me I was better even than certain adults: or it may be that I knew it all the time, and this was merely confirmation. ·
· · · This observance was part of a visual excitement which took its most extreme form in the photographing of everything catching that attention with a pretend camera, which was a small metal object, cylindrical, about half an inch deep and one in diameter, with a sighting hole and a clicking catch: I picked it up on a tip, with one too for Batesy, and I cannot imagine what it was designed for originally. A real camera I remember seeing only once, when my mother came down, it was probably the same weekend I first heard a buzzbomb: a camera she had borrowed, and managed to find a film for, as they were very scarce in wartime, or so I believed, and we took some snaps, I would call them, up on West Wycombe hill, near the Mausoleum. · · · · Letters from my father, from North Africa, from Italy, from Germany, photographed letters, small, the paper crackling, just reproduced largely enough to read: saying all the things we would do after the war was over. · · · · I was infected with the details of the war, with the war, wanted to fly, read every Biggles book several times, and the *Aeromodeller*, made models which rarely flew, when they were meant to, and solid models which I

wished were meant to, since they were easier to make. Even at one point started a programme of self-training to fit me for the Air Force as a pilot at eighteen: I think a book, some sort of training manual, came into my hands at this time, and it was this which started me off. It was my first great enthusiasm: and like others since I kept it secret, guarded it against the ridicule of others, the dampening of others. This must have been when the other boys at Mrs Davies's had gone, when I was thrown more in upon myself, that I kept it to myself. This enthusiasm for flying continued until the time I was due to go for National Service, when I opted for the RAF, told Dorothy I just wanted to make sure I flew in the next war, underwent aircrew selection tests at Hornchurch before actually being called up to see if I could make the thing a career, passed as a radio operator but was failed on medical grounds with the perforated eardrum scarlet fever had left me with as a child of three; and was discharged the service accordingly. · ·
Now I do not want to fly, have not since then wanted to fly: perhaps I may again one day as a hobby: yet I remember the passionate enthusiasm with which I wanted to fly, then, for years, and wonder at the waxing and waning of enthusiasm. Perhaps the only happy man is the one who has no enthusiasms: but perhaps that cannot be achieved without having at least an enthusiasm for not having enthusiasms. That is too easy: what use are such statements? · · Another enthusiasm at the same time, which must be connected, I think, have been incorporated in the self-discipline, self-reliance, was a secret society I formed with Batesy. It had its headquarters in a certain tree, difficult to climb, but low, hawthorn I think it must have been, where we hid all kinds of formulae, little bottles of pink Anadin liquid, the occasional unused Durex we found in its packet, matches, and other valuables. Two other kids we allowed to belong to this society, who were not very enthusiastic, who did not turn up to meetings very often: when Batesy and I saw them once some weeks later they did not even seem to remember belonging. But someone

found all the things in HQ, robbed us, and we found these two and accused them: they denied betraying the society, but we thumped them just in case. Batesy and I were bigger than they were, but not by much. This society was perhaps an expression of a desire to lead, to organise. Not that I wanted to lead—I saw nothing good in that—but that things had to be led, things had to be organised: and other people did not seem very good at this—, no that's not it, exactly. Some people were: Mrs Davies was well organised, Mr Proffitt and the school were well organised: but there were other things which were not, and if I did not do it then I saw nobody did. A common fallacy. But I did. I think I tried to arrange something similar, a society or a camp, in a furniture · · *CRAANGK!* · · Ah, yet again! · · Yes. Now, the secret society, flying, no, another society, this time in a factory where they made chairs, or rather the factory woodyard, a camp in amongst the great piles of seasoning beechwood, stretchers between each piece to allow air to circulate: but we too often were found there and chased out by workmen, especially when we drew attention to ourselves by riding a wheeled platform on those short stretches of rail intended for moving stacks of wood about the yard. On one occasion a great splintered shaft, of triangular section, fell on George, the sharp ragged side gashing his forehead and nose: we led him home screaming, streaming blood our handkerchiefs could not absorb, to Mrs Davies, who washed and bathed him and found the wound of course to be far less bad than it looked. That could not have been connected with the society, John, or George, was it? had gone home by then, gone back to London. But we played in the woodyards at various times at High Wycombe, not just me on my own towards the end. · · · · · Mrs Davies had a cousin who worked in a very good baker's shop in the town where we used to go on Saturdays and buy a lardy-cake, which was a wonderful cake, the lardy-cake, with— · · What bloody relevance has a sodding lardy-cake to me now? I've had enough of High Wycombe and being evacuated:

surely I must have exhausted it by now, the pain must be exorcised, the tedium of interest, of making myself regurgitate all this: for what? · · Think, then, analyse, then, this estrangement from home, from London, parents, younger self. · · · · ·

· · · Blank. · · What use are analyses, reasons, causes? All I am left with are just things, happenings: things as they are, happenings as they have happened and go on happening through the unreliable filter of my memory. But try. What else is there to do? · · · · · First, the obvious. The pain of being parted from my parents was far greater, and more real, than the danger from bombing, from dying. The given reasons for my being evacuated—that I would be out of danger, with its corrollary that therefore they were in danger—was unacceptable, or seems so now, for at the time I had no choice but acceptance. The thought of my mother or my father being killed, which I could conceive, was far worse than the thought of myself being killed, which I could not as meaningfully conceive. If any of us had to die, I wanted it to be together. This thought was often with me, but not exactly as a thought—I could not have formulated it like that then—but rather as a threat, as an accompaniment to everything I did.

· · Was the liberality of my parents—I remember having ten or fifteen shillings and sometimes as much as a pound a week pocketmoney in the years after I came home, immediately after the war, when I was only twelve or thirteen—was this in some way (for they had little money) an attempt to make up for sending me away during the war? A payment in acknowledgement of their debt for my neglect? Perhaps. Perhaps not. · · Yet I know of others in my generation who were evacuated and who look back on this period as a golden one in their lives, who were sent deep into the country, to great houses in Somerset, to America even, and to whom life has never been so wonderful with their parents as it was away from them, whose characters were beautifully formed and transformed by this transplantation from London to some alien place. Perhaps I went to a graceless

town, appropriately but not gladly to the working-
class part, as well, and perhaps my complaints were
too easily countered with promises that all would
be different after the war, that all lacks were attributable to the war: and of course this was not so,
and of course I was affected by the disappointment
that nothing was ever after the war as good as it
had been promised to be—as I have said, I repeat
myself.... · · · · Back, where I was,
where I am. Sleep. · · Long sleep.

Three parts of a moon tonight. · · · · The
sea swells and subsides, swells, swells, subsides,
swells, subsides, subsides, subsides, swells again:
impossibly consistent, constantly varied, continuously backing, sliding, rolling, foaming, breaking:
perpetually owning and destroying, breaking down
and synthesising, accepting and enfolding, encom-
passing and losing, giving and demanding in return, drawing.... · · · · · · · A far-
side bridge window frames a rectangular selection
for my vision: a screen of stars and sky unrolls upwards as she rolls, ends to give place to blackness
starred and streaked with the luminous foam:
which in sequence on the reverse roll has the stars
return, now rushing downward like pinpoint lem-
mings to the sea, over the teak cliff. · · · ·
No one on the whaleback, rarely is, it seems: once
or twice, rigging the cod-end derrick while we
were coming through the fjords, they went up on
the whaleback: not that any man would be there
from choice as she dips her nose into a sea and it
breaks hugely over the bow rail, one section of
which has been bent by some great earlier sea. The
spray over the whaleback tonight reaches the
pounds where men stand gutting in their smocks
and oilskin souwesters: it is rough tonight, force
six, they tell me, just bearable for fishing. They
stand there stolidly, ripping and severing, pitching
the disembowelled fish into the washer: and then
the military progress down the chute. · · · ·
· Duff's watch, but the Skipper is here as well: he

hardly seems to sleep at all. Even when I come up here in the middle of the night, the Skipper is still inevitably here, in his high chair, the green squiggles of the fishfinder cathode repeated distortedly in the mirror of the bridge's shiny ceiling. He talks to me as he watches, tells me of his boyhood in Ireland, his sailing out of Dublin at fourteen, fishing, and of his rise despite himself, almost, to command this trawler: of his fears that one trip he just will not find fish, that he will lose his touch, though he has a great reputation for finding fish if there are any to be found: of how other skippers have been emptied out of their ships, emptied out is his phrase, by the owners after unsuccessful trips. The Skipper is a hunter and a gambler, guessing and watching and feeling where the fish may be, his only written guide a notebook which records for years before what he has caught, and exactly where, at each time of the year. Most sane, most calm. Even when he swears it is sanely, calmly: Roll you bastards! he'll say to the seas, and if they could feel this it would hurt them far more than Duff's or Festy's comprehensive sexual and blasphemous imagery. The Skipper I have heard raise his voice only when men's lives were in danger: from the bridge starboard windows he keeps a watch on their movements as we haul, and shouts through the hailer down whenever someone seems about to put himself in jeopardy from the warps, or the great links of the dogchains holding the otterboards. He has never lost a man overboard, unlike most skippers, nor had one really seriously injured, on his ship. He tells me about his family, promises to show me photographs of them he keeps down in his quarters. He tells me how before the war they threw scampi back, except for some they cooked in a bucket for themselves, as there was no market for them. He tells me he goes every year to Dublin for a holiday, where the Metropole in O'Connell Street serves a most excellent plate of scampi, or Dublin Bay Prawns, as the Irish will have them. He tells me of the day they were buzzed by a Russian helicopter in these waters and shortly afterwards saw an irregular mass of flame shoot at great speed

96

above them: and heard it some considerable time after it had passed them. A Russian missile of some sort, on its way north to the testing ground in Novaya Zemlya, so it seemed. Suddenly he is tense. I feel this rather than see it, on the darkened bridge, glance at what he has seen: another trawler is cutting across us, on a line that will take her very close, a Norwegian stern-fisher, very new, all her deck lights far brighter than ours across the narrow sea. The Skipper does not give way: she passes relatively safely: and suddenly Scouse shouts Her gear's up! And there is no more tenseness. If she had had her trawl down, it is likely ours would have fouled it: but she was between hauls, and I can see the ramp at the stern up which the cod-end has been hauled. Duff talks to me about her design, saying they are still experimental, stern-fishers, but he does not really express an opinion: probably the benefit from not having to haul the net in by hand would be only marginal, would relieve the harshness of trawling very little. ·   ·   ·   ·   I lean again on the brass rail in the posture my body knows very well, now, relaxes comfortably into, which takes account of every movement of the ship except the very worst. There is a moderately heavy cross swell, and for the first time I do not object to the constant movement: not that I enjoy it, for I do not, but I can accept it now, even anticipate it most of the time, becoming acclimatised, no, becoming a seaman, or so I hubristically pride myself. ·   ·   ·   ·   ·   ·   ·   Duff tells me he caught the cook in the galley this morning crimping a meat pie with his false teeth, and asked him if he hadn't got a proper tool: Yes, said the cook, but that I keep for making holes in doughnuts. I laugh, yes, laugh a lot, then think it is a told joke, but nevertheless Duff enacts it very well, I cannot find fault with his telling. In any case, he theatrically withdraws into the chartroom, ducking his head to avoid the lamp in gimbals, leaving me laughing. ·   ·   ·   ·   · Scouse too tells jokes, leaves his bar to lean on the one next to me where Duff was, asks me What is the proper length for ladies' skirts? I cannot guess, he gives me little time to guess, before telling me A little above two feet, and laughs himself far more than I do, who laugh only at his laughing at such an Edwardian Xmas cracker joke. Scouse mistakes my laughter for enthusiasm and plies me with others: What is the difference between a tree and an aeroplane? I refrain from telling him the obvious, out of sarcasm, my sarcasm is beside the point, here. And there is a satisfaction in knowing the answer to questions, being told the answers, to any questions: not knowing answers, however banal or guessed at already, is frustration, is incompleteness, is to be avoided. So, One sheds its leaves and the other leaves its shed! Scouse roars, and I do too, entering into his spirit, reflecting at the same moment on the length of time since any aeroplane left any shed. This one's intellectual, says Scouse, Should suit you, you'll know the answer to this one: What was the difference between Shakespeare and Queen Elizabeth, Queen Elizabeth the First, that is, not the one now, it wouldn't work if it was the one now? And is delighted at my ignorance as, after the briefest of pauses to establish it, he says: One was a wonder and the other was a Tudor! And I really laugh this time, mainly because three years doing a degree in English had not enabled me to make a guess nearer than that indicated by the subjects' respective sexes, or sex, since some will have it that Shakespeare was a woman, and yet others that Queen Elizabeth (the First, of course) was a man. Another, says Scouse, roused now, What is the difference between a thought, a sigh, a motor car, and a monkey? I shake my head, accepting my ignorance, not having any idea what could conjoin these disparate objects. Ah, says Scouse, A thought is an idea, a sigh oh! dear, a a motor car too dear, and a monkey you dear! I laugh as before, but Scouse suddenly feels he might have offended me by calling me dear, that I might think him queer, or bent, so he hastens to tell me about his wife, to assure me that none of the things I have heard about sailors at sea happen on this ship: and indeed I have seen or heard nothing of the sort, there is no atmosphere, no hint of anything homosexual, on this ship. Scouse was married

98

two years ago, and has no children: I try bloody hard every time I'm home, he says, But so far no luck. On his last ship, he became stuck in a cycle of three-week voyages that meant every time he was home his wife had the painters in: I felt like bloody Dracula, he says, in this Liverpool accent. And since trawlers are turned round in less than sixty hours, it gave them little chance, Scouse and his wife, less than the best chance, of her conceiving. The only way for the cycle to be broken was for him to leave that ship and sign on another more propitiously timed. In any case, Scouse seems to think the move was a good one, as this Skipper, he nods and lowers his voice, catches fish far more consistently than his last one did. This last time home, Scouse tells me, his wife having been told by other fishermen's wives that three in the morning was the most favourable time to conceive, she was setting the alarm clock and waking him up for it.   ·

·   ·   ·   ·   The ship-to-ship phone burbles our name, twice, briefly, and the Skipper leaves his seat to lift the receiver from the rest where it vertically hangs. It is a nearby vessel belonging to the same owners, and the Skipper gives him the size of our last haul. I notices that he underestimates it, Thirty baskets, he says, when, from what I have been told, I can judge it to have been nearer forty. There is this rivalry between ships, each captain for himself since each is paid directly proportionately to the amount of fish he catches: so when they are on fish they keep quiet about it. Whereas the ships of other countries co-operate much more closely: when one trawler of a Russian fleet finds fish, for instance, he radios at once to all his sister ships and the fleet joins him to trawl the area clean. Not that we are at the moment on any large quantity of fish: the fishing is mediocre, not good, not bad. It is now about an hour since we hauled, and they have nearly finished the gutting: so that the deckies will have a good hour before the next haul in which to relax in the warm mess, eating if they wish from the cheese and oddments the cook leaves out for the watch every night. I remark on all this to the Skipper, who tells me of the harvest years just

99

after the war, when the seas had hardly been
trawled for five years and were crowded with fish,
or so it seemed, of how one haul at this time would
not be gutted before the pounds would be overflowing with the next, men working every second
of their eighteen hours' watch: tells me how skippers would in these circumstances give their men
a four hours' break to sleep, and then put the clocks
forward two hours and delude them into thinking
they had rested twice as long: and how there was
no need for such deception now, when every year
less fish was brought to market, when more and
more countries increased the numbers of their fishing fleets. · · · · · We listen in to, eaves-
drop on, a long, boring, almost oneway conversation about cars, on the ship-to-ship shortwave
radio. Some captains yatter all bloody day and
night, says the Skipper. But he keeps it on, listening to this man's sporadic and repetitive accounts
of an accident with his Zephyr: the other captain to
whom this man is speaking hardly replies at all. In
the background pop music can be heard, and I ask
why the deckies do not have it on our ship: They
don't need it, says the Skipper. · · · · · On
to the deck below a strange gaunt figure, out of
keeping in a naval greatcoat and peaked cap, wan-
ders, the long spout of an oilcan protruding from
one sleeve, as though in place of a hand. Without
looking up he goes to the great steam winch below
us, directs the spout and ejaculates oil into the
womb of the slowly hissing machine. Then he turns
and returns, an old man for this life, the Second
Engineer. A curiously bizarre incident, the oilcan
a bizarre instrument with which to minister to
such a monster. · · · · · · · · I hunger
for fruit. We have fruit only for Sunday tea: last
Sunday tea we had tinned peaches, the only Sunday I have been aboard, but these are so little like
real fruit, tinned peaches, at least unlike the acid
biting that I require at the moment, of a good
apple, or an orange, or I could even welcome a
lemon, as it is, that tinned peaches seemed not
really fruit at all, though I did eat them, several
helpings, hoping they would stay down, but no, I
100

was sick immediately afterwards, as so often: up came the tinned peaches with the pork and stuffing we had, too, Sunday at sea is like Xmas, every Sunday at sea: but up it all came. Relief that I have now gone a day and a half without being sick, perhaps I have grown used to it, at last, have found my proverbial sealegs. Certainly I anticipate the movements of the ship far better, now, and though I always feel as though I might be sick, I can fight the feeling, and win, and not be sick. ·   ·   ·   ·
I sit in the wireless room, with Molloy. He says little, Molloy, but what he does have to say is interesting. Of being shipwrecked on a desert island, yes, in the Pacific, in the war, and being rescued by a negro. The chair I sit in rocks and slithers to the limits of its restraining tether. Apart from this movement, being in the wireless room with Molloy is not like being on a ship at all, here is the place on the ship least like being on a ship. ·   ·   ·   ·   ·
·   · But I hunger for fruit. I mention there not being much fruit in our diet to the Skipper, who looks at me, then says there is an orange on the ledge in his day cabin which I can have. He always brings ten pounds with him each trip, he says. I am grateful, decide at once to have it now, and leave the bridge on the lee side, another indication of my new seaworthiness. Down the bridge ladder, holding firmly to the rail as I have learnt to, everywhere, through the brass-fitted teak door, out of the weather, past the gyro steering unit nodding away to itself on the top landing of the scuttleway: and through into the Skipper's quarters. The finest part of the ship, soft seats round two sides of the day cabin immediately below the bridge, curtains at the portholes, carpet, furnished incongruously like a perhaps lowermiddleclass best sitting room. I see the orange, and take it, a medium-sized one, not South African, I am relieved to see, which means I have avoided a moral dilemma in which I would have had to concede a principle. ·   · As I leave the Skipper's day cabin I decide to eat my orange by myself: and the only place I have found on this ship I can feel I am by myself is on the boatdeck, at the stern. I move straight out from beside

101

the Sperry, therefore, along past the engine room skylights, the galley funnel, self-inflating liferafts, past ventilators and the jury steering gear, the lifeboat falls, to the rail at the very stern. Ah, I see now, how could I have not seen it before, that this is where the emergency exit from my cabin comes out, the escape from the transom cabin. · ·   The moon a pendant—orange: stars like—no easy image to hand. Perhaps this will be the night I see the aurora borealis. Both hands are needed to peel an orange, so I lock one leg through the lower rail for purchase against the pitch and roll, bite the skin near the starred dimple, and spit the piece into our wake. The other pieces I also throw into the sea, watching them sink and vanish into the yellow-green foam, then sometimes bob up yards farther on: pleased that I can do this at sea, unguiltily, whereas on land it would be unsocial: the sea takes this rejectamenta as all other, and assimilates it: this orange peel will be broken down into its constituent elements very rapidly, before anyone could ever see it, in the sea. I think. · ·   Ah, a good orange! A fine orange! Juice, a minimum of stringiness, a most welcome orange! Eat all edible pieces, waste no tiny piece, a precious orange! How welcome, how satisfying, how depressing it will be when I have finished it! Yet I was warned that I would miss fresh fruit, and therefore ought to take some with me by the official who dealt with my application to come on this trawler, who agreed to let me come on this voyage, at the same time as he told me I would find the ship's tea strong and liable to react strangely on my stomach. Very accommodating, this man, and these owners, to let me come, to provide me with seaboots and oilskins, a donkey's breakfast to sleep on, yes, very kind. · ·
And a taxi arranged to meet my train when I came up, in the middle of the night, for she sailed on the morning tide at four, on the thirteenth, as it happened, though not on a Friday, a Thursday, the thirteenth of October, at four in the morning. I had like a condemned man my last good meal on the train coming up from London, a good meal indeed as train meals go, with a friendly waiter
102

who had few people to serve and who gave large portions if they were wanted, as they were, by me, thinking this was the last meal which I was fairly certain I would not see up again, for it would be digested more or less by the time the ship sailed some seven or six hours afterwards. And the taxi-driver very friendly, as well, used to these night calls to take men to ships. I don't know how they stick it, he said, of trawlermen, I've been out as far as the Spurn light vessel and that was enough for me. He said the men born, drawn or forced into such a job were rough: indeed, there were known to be at least two murderers, discharged after their sentences, sailing from this port. He lit a cigarette and then put it out almost immediately, saying he smoked too much as a result of being given tips in the form of a packet of unexcised twenty by men off the trawlers.   · ·   That conversation, that journey through the well-lit, ordinary, and deserted latenight streets, dominated by the dark Italianate outline of the tall tower, I remember well: perhaps I noticed it particularly because things familiar all my life as a city-dweller I was no to see again for three weeks, was leaving behind one life, what I had known as life, for something entirely different, something, a set of circumstances and an environment, completely foreign to me: where no one I knew, no part of my past life, could reach me, since I had told no one where I was going: I was then somewhat uneasy as I was driven in that Consul towards a ship of which I knew only the name, about to make a voyage I knew not where, since I was told the Skipper alone decided this, and often only at the last minute: a voyage whose duration was uncertain within a few days of three weeks.   ·
·   And as we turned along by the North Quay there were the trawlers waiting, tied up, first a grey, clean modern one, then another showing up whitepainted in the quayside lights, and farther on a dark, rusty-black trawler. O, let it not be that last one! something said in me, and with the first real apprehension—not for going to sea, but for going to sea in that dark ship—I felt the car not stopping at the first, nor the second ship, and I

103

wished it then to continue past the third; but the taxidriver was braking and peering at the name on her bow, and then said this was my ship: my apprehension was released by knowledge, by the acceptance of the known after the dismay of the possible. · · Only her bow, her bridge, and the boatdeck stood above the quay edge. I waited in my heavy coat, carrying a suitcase and a duffel bag, wondering where I boarded her. I could see no ladder and no gangway. Then someone shouted at me, and I saw a light just where the curved rusty rail of the ship touched the quayside, and went there, and there was this small whitehaired old man, shining a torch up at me and saying, You the pleasuretripper? I supposed I must be: the name of the ship was right, anyway: so I handed him my bags, which he took without grace, and I stepped across and down what looked like castiron gratings on to the deck. It was very dark in the shadows where the quay lights did not reach. The old man led, shining his torch on the deck behind him, along the deck, pointing out I should be careful over the high step of the door openings, into a passageway. Immediately I began to feel cramped, for I had to carry one bag in front of me and one behind, and either shoulder banged against the sides as I went. There was one light in a door off this passage, and in here the old man went. I was glad to put down the bags and feel freer in the opening, which I could see was the galley: long coalfired ovens with special divisions on the top to prevent things sliding about, obviously: I had suddenly a vision of a pot of boiling liquid flung over a cook by the action of the ship, a realisation of the hazards of cooking at sea. The galley was lit by a single carbide lamp which hung hissing from an H-girder: it was made of copper, with the ship's name on a brass plate soldered to it, and had a straight spout on the end of which the brilliant white flame stood. Seeing me look at it, the old man said there were no lights because the steamer had not yet come aboard to raise steam and start the generator. The galley was warm, and well-kept. The old man told me he looked after this ship while
104

she was in port, more or less lived on her as a kind of caretaker while she was not at sea: he had sailed in her until he retired a few years before. He had with him another man, about fifty, perhaps for company. They showed me the lavatory, and they offered me tea, for which I was grateful: it did not taste as strongly as I had been led to expect, was quite pleasant, though a different drink due to the evaporated milk with which it was made. They did not seem curious as to why I was going to sea: which fortunately saved me inventing reasons: I could not just say, I want to give substantial yet symbolic form to an isolation I have felt most of my life by isolating myself in fact, by enacting the isolation in an extreme form, by cutting myself off as far as possible from everything I had ever known before. The old man's mate said, I don't envy you your job, there's a force ten gale warning out for the Orkneys. I asked whether that would be on our way to wherever we were going, and they said it might well be: last trip the Skipper went to Iceland, his catch made £7,000, and he might well go there again: or to the Barents Sea, or Bear Island, in either case probably going up through the fjords. Before I could ask where exactly these places were, the old man said, You'll be sick. I told him I had tablets for seasickness. They'll be no use to you, he said, You'll be sick until you bring up your green bile, you've got to bring up the green bile that's been there maybe since you were a child. And once that green bile's gone, you'll be all right, he said, and his mate too said, You'll be sick, but you'll fooking eat afterwards! Doctors recommend sea voyages for bringing up the bile, said the old man, Once you've brought up your green bile you won't get TB, nor cancer of the stomach, nor any trouble with your gut at all. I had apparently chosen a bad time of year: the autumn equinoctials had well started, and a hurricane which caused damage on the coast of Florida had moved across the Atlantic and was blowing itself out in the North Sea. That was why we should probably go through the fjords. You can get dirty books in Norway, said the old man's mate, With girls in their natural state, though
105

the words are not in English. Then he seemed
anxious I should not believe all the bad stories
about trawlermen which he was sure I had heard:
though they got drunk on shore and did some
damage, they were not anything like as bad as
they were made out to be. Suddenly the lights
went on, and mate says the steamer is aboard. It
was nearly midnight, and I said I would like to try
to sleep a little before we sailed. I don't know
where your bunk will be, said the old man, But I've
put the box with your bedding and stuff in it down
in the transom cabin. I told him I had understood
I would probably have a bed made up in the
Skipper's day cabin, and the old man said in that
case he would take me up to the chartroom where
I could stretch out on a seat and sleep till the Skipper came: which would be about three. After he
had left, I went for a walk alone, feeling the deck
under my feet, the clean wooden boards lined with
pitch, and then up on to the whaleback, a word I
knew, and relished, and could now put a place to:
looked again at the two trawlers tied in front of
us, and at the low buildings on the quay: then went
back, feeling very tired, to the chartroom.   ·   ·   ·
·   ·   The Skipper startled me awake when he
came into the chartroom. I introduced myself,
thanked him for agreeing to have me on this voyage. He was not unfriendly, but not friendly: spoke
little: firmly indicated I was to sleep in the transom
cabin aft with the deckies, which was not welcome
to me since I had been hoping for something more
private, more comfortable: but I was prepared to
accept hardship, had prepared myself for it, so was
no more than disappointed. I found my kit in a big
cardboard box in the biggest of the three deckies'
cabins, bunks for six, right at the stern. Seven or
eight deckies sat around, some drinking; others
dropped in from time to time, talking of what they
had done when ashore. A short, not quite tubby man
of forty-five or so took me in hand, kindly, Festy, the
Third Hand, found me an untaken bunk, cleared
it of clobber—old seaboots, canvas bags, rope, a
small torpedo-like thing—and helped me to place
my donkey's breakfast in it. I climbed up into the
106

bunk, noticing at once and using the ventilator, directing the aluminium spout from the trunking on to my face. There was a small shelf on the bulkhead side: here I thought I would keep my pills, dramamine and aspirins and so on. And a pencil. I took a dramamine tablet. The deckies were not drunk, but certainly had been the evening before, were morose now, yet in good spirits, paradoxically. They talked of Mick, who had sung at a nightclub, central teeth to the canines missing, and another man who claimed to have started a fight at a dancehall. Yet again they were concerned for me to know, like the old man, that they were nothing like as bad as their reputation, plied me with drink as if to enlist me. Stagg, in particular, more drunk than most, nearly an old man, kept telling me almost aggressively that he was not a drunken troublemaker like I thought all fishermen were, and had to be reassured by Mick and Festy that I did not think badly of him, and even if I did, who cared? As soon as we began to move, I went up on to the bridge: out of interest and also, sentimentally, even fearfully, to take my last sight of land for three weeks, as I thought. Not that the land was much like land as I had always known it: docks and gantries and sea walls and flat, flat, flat. The Skipper said nothing as I came, nor while I was there: he seemed to concentrate almost over-intensely as he took us slowly out of the basin and through dock gates not so very much wider than the ship. In this he was aided by two or three men on the whaleback, the great figure of Duff amongst them, ordering and swearing, glancing up at the Skipper from time to time. The deck was lit, well but not brightly, and several men were tidying, one swearing at the fishlumpers who had left the ship in such a mess. Stagg came on to the deck, old and somewhat unsteady, to be sent back by Duff as not being needed, or perhaps because of his age, or because of his state. Once we had passed the dock entrance there was nothing to be seen but lights: and, though we had begun to feel only the slight swell in the river mouth, I already sensed that my balance was not as certain as it was and that head-

ache which is still with me began, is part of the
seasickness and of being at sea: so I went off the
bridge, excusing myself to the Skipper, down off
the boatdeck, to the rail, hanging on to the safety
line, where I stood hoping the air would cure my
incipient seasickness, or at least postpone it: where
Scouse found me, and talked, was friendly, told
me which the various lights were at sea and on
shore: every second I felt more and more sick, the
nausea hung in my head lower and lower every
moment: would reach my gut soon: did: I rushed
away from Scouse, half apologising, glad I knew
where the lavatory was, pleased that I had had the
foresight to have asked the old man just where it
was: where I collapsed over the pan, knees on the
dirty wooden grating, retching, felt some part of
me just below my solar plexus trying hard to force
its way up my throat: and spewed just a trickle
of acid spittle into the bowl: and, worse than I
had expected, this retching continued, though I
brought nothing up, had nothing it seemed which
I could bring up, except my solar plexus, or whatever it was under it that was loose, or seemed so,
and which now began to pain me every time I
heaved. I saw no sense in being there and heaving
nothing, and I wanted to lie down, remembered it
did help, or was supposed to help, lying down. As I
thought, I'm glad I've been sick. I'm relieved all
the wondering whether I would be or not is over,
for it's bloody awful but it's not unbearable, intolerable, I can stand it, I do still want to stay, I am
going on this voyage and I am not going to try to
back out now, or regret it. How did I manage that
companionway down to the cabin? Fell most of
the way, perhaps, but climbed into my bunk de-
terminedly enough. Festy underneath said Eat
something, and Johnny opposite said Eat, eat for it,
eat for crissake. And all I had was a green pear
bought in the market the afternoon before I came,
one pear out of three pounds, which were all I
could carry, ludicrously small amount now I think
of it, they were all gone in four days, those green
pears, spending but a brief while doing me hardly
any good. · · The last fresh fruit until this

orange, which was valuable, so valuable, that now I know I can do without more until we return, know that I have come that far, have gained that much control, will not have difficulty in not bringing myself to beg another from the Skipper. As I can stand standing here on the cold boatdeck, as long now as I choose, bearing the cold, bearing the wind, bearing whatever weather.

oooooooooaaaaaah · · · · worn edge · · · · · mahogany · · · · · worn · · edge · · mahogany · · ooooah · · · · · careful · · carefully lift head · · aaaaah · · not so bad, not so badly · · the head · · this morning · · if it is this morning. Arm · · lift arm, asleep, still, the arm, with the watch, yes, after nine, missed breakfast, no matter, not hungry, can wait till midday, yes, but look forward to it, not feeling sick, though still the headache, still that, I'm almost used to it, accept it, bear it, but I'm over the sickness, for the moment, I feel, how marvellous, yes, this happened the first time I was seasick, I seem to remember, the only other time I have been seasick, between Penzance and St Mary's, going across to the Scilly Isles, yes, with the Cypriot girl, whose name was · · · · · Eva, yes, Eva, who was sick too. We had come down to Penzance on my old motorbike, a BSA 250 it was, pre-war model, which I loved, but she could really only do sixty, and I always lied about her age, as too about Eva's who was twenty-eight to my nineteen, and married too, to a Cypriot who sent her to England occasionally to live with her mother, for cheapness, since he could not afford to keep her in Cyprus,—no, I am deceived, misled, it was Malta, she was Maltese, I used to buy her sweets and she'd say I like Maltesers and I'd wittily reply, I know, you married one. But she was only Maltese, herself, her mother was English, that was why her husband could send her home to England sometimes, for months at a time, and it was one of these times that I had met her, Ian and

109

I had picked up her and her sister at Richmond Ice
Rink one evening, and I had gone for the older
one, thinking it was time I found someone experi-
enced, and she was, though she was not wearing a
ring, and she never let me have it, the cow, never
brought herself to adultery, I suppose, being a
Catholic, though that mattered in this special instance very little, with Eva. She and her sister
were left alone at the time we met them in this
house at Twickenham, the mother was off abroad
somewhere with the father, who worked for a
foreign airline, El Al perhaps it was, or Air India,
Near or Middle East, I forget which, as a mech-
anic: and I would go over many nights, on my old
BSA, after working in an office all day, and sit with
her, Eva, or go to the pictures—some picture about
Lourdes was one we saw, I remember, shit I
thought it was, but it pleased her: and I was always
trying to please her. When we came back, or when
we were alone, sooner or later, we would kiss
deeply, tonguing and sighing, and I would feel
her breasts, which were good, and then slip my
hand between her knees, and so up her skirt and
over the elastic of her panties and—it was all very
juvenile, I realise—work my finger on her clitoris
until she had had enough, I never knew whether
she came or not, probably she did not, I suspect:
but she never returned the pleasure, for me, when
I embarrassedly indicated that she could, that I
would welcome at least that, she said once I knew
where I could go if I wanted that sort of thing, up
Piccadilly. Whether we should have it properly
was decided very early on, as I remember: one
Sunday afternoon, after she had cooked spaghetti
for lunch—she taught me how to cook a good
spaghetti—I offered to wash up and she went upstairs to rest, she said, in her room, and of course
I later followed her. She seemed partly drunk, and
indeed we had had some wine with lunch, but not
much, and I lay with her on the bed, and fondled
her, and she said Take me: yes, just like that, it
was, and I being nineteen and unpractised, thought
hard and was prepared contraceptively, and went
outside to the lavatory: and while I was there, just
110

about to put the thing on, this lodger came in, downstairs, and went into the room next to Eva's, and somehow I could not with him there, and I went downstairs again, and sat and stared at the photo of a nude baby on a plump cushion that was Eva young and nearly cried over my innocence or lack of experience and knew that we would never, just knew. When later she woke up, she asked why I had not taken her, and cowardly I told her I had no contraceptive, and she did not want to have a baby, did she? And she was horrified, or pretended to be upset, about my thinking of using a contraceptive on a Catholic girl. And there sexually we stayed for months, she not wanting me to use protection and me not willing to risk committing myself with her to the extent of starting a baby. We even went on holiday together, that summer, it only lasted spring and summer with Eva, down through Devon and Cornwall to Penzance, where we stayed the night and left the BSA and crossed next morning to the Scillies. The ship looked quite big when we first saw it beside the quay at Penzance, but even before we were off Land's End it seemed very small compared with the waves. I was seasick within perhaps half an hour, after eating an apple and seeing someone else sick, and was led down far into the ship, where I lay down and was slightly better. But I can remember still the pulse of the engine, faster as the screw came out of the water, slowing as it was immersed again, and the slowness of time passing. Five hours it took, that day, I think, and it was a rough passage: in any case, it was a rough stretch of sea, for seven currents we were told met in those straights between the Scillies and Land's End. Eva would not let me have it on the Scillies, either, of course, though we had an interesting enough holiday. I was such a fool, an innocent, really, for standing for it: it taught me not to, later, though. The voyage back to Penzance was calm, I was not sick, and remember recovering very quickly from the outward trip · · Not here, as there is never a chance to be still, three weeks of movement, my body never still. · · Eva's face.... · · She had a flat

111

face: oh, that is not to say that her face did not
have its promontories, its protrusions, its irregulari-
ties, for it did, but it seemed flat, her face, flatness
was the impression one gained from looking at her
face, that I gained · · ah, a face just like · ·
rather like · · the green pro · · · · ·
the cow · · made my left eyelid twitch, Terry
noticed it drooped after that shame, my two eyes
became different from each other, I noticed it
twitched, could feel it irritating, but could not see
it in the mirror when I tried to catch it doing it, so
no one else can have seen it, and · · good, I
have not noticed it doing it since I came on board,
this trip has at least rid me of that, so far, of my left
eyelid's twitch, that was upsetting, so it must be
therapeutic, this facing of the past, of all of the
past, must be, I've lost my twitch! Good! · · ·
 · · That face like Eva's. Eva went back to her
husband on Malta, as soon as the summer was over,
she did not like the English climate, Eva, returned
on a mailship from Southampton, where I saw her
off, was surprisingly allowed the day off from the
asbestos firm where I worked, wept as I left her, yes,
wept at our parting, like a woman or a child, she
must have been embarrassed, but I left her before
I need have, she wrote nastily afterwards, a card
from Lisbon, or Gibraltar, that she had hours to
wait on her own at the ocean terminal, because I
had rushed off, weeping, could stand it no longer,
and her one or two other letters much later were
nastier, she was having a baby by this useless
husband, and wanted nothing more to do with me,
at which I felt sorry for the last time, then swore
at her, and determined to learn by this experience,
from which I had little else, that I would always
take at least sexual satisfaction from such as she,
as Eva, with her flat face, or give them up, did too,
yes, Laura, for one instance, Laura was more a success, I did make love to Laura, yes, very satisfac-
torily, perhaps as a result of my experience with
Eva, some two years later, perhaps eighteen months,
not that she was not keen, or that I had to push it
very hard, for she was, and I did not. She was the
first I ever had without the sheath, it was good, I
112

remember her for that, Laura, I do remember her for that, at the very least. And for what else? She hurt me, too, had me on the rebound from an Arab student, who returned, saying he would send for her, to marry her, which he did, in the end, and not so very long afterwards, though she had to pay her own fare. She used me in a sort of revenge, a sort of cocking an English snook at the Arabs, I suppose, for committing her to them. She worked on Wages in the same office as I did, and the physical attraction between us was such as I had never known before, like that of a magnetized steel bolt for its appropriately polarised nut: so much so that I do not remember any real preliminaries, like going to the theatre, or to the pictures as being necessary— yes, we did, we went to see *Hedda Gabler*, at the Westminster, I think it was—but this was merely for the sake of form. Very quickly, it seems, she had invited me round to her room, which she occupied as if it were a bedsitter, in her parents' house in Kensington, and we were immediately kissing as soon as I had arrived. Suddenly she broke away and muttered about changing into something more suitable, a readymade phrase, that, from any number of romantic stories, and I stood there fingering my stand, and she came back quickly, from the bathroom, I think it must have been, with only a long, loose, nearly transparent dressing gown on, and stood up against me, and dragged my flies apart and undid my belt and slid my trousers down and pulled at my briefs as I took my jacket off: and took in both hands those this disinvestiture had all been directed to: then pulled back her dressing gown and lodged me between her legs and threw her arms about me to bring it to her closer and keep me close: and at one point it slipped out, as I was taller and it had of course a natural bent up- wards, and she eagerly, yes eagerly, pushed it back again and then shortly decided this initial coquetry was unnecessary and pulled me down on to the bed and at once sought to take me between her thighs, who had expected more preliminaries, but was not by any means insisting on them, she pull- ing up my shirt so that our flesh met the more

113

closely and introducing me all unsheathed as I stood into the soft sheath of her vagina: a stroke, a second, and I came, so had I been excited, so could I no longer contain myself: but still stood, I was surprised to feel, so kept on with my stroke until, it seemed a long while later, she said, Have you finished, then? And it was all slightly embarrassing as I stood up, pulled my shirt tails down, and searched for my pants, elastically reduced to an easily-lost article: but she eased the embarrassment, Laura, gracefully indicated she was satisfied with my as if tyro performance, while at the same time giving me security in the continuance of our loving, by saying And next time take your shirt off!

· ·   The other times were eight, I counted them, we lasted only three or four weeks: and still unsheathed, she using Gynomin, herself. Usually I would come round in that time, those three or four weeks, after the Latin lesson I had in the evenings with a tutor in Holland Park, perhaps at eight or so, and she gradually became less and less interested in me and she talked about her Arab and took a parttime job as an usherette to earn more money to pay her fare out to him while yet denying to me that she was doing this. And though after the fourth or fifth or sixth time I did not exactly have to force her, once she said, How did that happen? afterwards, as if she had decided not to let me any more but her will had been too weak. And she would not take her clothes off or help me in many ways, so that I had to push her briefs down at the front as she lay and insinuate myself into her: which was not uncomfortable or difficult, I was surprised and pleased to find. But soon her will held, and she would just not let me, and I was of course, angry, and ruined whatever bases of a real relationship there were. I see now it was wholly physical, on my part too, and that she grew tired of it sooner than I: but at the time I wanted it to be a lot more, a lot more, and was hurt and bitter when it finished, for it was love, of a kind, and not to be rejected as I thought she had rejected it. Obviously it would have been intolerable to remain working in the same office as Laura, so I used a slight cold as an
114

excuse to take a few days off from those commercial bastards and found myself another job in another office but far away from Hammersmith, in the West End: a better job, too, and I had been meaning to leave for a long time, but had not done so, out of laziness, inertia, and so it was good in a way that this trouble with Laura forced me out into a new job: not that I stayed in it long, for I did not, the new job, as within a year I had taken my Latin and been accepted to do an English degree course. But that last evening with Laura hurt! My parents —I had had some duty visit to make with my parents—to the country, my father drove us in a hired Vauxhall— · · What interest is that? · · I had an attack of herpes on my lip, at the corner of my mouth, felt the small vesicles swelling and irritating all day long, tried to reduce the unsightliness at a pub we stopped at for a drink in the early evening on the way back, but succeeded only in making the sore place bloody, suppurating and more obvious. He dropped me off at Kensington High Street, my father, and I walked the rest of the way to Laura's, said my good evenings to her military father and stunted mother in the hall with the first middle-class pleated silk lampshade I ever saw, and went up to her pine-partitioned bedsitting room. She would not kiss me because of my herpes: it was as simple as that, this temporary ugliness was made the reason for the unwantedness of myself, for her. There were ugly words said as well, and an ugly scene, to complete the romantic cliché of it all, to end the same sort of affair a million million others have had. And I left, after forcing on her my ugly herpes in a kiss that smeared her with the harmlessness of my blood, the ugliness of my lymph. Trite, the affair with Laura, casual sex, if anything ever deserved the cliché: but I wanted it to be more, I wanted it to be more! She made it that, kept it small, not me, she! I was even prepared to offer her, did offer her, that I would give up my Latin, abandon hopes of going to university to do an English degree, if she would stay with me, which meant marriage, and I swore I would become a successful accountant, as then I was a

clever accounts clerk but contemptuous of everything to do with it, if she would stay with me, not
go to her Arab, marry me. It was as well she did
not, of course, I too would soon have exhausted the
physical side, and she was dim, of course, of 'good'
parents, middle-class Presbyterians, she after an
expensive education took a job as a cashier at a
serve-yourself in Kensington High Street, which is
where she met her Arab, ah, the whole thing bloody
disgusts me! · · · · · But the sex was good,
at first, I'll say that for her, Laura · · · · · I
soon made sure I recovered from that wound,
having learnt from Eva, yes, I took too a lesson
from Laura and her Arab, went straight out on the
romantic rebound and found another girl for myself, picked another up within days when out with
Jerry in Edgware Road, Joan her name was, lived
in Sussex Gardens, went back with her the first
night— · · I've been through all that once, not
again, · · the cupboard bathroom and the
missing letter—no. Yet now I think of it, why did I
not think, remember, that I had had it without the
sheath with Laura, when I was with Joan? · ·
Oh, what matter. · · I counted with Joan, too
and I only managed it nine times with her, as well,
for ages that haunted me, that record, that with no
one woman had I ever managed it into double
figures, no, a strange intercession at this last digit
of those invented by the Arabs—no, that too could
be no more than coincidence, with Arabs! But I
still felt pain at the defection of Laura, as I saw it,
for years afterwards, could remember her small
face and the way she slightly dropped each shoulder in turn as she walked, for years, and that first
way she came into her room in the loose dressing
gown and how she almost sucked me into her, took
me naked deep into her woman's mysteries: such
expressions. · · · · · Yet thinking of what I
so easily term her betrayal, it may be I am too harsh:
she told me right from the beginning she was involved with the Arab, I cannot complain of deception, and what I do complain of is perhaps no more
than that she did not do always what I wanted, was
not always or even ever what I desired. My fault if
116

anyone's: again. · · And did I love her? Certainly, no one till Gwen did I feel so hurt about, and certainly I loved Gwen, certainly. · · At last I come to think about Gwen, who have tried so long to put her from my mind, now, four years later, have succeeded this far, in not thinking of her on this voyage at all: she was a wound, yes, an area of pain, a death of a certain part of me, of course, but not consciously, no, just as so much smegma under the prepuce of my consciousness— · · what am I doing, I ramble, when this should be important, this should be selective, I should not just think of Gwen generally, of the happiness, for there was happiness, of the love, for there was love, I did love, no, but of the significant, of the meaningful, of that which has since formed me, influenced me, twisted me into a solitary, if it has, that force which has set in train the constant movement of this voyage, and my mind, my self. For her leaving was far worse than Laura's returning to her Arab, saving her fare in shillings to fly to Iraq or Lebanon or wherever it was, far worse than Eva's going, which I could weep over, sincerely: for Gwen's failure was such that I could not weep, was beyond crying, wanted only to be on my own to celebrate this death within me. So think: only those things relevant, and happiness, such joy as there was, is not relevant, not important to me now. So think, selectively. · · The German Tour. Something of a release from that useless study of Anglo-Saxon, a tour lasting perhaps three weeks, to German and Danish universities with a play, Shakespeare, of course, *Much Ado About Nothing*, good title, not my choice, chosen by academics in both England and the countries we were to visit, but I was chosen to produce it, or direct it, as I preferred to call it. My first real experience of the isolation of command, the only time since those early attempts to lead in the landscape of my evacuated childhood. And I did not enjoy it this time later, either. For it was not as though they were professional actors who could be replaced if they would not be disciplined, who were used to discipline: they were students who had to pay £25 each to-

117

wards the cost of the tour and who saw it therefore
as much as a holiday as a performance: and who
were undisciplined as most students are, seeing
this period as their last chance of real freedom before the iron gate of responsibility clanged to after
them. And I have no taste for authority, for ordering: the acquisition of it does not interest me, and
the exercise of it bores me. I agreed to direct this
play because I thought that having to study the
mechanism of it in such practical detail would
show me how it was done, how it worked, that I
might learn from it something of use to me: in this
I was mistaken, for it taught me nothing that I did
not know already, and for weeks put me in an
exposed, isolated situation of great anxiety and
self-doubt. And before it was over I felt humiliated,
too, by some attitudes of unreasonableness, I felt,
on some of their parts— · · This becomes
woolly, tortuous: pull it together. · · Gwen
was my Beatrice, then, and because of a late defection I was compelled to play Dogberry, the fool to
her beauty: which was in many ways a true reflection of our relationship, for I was foolishly in love
with her. That is, was made foolish, to look and act,
by the singularity of my love for her. People said
I had given my mistress or lover or girlfriend the
lead in this play out of partiality: but I am sure that
she was the best actress of those available: and also
that she did the part very well. And if being director did isolate me, she at least had other reasons
for being on my side, at least had other reasons not
to disregard my orders: which orders were only in
the interests of producing the best performance of
that mediocre, oldfashioned play which was possible in all the circumstances. But many of the cast
were just not interested in that side of it, were
irresponsible. · · · · · —Oh, how miserable
and unworthwhile the whole thing seems to me
now! What embarrassment, shame, and humiliation it recalls, the German Tour!—bloody get on
with it, then, selectively. · · · · · It is a
measure of . . . something . . . that I was so in love
with her, perhaps, of course, that I cannot remember the cause of this great row we had, Gwen and I,
118

at this place called Hald, in Denmark, an old house
not like an old house, in wooded grounds, largely,
where we were to perform before students (Hald
was a student organisation) yet I remember it as
the row which finally established that we would
never be closer, even though we went on for four
or five further months, I in my delusion, she taking
what she needed from me and deceiving me for the
rest— · · Oh, this remembering is not only so
painful, but so boring to me, I have no enthusiasm
for it! · · · · · · · Hald, I must remember Hald. At least I can do the bloody scenery.
At least. A fairly large house, red brick, stone
facings, Dutch gables, a circular drive to the door,
entering and leaving on the same road through an
ungated pair of piers—"and when I say piles on
piers I do not mean 'aemorrhoids hon the harse-
holes of the haristocracy", the old joke about elm
and its uses, from Gordon. There were many
wooded areas, few open ones, a goodlooking lake,
with a ruin on one side, not romantically, it was not
a romantic place: the trees being firs mainly, occasionally deciduous: were they, I don't know, why
should I know the trees, have taken note of the
trees of this student guesthouse in the middle of
Denmark? I am not like that. The house itelf was
good, of a kind, pine panelling, a fine hall and
staircase kept rich and authentic. Elsewhere the
rooms were students' functional, the same as students' rooms all over Europe. But there was auxili-
ary accommodation in sheds, huts, whatever, away
from the main building, students' rough ironframe
bunks: and perhaps what started my bad luck from
which the row led, was it, was that I was one of
only three men who ended up in this inferior bedding, I, who, without standing on my dignity, or
perhaps it was being pompous, to expect as director
and as leader (when anything awkward needed
leading) I should have slept in the house, more comfortably. · · I still cannot remember what the
row was all about, but it was violent, bitter on my
part: I feel sure it was that she would not do something that I felt she should, that it was her duty to
our love to have done: or to what my concept of

119

our love doubtless was. But I do remember walking out into the night, burning with the injustice of her action, indignation riving my self, out into those cold woods, wet with dew, or rain, my brain hardly containing the frustration of it: for what could I do? I could not break with her there and then, as I would or might have done at home, privately, could neither leave the tour nor publicly break with her—ah, no, I had not the courage to do either: preferred to isolate myself within my self, bad, ah, bad! And anti-romantically I preferred not to stay wet out in the dank woods, so came in and went to bed early, very early, and this was our first night at Hald, to shiver under insufficient blankets, rage hammering at my sanity, my rightness put in jeopardy by her wrongness, her stubbornness—how odd that I can remember so well the state and not the cause of it! There must be something relevant in that, there must. · · And that uneasy place to sleep: sleep is important to me, I can endure a lot when I know I have a place to sleep easy. And I could not sleep for hours, in that place, listening to sounds from the house, of music, of dancing, like a servant in the outhouses hearing the junketings of the great in the great house, and this was added to my resentment, that I was excluded, to my bitterness against her, for causing it. And the embarrassment of knowing that the others knew, that one of the two who slept near me would nod at my buried shape on the bed, and grin, knowing I had quarrelled with her, and would be glad, for one envied me, perhaps, or because to another I was the representative of authority or power or something. But the other, in fact, the only one who did come while I was awake, was kindly when he did come, sat on my bed and talked to me about ordinary things, served to remind me there were ordinary things, suggested without saying that he sympathised, was good to me, in short, for which I was grateful, and afterwards I, who was so meanly prone to keeping myself to myself, went out of my way to repay him, Patrick, yes, whose qualities I just because of this began to notice, more than I would have otherwise done,

120

and am grateful to him—I was a mean bastard
then—for they are fine qualities— · · I ramble,
I ramble, my constant fault, these are irrelevancies.
Think what it was I rowed with Gwen over: it
makes it laughable if I cannot know what caused
so much pain! · · · · · · · I cannot: it
is laughable. · · · · · · · We met next
morning at breakfast, Gwen and I, and— · ·
Oh, the pain, the pain!— · · and the only thing
I thought of to avoid making the courageous steps
of either leaving the company or ignoring her for
the rest of the tour was to climb down, to make the
overtures, even to pretend it was my fault, even,
even, to humble myself before herself, with her
wrongness, her solitariness · · Ah, that is it,
THAT IS IT! · · No, anyway, she saw the advantages of this approach, of this solution, for she was
in the same situation, then, really, now I come to
see it, and gave in with little grace, who had great
grace, and knew that something had been established, and that even if it had not been then the
same battle (whatever it was) could be fought
again on more favourable ground at a more favourable time. So we were one again, ha-ha, and had
a brief scene that morning in the room she shared,
locking the door, that no others could disturb us,
in which we both said we were lonely, would
always be lonely, and that therefore we could never
really love anyone: that sounds romantically silly,
now, and at the time I was concerned only with
expediency, with making it up, so that a face
should be put on things, until we were home. And
I forgot about that declaration of mutual individu-
ality immediately afterwards, lapsing into my illusion again, that we did love, that she loved me,
rather, for certainly I loved her, certainly that was
no illusion: it is an indication of my love for her
that I could delude myself about her part of it,
her reciprocation. But later she was to say, when I
was bitter at her failure, that she thought all had
been made clear at Hald— · · I have been
through some rough old emotional times, it becomes clear, yes. So have the women, to be fair.
Always I was trying to make them conform to some

121

concept I had of what a relationship could be. If I could conceive it, then it should be attainable: a dangerous concept, I see, if applied to many things, to any other thing, perhaps, demonstrably untrue, in fact, but I certainly believed it to be true of something I could see between man and woman, and still believe it, still search for it. And Gwen conformed when it suited her petit-bourgeois mind, and deceived me when it did not. Circles, I go round in circles. So then: what else about Hald? · · · · · · · The performance we gave was poor, as I remember: the stage had no more than a twelve-foot opening, and the amateur conditions gave rise to an amateurish performance when we were capable of doing much better, did do much better, in other places, on proper stages. · · Running heavily through the woods in my thin cheap gold and black dressing gown to bathe in the lake, with her and Patrick and others: the pine-mast, if that is the word, yielding dankly under our feet, the same slimily present as we entered the lake, shallow at this point, unpleasant underfoot, that we were glad to breaststroke off, kick our feet clean of that slime. And there were leeches, too, that's right, when we came out there were leeches cupped on our feet, not painfully sucking, but loathesome enough in their possibilities, and Patrick made erudite jokes about medieval medicine, which made it more bearable. And the ruins we visited, too, taking photographs of each other in the ruins, on the walls, one of Gwen where her bathing costume was so similar in tone to the sky as backcloth that she appeared to have nothing on, until you looked very closely. · · · · · What else? Dining room scenes, with announcements in several languages, which we actors parodied, once, quite funnily, to us, yes, but not probably to them, perhaps even embarrassingly, I don't know. That will do about Hald. · · Anything else on that tour? · · · · · Photographs taken there too, in Hamburg, · · could look them out, if I had them here, to help with the memories, to establish the causes, manufacture the reasons, evolve the bases, confirm the findings, oh

122

Christ this is getting tedious! But it must be exhausted, the subject, of its possibilities, in case the key, the whole point, is there for my finding. ·

 · · · · · · In Copenhagen there was a party for us in an upstairs room at some students' union, where we all were drunk on Carlsberg and akvavit and where Gwen and I came closer, enjoyed at a window throwing telephone directories to a Welsh member of the company outside who took them, ran, dummied, and kicked for touch. Where some sort of local police came and enquired what was going on, as was their duty, and being honestly answered that it was a student party, left us civilly to become drunker, after accepting each a bottle of lager themselves. Where the Raven, one of our rustics, made a spectacular exit through a door, theatrically crawling backwards to gain attention, having forgotten that there was a steep flight of stairs immediately outside that door. And where Stuart and I fought a duel through the streets of that capital, holding our blunt prop Naval ceremonial swords by their wrong ends, laughing all the way. Eventually to collapse on to student bunk beds where on the bottom of the one above mine I cut my knee badly, after bouncing, felt no pain, but woke in the morning to guilt about the blood low on the sheets, as if I had been raping dwarf virgins all night. · · · · · The performance at Copenhagen was disastrous. We acted on a bare dais in a ceremonial panelled hall, with blackouts instead of curtains, and two poor entrances: one was a door with a step down and behind it a landing of a marble flight of stairs, the other door was at the foot of these stairs, after passing through which the actors mounted by a wooden flight of steps to stage level. This flight had a handrail on one side only, and I suppose it was lucky that only one actor throughout the whole performance chose to step down on the wrong side of that handrail in the dark. The blackouts confused the props men too, who, altering scenes, were often caught in jeans and shirtsleeves in renascence Italy. For no reason that I knew, during the second act this ornamental staircase—green travertine and bronze

balustrade— became flooded with water: that is to say, water came from the upper storeys, gently, half an inch deep, taking the stairs as a formal waterfall, just wetting to our uppers, and continued down into the basement where a dance orchestra played just loudly enough to be overheard in the auditorium. But the audience, such as it was, fifty poor Danish souls or so, took it very well, quickly entered into such spirit as we were able, considering the wrongness of everything, to assume, and clapped the itinerant sceneshifters as they were caught, who took a bow, appropriately, and thought themselves very Brechtian, and at the end we were clapped mightily, several blackout calls as if we had given *Much Ado About F.A.* the finest, most definitive performance ever, and we went out on a final appropriate note by half the cast being caught for an unexpected call. This lighting was by a man called Chance, Lighting by Chance, it said on our programme, and so it bloody was that night. · · · · · Whereas at Hamburg everything went well, the right size stage and neutral setting for our scale of acting and paucity of props, a good audience and efficient control of things of which we were glad to have been relieved. And at the beginning, since I was not on for some time, I quietly went round to the back of the hall and there watched part of the play, and was pleased at what was my production, seeing it distanced, my only real moment when it was all worth while during the whole tour. And Gwen was really so good as Beatrice, she gave a new kind of life to Shakespeare's fustian lines, for me, made his oldfashioned overwrought convoluted phrases sound like sense even to Germans: which was more than I could relatively do for the plot, or anyone could do for it, for that matter: Shakespeare is a great poet but a useless dramatist on today's stage. · · And in Hamburg I was at peace with Gwen, for some reason, this city was the setting for one of the good times, and even when a man called Falke—My name is Falke, he said, Like Falcon in English: and he flapped his arms—even when this organiser of our visit kissed her theatrically, in a fatherly
124

manner, I was not jealous, for the first time, who was generally jealous if any man so much as looked with more than general interest at her: a sign of my insecurity, of course, and in this case of my temporary sureness of her and of our love. And in Hamburg of course we went to the Reeperbahn, as all tourists do, after our performance on the first night, and went to a jazz club where the sharks let us listen to the jazz for buying one drink, which cost a great deal of my little money, but did not bother us after that. A Swedish band it was, I remember, and the drink was not real alcohol or even real Coke with it: which latter annoyed me, but not Gwen. Oh, and before we went into this jazz club, we went into a pintable place and an attendant asked me if Gwen was over eighteen, in English, we must have stood out as being English, and we laughed, for of course she was, but afterwards she was slightly annoyed rather than flattered by this. ·
· · · · And on our way home, or back to our digs, hers in one and mine in another, place, that is, on a tram, a disturbing, Kafka-esque thing happened to us. First of all, the tram seemed not to pass through the place where we were sure it would, had been assured it would, where we wished to get off: and then, on the first time past this posited place, I glanced at the conductor a few seconds after I had looked at him before (or so it seemed) and it was a completely different man! All sorts of rational explanations for this came to us then and later, but none really explained it. And, after the third trip on that same number tram, twice in the original direction with once in the opposite direction in between, we gave up and took a taxi, first to her digs and then I took it on to mine. · · I still remember Hamburg with affection, as being the one town I saw to which I would like to go back, to spend some time in, in Germany, except perhaps for Munich, yes, but Hamburg! And one member of our cast went sailing for an afternoon on the something See, and overturned and had to be rescued by the local water police or whatever they were called, and they came round to our digs the next day demanding some sort of fee for rescuing

125

him: I do not remember how that ended, whether he paid them, or stalled them off until we were on our way to wherever next, which I believe was Munich, far down in the south, in Bavaria, the tour was not very well organised geographically, there were these great long train journeys in between. But Munich as a city I took to at once, as so many do, I find, its great wide streets, Baroque churches, beergardens and halls, and the great Rubens in the Alte Pinakothek. We swam in the brown Iser race by a footbridge, one afternoon, I remember, and one morning were invited by the Mayor to break-fast in whatever the German equivalent of Parlour is, the City Hall, anyway, the whole company. Where I sat next to the Mayor, who showed me how to deal with the fat white hot sausages we had for this odd meal at eleven: he cut his in the middle, stuck his fork in the end thus exposed, of one half, cut straight along the skin towards the tied end, and then, holding down one flap so formed, rotated his fork to peel the skin neatly off. I was impressed, and cut decisively across my sausage as I had seen him do: a jet of hot white water shot a good eighteen inches into the air, most of it returning to my plate. Ha! said the Mayor, nothing more. These sausages were made of tripe, I supposed, or that at least was the only reasonable thing I could think of to account for their colour. They tasted quite pleas-ant with the stein of beer each of us had as well. Gwen I could not talk to, we had been separated by some kind of protocol. · · · · · They made us very welcome in Munich, and I still feel guilty that the standard of our production was not really worthy of them, or of me. · · · · · God knows where we went from Munich. This is all out of order. Back to Cologne, probably, where we spent our first night, on the way to Frankfurt, in a converted air raid shelter, built of massively thick concrete in the shape of a church, hopefully to escape the attention of bombers which in any case at night could hardly distinguish between houses and factories, offices and churches. When our party arrived there that night it was interesting how those men who were paired off with women

already quickly arranged to take double rooms together so that a later change could easily be made
to allow the pairs to sleep together: it was an automatic pairing, without any previous arrangement
being necessary, an instinctive decision, as we saw
that another man's thoughts were the complement
of ours. And the girls did the same. I thought little
about anything except sex, at that time, at that age,
twenty-five, and nor it seems did others: in that at
least I was with them. As a result of these arrangements, Gwen and I shared a cell-like room without
windows, tired after the train journey from London. And the performances there on the way back
were mediocre, the whole stay in Cologne was
boring, mediocre, being the fag-end of the tour,
all of us tired of new things constantly, the one- or
two-night stands in strange cities. · · As I am
now tired of remembering the whole thing, which
brought me so little in return for the great amount
of emotional energy, time admittedly willingly
filched from my degree, love, yes, love, wasted on
a poor play and an uninterested cast. Forget it. ·
· · · · No. Finish off Gwen. · · · · · ·
· · As soon as we had returned, in the train from
Dover to Victoria, in fact, when we were all revert-
ing to being our own individuals again, I relapsed
into very painful anxiety for us, for our love, and
also worried that she might see again an old boy-
friend whom she had confessed had broken her
heart— · · How trite this all seems now! Good!
· · —during the rest of that summer vacation:
which disturbed me greatly, and all the peace we
had had, for despite the quarrel at Hald we had
been together more continuously than at any other
time, as if in marriage—this now disappeared and
was replaced by unease and a foreboding of future
pain and loss: through which I could feel myself
already achieving a kind of piety. It was agreed
that we would marry the next year, after finals, in
almost exactly a year: and I knew that the test of
those coming months, and the ultimate test of
whether or not she would actually marry me, were
going to be very painful indeed, for me. And somewhere, very small, all but disregarded, I also knew

that I was not quite sure of our love, or that she was what I wanted, that she would be the answer to my questions about sex, about love, about art. Yet what else was there to do but proceed as though she was in love with me as indeed she said often enough she was, and that it would work out well? At the Tivoli in Copenhagen one evening we exchanged money for disc tokens to gamble on fruit machines, and, when we unexpectedly won and went back to the woman who gave change to convert our winnings, the woman's face showed scorn, such enormous contempt, at our hope for this, without needing to use a word of rejection: from that moment, I feared seeing that scorn on Gwen's face, that I should expect her to keep her word, to mean what she said about loving me and marrying me. · · There were several months of that fear before I did see that scorn, that contempt, before she betrayed me, Gwen. And still I went on seeing it, during that uneasy period between love and hate after betrayal, and into hate, for five years of hate, until now, when I begin to feel indifferent, certainly do not hate, no, merely want to understand. For years it was with me, as, hearing accidentally of some new betrayal, or realising some new betrayal, I would think of what I was doing while she was betraying me: and however good that thing was, this betrayal would ruin just the memory for me, the memory even tainted by it. When I heard of her taking up a job after we left college it came as a shock: I had not liked to think of her as having any life at all outside me: the effect of which was to set me worrying in a further way, I had the hell of the thought of her marrying and of the news of her marrying being given to me at a moment when I could not take it, would break under it. · · And once, when I went to stay with a friend in Cambridge, a friend of hers spotted me and followed us into King's College Chapel, stood talking to us, I hated him, questioning me at length as to what I was doing now, presumably to retell to Gwen: and said I would not have liked Cambridge, which was full of pseuds, should be glad I had gone to London: whereupon I enquired
128

how he should know what suited or did not suit my character so well, and he replied that he knew my character because he knew what Gwen was before she met me, and what she was now. This hurt me, that she should take from me so without giving what I needed in return, what I felt I had a right in all equity to receive in return! And I hated any conversation in which she was mentioned, it disturbed me, sullened me, especially in this place, whose late perpendicular would now always be associated with this mean man, who said also that Cambridge students of engineering would not come into the Chapel since no one could understand logically how it still stood, stupidly, as though we were tourists; and associated with that woman: Gwen. · · · · · So, not in mitigation of past love and enmity, just-passed hatred, of her for what she did, but because this is as much hers as mine, something we had, or seemed to have.... · · This is woolly, indeterminate. · · · · · I must try to analyse more, not just go over things, over and over things, the past, glorying in, almost, rather than analysing, now the hurt is past, over, enjoying the sex, vicariously, too much on sex, perhaps, no, it is important, so little else seems really relevant, though there were of course long periods without girls, or with useless girls. · · · · · Time? I ought to get up. Time? Headache still, always, but not sick, ten, half-past, yes, get up, wash, watch the gutting for an hour, or so, lunch, they call it dinner, will give me a good excuse not to stay out on that cold deck in this cold weather, for longer, unless I choose, can stand it, no. · · · · · Up then, no trousers to put on, sleeping in them, just a sweater, just as well, there's a lot of movement on her today, weather must be rougher, blowing up, I suppose, but I'm used to it now, more or less, which is not to say I cannot be thrown about, was yesterday, in the galley, returning a plate late, was thrown by a sudden movement, barked my forearm on a vertical girder, yes, still hurts, head just missed, legs folding under me, plate and spoon took off across galley, felt a fool, though only galley boy there, who was nearly

129

thrown as well, so neither of us laughed. So careful! The price of safety is eternal vigilance, in this case, again, the verity of the cliché. So one hand out for self, holding on, up the steps, through the hatch into alleyway, along, along, on to the engineroom gratings, along past the dully bright cylinder-head cover, the asbestos-covered pipes, the blasting warmth of the silver-lagged boiler, to the officers' quarters under the Skipper's suite, where I am allowed to use the washroom and lavatory. · ·
One hand holding for self, again, it is difficult to pee like this, with the target moving, or the projector moving, ah, reminds me of pissing on people's lavatory seats when a kid, to annoy them, to pay them back for whatever it was: no room for such gentility here, it is beside the point, marginal, every time someone leaves the porthole open, forget to secure the brass butterfly nuts, a sea splashes in and cleanses it out, the Great Jakes, the sea, and so on, and so forth, as I said before. So: now wash, easy enough to do with one hand, yes, shaving would be almost impossible for me, though the others all shave, it seems to me, not every day perhaps, but certainly they are not noticeably growing beards, as I am, as I decided to, though she did dare me before I came to grow one, and keep it for her to see; scratchy, it feels, of course, prickly, growing slowly after an initial sprouting, twelve days now, (is it?), hairs grow in all directions so that it looks most random, untidy, sloppy, unseamanlike, and though it started off fair it has now turned a kind of reddish brown, as if I had not fathered these hairs, illegitimate hairs, hirsute bastards: but it does feel good upon my upper lip, to brush back gently with the pads of my index finger and thumb, to feel the length of my moustache: and the hollow beneath my lower lip, too. Ah, evacuate, and piles, too, pain, pain, as if this voyage were not already enough of a paradigm of the human condition, piles, the unmentionable condition, so many people have them, they say, but no one talks about them, paradox, merely suffer them, treat them with suppositories, like these, the best shape, this make, like bullets, dum-dum bul-
130

lets, really, not allowed by the rules of war but very comforting to those fundamentally afflicted, dumdum, roundheaded, but tapering from the shoulder so that, pushed in a little way, they go the rest themselves, a most accommodating shape, made by Messrs Boots the Chemists, very well, the most shapely of all the suppositories I have come across. But nevertheless difficult to insert, they all are, need both hands really, but judge the pitch, allow for the roll, made it, hole in one, but one of these days something unexpected is going to happen, like yesterday in the galley, and I shall be found dead or unconscious in a very peculiar situation indeed. · · · · · · · So out, to walk the thoughtful walk of the man with piles, in these noisy oilskins and slummocky rubber boots, to stand alongside the men gutting, among the pounds, though not to use a knife myself. Ah, the sea is getting up, the weather is noticeably worse than last night. Hang on to the strung cable, do not touch the warp, directed round the double drums of the fairleads, across the deck, stand just ouside the pounds, announce I have come to read the entrails, smile: Festy, Mick, Stagg, Scouse and the deckie-learner do not smile, but look up, seem glad of any diversion, though, rib me about my seasickness, the while gutting. · · · · · At closer quarters, the gutting impresses me even more with its speed. I time Scouse on one of the bigger fish, a sprag, he calls it, which is a mediumsized cod, small ones are codling, and really big ones, of which we seem to have caught few, are presumably cod: it takes him nine seconds to despoil this great fish of its intestines, throw the liver into a basket, and hurl the remaining twenty pounds or so fifteen feet through the air into the washer. · · There is an athletic dedication about Scouse's gutting, a certain sadistic pleasure in his cutting strokes. But Stagg stands there stolidly, cloth capped, gutting automatically, economical of movement, saying nothing, thinfaced, gaunt even in the artificial bulkiness of his yellow skins, just as he probably has done the last forty years, or more, from a boy of twelve. Mick talks

131

as he guts, intermittently, usually to rib the deckie-learner, often quite harshly, intending to hurt a boy of sixteen, for what reason I cannot think: none of the others reproves Mick for it, and certainly I cannot interfere. Yet suddenly, when Stagg notices a metal marker on the tail of a jumbo haddock, and hands it without a word to Festy, it is Mick who insists that the fish, worth five shillings for the evidence of its travelling when taken to the fisheries research laboratory on shore, be given to the deckie-learner, insists it is his by tradition or some sort of right. Then a moment later he throws a catfish across at the boy, a cruel joke, since the fish has a wide mouth vicious with pointed teeth which can wound dangerously. Festy tells me about this catfish, since it is the first I have seen, long and somewhat eel-like with a fluttering continuous dorsal fin, mottled darkly on olive, the squat head nearly all mouth: says some trawlermen will deal with it by offering it the warp to bite, which it will do tenaciously, and then it is hanging in an easy position to gut. The deckie-learner, however, picks it up through its gills in the usual way, in its turn, avoiding the savage mouth, guts it efficiently, and throws it away from him, all without apparently noticing Mick. · · Festy points out such other curiosities as there are in this haul: several half-halibut, not really halibut but a bastard breed produced by some miscalculated union in pre-history, which are worth keeping, however, for the reasonable price they fetch; something like an overblown version of the catfish, but bigger and black and called a jellycat, which Festy stabs cruelly in an orange-coloured eye and heaves overboard, saying we would only catch it again and even for fishmeal it is not worth keeping, as so much of it consists of water; dab, small flatfish which are not kept; and small skate, which Festy says they call ginnies, and which he shows me to have genitals to copulate to reproduce like mammals: speaking of this with a delicacy which contrasts oddly with the dirty stories he tells me at other times, and saying also that he thinks the Skipper is wrong not to be keeping these small

132

skate this trip, as they are worth something, are very sweet to eat, and he throws the one he was showing to me into the basket which goes to the cook for our meals, for there is fish as a choice at every meal: I must try a ginnie, which has another meaning for me, but not now to think of that; and a great, squat, green, lumpish, bulge-eyed concertina'd parody of a fish, which Scouse seizes, balances on one hand with the other held flat at right angles across the thing's eyes, a mime I do not understand until Festy explains it is a camera-fish, and Scouse says he has taken a snap of me with it, before he pitches it weightily overboard; there are, too, lumps of a cream-coloured petrified substance which Festy tells me they call duff, and he looks round for the mate, as it too is like suet-pudding, some vegetable matter which grows on the seabed in this area and of which the net can become full if the Skipper does not avoid those patches experience has shown him it grows on. The other fish I know: cod, handsome, gleaming olive green, most unlike the sad grey slabs I have seen hitherto at fishmongers, for cod seems to lose most of all in appearance by being long out of water: haddock, with thumbprints either side of the neck and a black line down each flank; redfish, their great deepsea eyes burst, their mouths bloated with a bubble formed from some depressurised intestine to make them look as if blowing bubblegum, their spiky fins perhaps raising perch-like once or twice before they, sooner than most, die; and coley, or saithe, long, snouted, plump, dark green, handsome. I ask about dogfish, seeing none, ask if they come over the side barking, at which, surprisingly, they laugh, but are rather disgusted when I say I eat it often in London, that as rock salmon or rockfish it is popular, for to them it is a scavenger, looks like a small shark, is of that family, and therefore not acceptable to them when there are so many clean fish to be had. Their favourites are the small codling or baby haddock, eighty or a hundred fillets of which the cook must prepare, fried in egg and breadcrumbs, or batter, every day. Stagg and Scouse, gutting in the deepest

133

pound, fish up to their knees, now slide with their boots sideways a mass of fish towards the others. Mick raising a pound board to allow them to pass under. Flat on the deck lies a huge skate, four feet across its wings, and I remember now seeing it caught up in the mouth of the trawl earlier, and the Skipper assuring me it would be washed down into the cod end sooner or later: this haul, in fact I see now. Stagg guts it where it lies, white belly upwards, then gestures for Scouse to help him throw it into the washer. Peering at the mass of guts and green excreta which now begins to outbulk the remaining fish, I notice that there are small fish in amongst them, far too small not to have slipped through the five-inch mesh of the net, and upbraid Festy jokingly for catching the small ones: he looks at me, does not answer, but seizes the largest of the sprags still lying near his feet, rips at its belly, then cuts delicately and removes from the sprag's stomach a small haddock, perhaps weighing half a pound, the silver of whose scales has only just begun to be dulled by the sprag's digestive juices: which he hands to me with a grin, watching my fascination and disgust. This gives Scouse an idea, for he says, Come and look at this, pleasuretripper! And he fiddles carefully with the guts of a flat brown bastard halibut, snicks twice into the thick mass and then lays on the flat top of the pound board a bloody piece of gut, which I quickly see to be pulsing and very soon afterwards realise to be a heart, still beating, beating, a fish heart still with some kind of life left in it. I've known a heart go on beating for half an hour, says Festy: Three hours, during the whole time we were gutting, says Mick: A whole watch, says Scouse: and I know they are kidding me. I peer at this entrail, watch its life beating away, interested and disgusted yet moved: and think of several different omens this particular sacrificial object could portend. · · I feel the cold, as a result or not I cannot tell: but I feel cold. I cannot understand how these men can tolerate the cold for long stretches like this, gutting on an open deck on a day like this, when an occasional wave will break hard against the side and
134

send spray like a shroud over them as they work in the pounds. Obviously they are used to it—yet yesterday Scouse said that no fisherman ever gets used to it—accept it, at any rate, for the money it brings, they say, but there must be more to it than that. Perhaps they are all that physical type which can withstand pain more easily than others, is relatively unaffected by it, simply does not feel it: but, to look at, these men are physically so disparate.   ·

·   ·   ·   ·   From down a hatch to the fishroom a voice bellows Is the pleasuretripper up there? And Duff's head follows it, just his head, like Jokanaan from the green cistern, but grinning, alive, a little red tam o'shanter on his head. And he invites me to inspect his fishroom, which I am quite glad to do, imagining at first it must be warmer down there than on the deck, then remembering that the fish are packed in ice. Down through a coalhole-like hatch, dropping straight on to a pine fish-slimy inclined chute, fortunately just four or five feet long, landing on my feet, crunching ice: a great sprag nudges me in the back immediately afterwards, kicks once, and is then seized both handed through the gills and round the base of the tail by a man whom I have not seen before, which seems incredible, did not know he was on board: perhaps he lives down here: no, impossible. He lays the sprag neatly next to others, of a similar size, packs ice round it, and sockets into place a wooden board. I see now that part of the fishroom is skeletal, with metal supports which are made into compartments with boards, some wooden, others of corrugated aluminium: here are packed layer upon layer of fish in ice, according to size and according to kind, the cod with the cod, the haddock with their kin: solidly, we stand on one eight-foot layer, we have caught that many, and are now filling a second layer, perhaps another eight feet deep, the width of the ship and half its length: a great many fish, measured in kits, each of which equals ten stone, packed like sardines, ha-ha, sometimes still kicking in the ice as they are put down: occasionally if such movement annoys a man at his neat shelving he will bash the head with a piece of ice or the end of a board. The

other one of Duff's assistants is Joe, an older man
I have seen before, who silently shelves haddock,
methodically, tidily, mechanically. The area for
working in is relatively small, since the space without fish in it is packed with ice: as the ice is taken
for the fish, so more space is exposed, more skeletal
forest, for use as storage. Duff asks me if I am cold,
sees I am, and hands me a pick and grinning points
to the ice wall forward, behind the chute. I take
the tool and, bracing myself carefully against a
support and timing my blows within the movements of the ship, I begin to break down the ice,
crushed originally but now adhering together in
a mass, into fragments which form into mounds at
my feet. When the freed ice is nearly up to the top
of my seaboots, I take a shovel and send it in great
arcing showers to the feet of Joe and the other
man: and soon I am very warm, take off my scarf
and skins, work in sweater and trousers like the
others. For a breather, I watch the care with which
they pack, remember someone saying before I
came that this mate has a great reputation for the
condition in which he brings his fish to market: talk
with them about this method of storage, presumably the best, for some reason, though to my eyes
packing the fish at once in boxes or kits at this stage
would save the trouble of it being all unpacked
from the ice by fishlumpers in port and then put
into boxes. · · I am well warm by the time
Duff calls me off for dinner. · · · · · · · ·
The Skipper is worried about the weather, says we
shall have to give up fishing for a while if it worsens
at all. I say that I have noticed the occasional bad
roll which submerged the concrete scuppers alongside the rail, even submerged the top of the rail—
submerged it, not just broke over it: and Duff re-
assuringly says he has seen it do that up to the
engine room skylights, which are up on the boatdeck and on the centre line of the ship: Mind you,
he adds, I was bloody scared at the time. Fear of
this ship sinking is one thing I do not have, cannot
conceive even, for she is so demonstrably well
fitted to her element, to her job, that I cannot
imagine what conditions could overcome her: she
136

rides all the seas I have seen—and we had force nine across the North Sea and off the Norwegian coast—as successfully and confidently as I, a landsman, could wish. I can see why Corb took some of his examples, parallels, from ships: this trawler is indeed a machine for going to sea in, a machine for catching fish; shipshape; and in this bare functionalism lies her beauty. Certainly, she has no conventional beauties, for me, which is to the good: she has a very narrow beam for her length, for her less than eight hundred tons, but function, function, function! The whole ship is dedication to the concept of function and that is what makes her so beautiful to me. Except when, as now, she throws custard about, soaks my trousers with the sweet thick custard from the enamel jug as I attempt to pour, both burning and messing me: simultaneously from the galley through the hatch the sounds of two voices cursing as she threw something at both the cook and the galley boy. · · · · · I retire to my bunk to change the trousers, wash off the custard, hang them in my very efficient airing cupboard, and then decide to spend a while in my bunk in case of further accidents in this weather.

The only other time I lived this kind of corporate, community existence was · · in the RAF, for a short time, since I was in only a short time: and that only in Reserve Flight at Padgate, with the other rejects who were waiting for their discharge, all sorts, the odd serious disease, and three or four like me with perforated eardrums: they did not like people with perforated eardrums in the RAF, I never did find out exactly why not, some said it was because if the other ear went they had to give you a pension for the rest of your life, which would in many cases be a very long time, others said it was because you might have to fly high and unpressurised and you could not do that if your ear was perforated; others said—and the idea has never left me—that it was because meningitis bugs could go straight through to your brain: anyway, they never told me why, just made me step out for being hard

137

of hearing in that right ear at a medical inspection, and then a doctor tested it, banging a huge tuning fork in a deep score mark on a table and pressing it over various parts of my head, the while saying, Can you hear that? and me saying No, or Yes, as the case was, and when the doctor went out one of the erk orderlies said Looks like you've worked your ticket, mate: and I thought, Christ, now I shall have to think of getting a job, of deciding on this career I am expected to devote myself to. And they did discharge me, with a certificate excusing me from National Service on the grounds that I was unlikely to attain full medical fitness on account of a suppurative otitis media: which I must say has never given me much trouble, only discharged a custard-like, ha, fluid which stank when I was a kid up to about fifteen, and only did that when I had a cold. I am very slightly deaf in that ear, and I suspect also that this perforation is the reason why I can never tell any difference between mono and stereo. They found this imperfection on my second day at Padgate, the reception camp then, which must be known to thousands of my genera-tion as a damp and foul dump near Warrington in Lancashire: but they kept me three weeks before my discharge came through, in this Reserve Flight, which had nothing to do with flying but was a scruffy nissen hut in which all we rejects lived and slept. And though we had had no training we were still expected to march up to meals at the canteen as though we were trained airmen, and as we could not march properly were brought back in the even-ings in what would otherwise have been our free time to learn to march, for hours it seemed, the bastard of a corporal, this was, in charge of us, and we drilled, drilled, drilled, drilled. I quite came to enjoy it, but for the compulsion, saw a possibility of the pleasure of doing something simultaneously with others that I only ever felt before whilst sing-ing in a choir. · · And we had only parts of uniforms: I had a couple of shirts, socks, and boots, no blues, best or working, which I was rather sorry about. And they made us bloody bull the hut, too, polish the floor till it shone immaculately, without
138

any polish, too, officially, and lay our stuff out on
our beds in a way we had not been officially shown,
and generally be like real airmen when we were only
passing through, were not to be airmen yet were
treated as though we were. Yet in some ways we
were luckier than other huts because we able-
bodied Reserve Flight men were sent to work in
the hospital each day, cleaning floors like chars,
and we could steal polish to keep our floor bulled
for the officer's inspection. The hospital was an
interesting place, though the work was boring and
there was not even enough of it. I would try to
work it so that I had the floor of a matron's or nurse's
room to clean, work like hell, and then relax and
read her medical handbooks, particularly those on
sex, sex being my first choice in medical reading,
at this time. I never saw the matrons or nurses, pity,
they were always out, working I presume. The only
women we did see were Naafi bags, as they were
known, in the evenings, when we bought Naafi
food, which was only marginally better than the
issue, which was terrible, eggs in cellophane
jackets, tinned beans, tea thick with tannin and
bromide. And we used to cook toast and stuff
we bought in Warrington by the cylindrical
donkey fire in the middle of the hut, which was
CRAANGK! · · We're hauling—that's early—
the weather must be so bad that we're giving up
fishing till it blows itself out. Where was I? · ·
The hut, we were proud, if that is the right word,
since we had to do it, of our polished floor, so much
so we kept squares of blankets inside the doors for
anyone coming in to step on and traverse about on.
This had the pleasingly dual effect of protecting
and polishing the shitbrown lino: anyone who did
not use the squares had in the middle of the night
his bed turned upside down on him. There was no
privacy, · · as there is virtually none here · ·
which I missed, which I lack. · · I heard some
new jokes, to me, at least, and the sex stories of
other youths which may or may not have been true
but which were certainly interesting. I learnt to
sew buttons on for myself, and to patch a tear: but
not to darn. I contracted the worst cold I have ever

139

had, which lasted for weeks after I had finally been presented with my ticket. I saw the sex films meant to put erks off dirty women who could give them VD, and was accordingly disinclined that way for several days. I did no firing, held no weapon even, and the only aircraft I saw there were the decorative Spitfire and Hurricane preserved like modern fossils on patches of grass at the camp main gate. I made no friends, hardly an acquaintance, talked little even to the men in beds either side of mine. I read a lot, brooded a lot on a girl called Dorothy who was in effect affianced to me at the time, we were that close, ha-ha, designed a model aeroplane based on an amalgam of all the features of all the designs in a book I had on aeromodelling. My brooding over Dorothy—her lowermiddleclassness, the way in which she was directing our to-be-married life, the direction in which she was forcing my life—was very much involved with brooding on my future now that, very unexpectedly as I had since fourteen been conditioned to accept that my nineteenth and twentieth years were only to a very limited extent going to be under my control, I had seriously to think of a job that would as soon as possible enable me to marry and soon as possible afterwards provide me with enough money comfortably to support a wife and in due course, or sooner, children. This brooding depressed me, for marriage seemed both desirable and dull, inevitable and avoidable: certainly not an end in itself, as which it was presenting itself and presented to me. What I earned money from was made to seem by this irrelevant, arbitrary, and I felt it should not be. One thing I did decide, was sure about, was that I was not going back to being a bank clerk as I had been in the six months between leaving school and being called up: I could not stand any of the work, the people, the atmosphere. But what I would do I just did not know, and could not think: and I could not even think of anything I would like to be, except the impossible things, like a writer, or a film director, or just rich. I had gone at fourteen for two years to a secondary school which specialised in turning boys into clerks and

140

accountants, and girls into typists and secretaries: and I could therefore keep accounts, type, even do shorthand, though very slowly, and was fitted, even trained and qualified, after a style, to be a clerk in some sort of office: which fitting was dismaying to me after my experience at the bank. The whole point was that such work involved repetition, often quite complex repetition, but nevertheless basically the same sort of thing day after day after day: and that while I was sometimes interested in doing a thing, and I have always been interested in doing a thing for the first time, even for the second time, until I had learnt, not to say mastered, it, my interest would go immediately I had done so, and I would then be bored almost to shouting with it. I have always liked the new, though not in all things, not in marriage, for instance, a condition of which seems to me exclusion, oneness, with one person only. · · · · · My parents in all this seeking of appropriate employment were no help and no hindrance: that is to say, while they made no attempt either to press me to take a certain type of job or to dissuade from another certain type of job, they yet did not indicate to me what jobs there were to be had for our sort of class, for the sort of person I was, from the sort of background I came. The examples even of the rest of the family—a driver, greengrocers in the New Kent Road, the odd labourer—were not of much use, and certainly neither my father nor I wanted me to follow in his footsteps as a stock-keeper. So I brooded on this, there is no other word for it, unfortunately, I even came to resent the disability—left as some sort of medical legacy after having scarlet fever as a child of three—which had resulted in my so having to brood and think of my future two years earlier than I had expected, almost had hoped: realised too that, though there were obviously unpleasant sides to National Service, that indeed these might form the major part of the life, there was also a better side, the companionship, the fitness, a sense of some purpose even if I disagreed with it, a chance to travel, and a freedom from having to make serious decisions. And I had felt when I went

141

in that in some way National Service would improve me, harden me, and save the love I had for Dorothy, which wore away daily through her bourgeois aspirations and my regression into workingclass habits in self-defence, in defence of my self. Perhaps though it was fortunate that I was rejected by the RAF, for it might have coarsened and dulled me as well as toughened and honed me, and I might even now be stuck with an unsatisfactory wife, or divorced, or some such mess. As it is . . . it was very painful at the time, since in classic middleclass style she found someone else whilst still at least nominally attached to me, not engaged, that is to say, but attached, betrayed me, which hurt far more than her loss: I am glad I did lose her, now, and was not . . . · · no matter. She is not relevant to this present enquiry, this present state. · · Even our lovemaking was bourgeois and petty, incomplete and unsatisfying. And I hardly remember anything of her now, only things, comic things, like how her nose was in the way when I first kissed her, which was in the pictures, in Richmond or somewhere like that. · · No relevance, no interest, go on to something else. · · · · · · · When I take my mind off, I feel the bucking, I must force myself not to be sick again, but thirsty, yes, drink, I have a can of beer somewhere, yes, in the corner between my mattress and the bulkhead, open, difficult, and it will splash, fizz rather, IPA, spray, all over, can't help that, no, lever in the point, hold face away, spray, ah, spray! Can't even be bothered to wipe away. Who's to condemn me, here. · · Brace myself between the side of the bunk and the side of the ship, carefully judge the can in hand in relation to my mouth, drink, a delicate manoeuvre, a tricky judging. · · Ah. This beer is strong, straight from the punctured can. But not cold, since I keep it here, and this cabin is kept very warm, comfortable for us, but not good for keeping beer, but better than nothing, now, or going up to the Skipper's day cabin, to the case of beer he let me buy from him, where it is not so warm, where it keeps that little cooler. I asked the cook if I could keep it in his
142

cold store, but he said it would be frozen solid there, suggested I leave it out on deck somewhere, certainly it would get cold enough there, but who's to know if a sea might not wash it overboard, or someone take a thirst to it? As it is I keep it in the Skipper's day cabin, yes, and the bottle of whisky he let me buy, too, which he does not allow everyone on board, for drunkenness at sea is diabolical, to a seaman, apparently, a matter of endangering life, and so on. But he trusted me with a case of cans, twenty-four, and a bottle of whisky. Perhaps this export whisky is purposely different, for it has a strong, burnt taste I have not noticed in this brand at home: or perhaps it is that my taste is so affected by the seasickness that nothing tastes as it once did. The beer, too, is not what I would have chosen, myself, being a strongly tasting IPA, but the deckies seem to like it, it was chosen by their popular vote: they have two cans a day each, given out at midday, a ration they call it, I have heard no complaints that it is too little, and they pay for it themselves, cheap enough, on board, no excise, nor on cigarettes, nor chocolates, for some reason the Skipper keeps chocolates as well in the bond just outside Molloy's room, I had a box, at the start, but my stomach let me eat just two. But the beer I drink cheerfully enough, though it is not exactly to my taste, the taste is not particularly mine, for I am thirsty a lot on this ship, I drink it to break my thirst, one swallow from the can, straight, until I feel the click in the back of my throat, which breaks the thirst, I drink it to break my thirst, not to get drunk. The whisky I am sorry I bought, though it was only a few shillings, for I do not enjoy it: perhaps I can take it ashore, home, or give it away on board, have a farewell drink with the deckies—That's the first time I have thought of the end of the voyage! So there is an end! There will be an end! Yes, already we must be over half way through. And it seemed—not endless, that's a stupid word, but indefinite, though I knew three weeks as a length, as a unit, it was less than a month, which I knew about, well enough, but during those first few days out, across the North

143

Sea, it seemed indefinite, the length of the voyage, and very quickly the deprivation of the sight of land for that length of time was grievous, unexpectedly, · · And when, the weather in the open sea being bad enough to justify the cost of a pilot in terms of time gained in steaming speed, the Skipper decided to go through the fjords, I was relieved, delighted at the prospect of another sight of land: even though it had been only three days, or so, this was the fourth day. And carefully I watched from the bridge, on the first day I really felt that I might be able to withstand the voyage and not jump overboard, or die, possibly, for the first lump on the horizon which they told me would be the southernmost stump of the Lofoten Islands: and for about fifteen or twenty minutes they said they could see it, and I sectored that horizon again and again but could see nothing: until at last I did, a burr on the port side far forward, and realised how much keener than mine their eyesight was, how much better adapted to seeing at sea. And as the Lofotens came up one by one, mere great rocks at first, I was pleased for the first time that I was at sea, I, who had not expected to see land for three weeks grasped at the visual relief of these variations on the flat horizon of my outlook, and was glad. And it was then too that the Skipper told me we might land on the way back, at a place called Honigsvag, where we would pick up the pilot for the return through the fjords, if we needed fresh water: but that we would not that day put into the southern port for a pilot as they came out by boat to us waiting in the channel. As they did, two pilots, friendly but austere, to leave us at this Honigsvag, which I saw not to be much compared with most towns, but which I certainly hope we stop at on the way back, fervently, almost, I hope we put in at Honigsvag for water, even if it is only for a very short while. · · Surprisingly, as we came out of the fjords after twenty-four hours of smooth water and she began to roll and pitch again, immediately I was seasick yet again, just as I was the first few hours out. It was as though I had gained no immunity, as it were, from the earlier sickness,

144

but as soon as she started rocking after a smooth spell, there I was, back where I had started. · ·
Now try to sleep, the beer helps, ah. · · Ah.

greenblue · · · · mahogany · · beer can
· · the wood · · the polish, sheets, no pillows · · sleep · · · · · no movement ·
· no movement! The ship is not rolling, or pitching! Or hardly. Up then, not sleepy, time · ·
Christ, it's seven, I must have slept all of twelve
hours, more, amazing, my capacity for sleep, now,
here, there must be some physiological or bio-
chemical reason for it, surely, yes. Now: what has
happened, why are we still? Not in port, we must
still be at sea, yet last night the sea was violent,
and we were far out of sight of land? Festy, is
Festy underneath? No, and Mick's asleep, dare not
wake him. Get up and see, then, only thing to do,
good to be up for breakfast, for a change, anyway,
half an hour, up on the bridge then, for a little
while, then, dress, easy now, no movement, I
should seize this opportunity to change my under-
pants, or otherwise my balls will be in danger of
rotting off, ha, with the dirt, no chance to bath
yet, or wash down even, filthy, but there are so
many more important matters, than washing, that
really it is marginal, of little account. · · So
then. Clean pants in airing cupboard, my locker,
warm to the touch, to put on, good. So: clean shirt
as well, push hair back, feel brighter than I have
done for days, purple sweater on top—my overcoat, just remembered, seeing it, that I brought it:
but have not needed it: either I am in the warm,
needing only a sweater extra, sometimes not even
that, or I am out, in the cold, on the deck, in skins.
· · · · · · · The Skipper greets me
with theatrical surprise as I come on to the bridge,
asking if we are to have the rare pleasure of my
company for breakfast, and smiling as I peer out
to port to see land just near us. He tells me we had
to run for shelter as the weather deteriorated
quickly: fog thick as guts, as well, he says. We are
145

now in the lee of the land near Vardö. We ran for
Norwegian shelter rather than the Russian coast,
not for any political reason but because the former
gave more protection from the WNW wind.   ·   ·
Now we wait for the weather to lift. The atmosphere on the bridge is quite different, the Skipper's mood is almost lighthearted, though he is
obviously impatient at the weather. But there is
nothing he can do about it, so he, and everyone
else, can relax. Ah whale, Said the sole, the Skipper
says to me unexpectedly and whimsically, Ah sole,
Replied the Whale. I fall about laughing. Stagg, on
watch, does not laugh, does not move, gives no sign
he has even heard: perhaps he has not. The Skipper
shows me where we are on the chart, and I make
one of my infrequent checks on the Sal log to see
how far we have steamed since leaving: 1642, I
make it: I had a chance to note the figure when we
started, for I stared at it a long while before I slept
that first night aboard.   ·   ·   ·   ·   ·   At breakfast the Chief is more talkative, as well, and says
to me Why don't you come and have a look at my
engines? Why, takes up the Skipper, Is something
wrong with them? Everyone laughs, except the
Chief.   ·   ·   ·   ·   ·   ·   ·   ·   I walk out on to the
deck, strangely level, though there is a slight swell,
stand by the aft gallows looking towards the land.
Fairly low-lying, no great fall of cliffs to the sea, a
green cap, surprisingly, to me, who had not expected green, of this shade at least, yellowish-
green, though the sea sometimes is green, that dark
transluscent green, a threatening green, really, yes,
threatening. No habitation, no buildings, no animals on that green ledge, as far as I can see, no port,
it must be round that point, beyond the arm to
starboard and astern. The clouds, grey streaked
with black, move quickly everywhere above: bearing rain, or even snow, I would think: I cannot tell
how long it will be before a break comes, but at
least it is not raining now, nor is there fog, and the
wind is nothing to what it was yesterday afternoon,
when I had to hold starkly to the rail down from
the bridge, to avoid being taken off into that
threatening green sea.   ·   ·   Jack calls me, from
146

the liver-house, Jack, who keeps interesting things for me, curiosities which turn up in the trawl. Today he has a dogfish, the only one caught so far, stiff and bent rigorously by the shape of the bucket it has lain in, about two pounds in weight, looking just like a baby shark, vicious enough for its size. Jack cuts off its fins, then flenses it of its white and blueblack skin, for me, he says, to try to persuade the cook to fry it for me: You said you liked rock salmon, says Jack, so here you are. Jack was not there when I said this, I know, so someone on Festy's watch must have told him: and then, word for word, he says, This one came over the side barking! This is not the first time I have noticed the repetition of my remarks: after all, there is little new to talk about, anyone new at all is a diversion: and I have given little to them really, because of my seasickness. Jack also has best part of an enormous crab, legs here and there being missing, a spider crab, just like the illustrations on Russian crabmeat tins, which contain very good crabmeat, but the crabs themselves are not the same kind as English ones. And this crab is red, as though it had been cooked already: I tell Jack that I think he is kidding me, as I know that lobsters go red only after they are cooked: but he assures me that this is how the crab came out of the sea, and that if I do not believe him, I can watch every haul until they bring up another, and thus see for myself. I apologise, for he has taken offence I did not intend, and to cover up our mutual embarrassment Jack shows me at the bottom of the bucket the brown flatness, flecked with orange spots, of a plaice. As he puts his hand in, the plaice flaps twice before he can hold it through the gills: looking at me as though about to reveal a secret, he suddenly reverses the fish to show that the bottom two fillets have been cut away. That's what I like about plaice, Jack says, They do keep trying. This cruelty, as many would call it despite the anthropomorphic fallacy of such a description, does not disgust me, does not make me feel for the plaice: it might have done on land, but here the life itself is so near to cruelty, the sea so merciless, the air so biting, that

147

keeping a plaice alive to make fresher fillets for a trawlerman's tea seems a very minor thing, nothing to bring down the RSPCA about, no. Indeed, I ask Jack if we have caught any more plaice in order that I may have fillets for my own tea, but no, like the one dogfish, this is the sole plaice that has been seen on this trip. Jack tells me that most things like this never reach market, that if a salmon were by chance to be caught then there would be little likelihood of it reaching shore. Life is that hard, I see, that such diversions, such small delicacies, are so welcome, so esteemed. If it were a dozen salmon, of course, or a kit of plaice, it would be a different matter. · · Jack shows me how they boil the livers in this little space at the stern, this fairly stinking little liver-house. They all like to show me their parts of the ship, their function on it, all of them, the Skipper, Duff, Festy, the Chief asked today, and now Jack: at least I am that much to them, provide them with some relief, some conversation, allow them to reassure themselves of their identities, as a pleasuretripper. I am not very interested in the liver-boiling, however, especially as I learn that codliveroil can also be obtained from haddock and most other livers available. And even though the liveroil is doubtless a highly-valued commodity, not only by us, but by seabirds, as well, and other fish, still these facts do not make me more interested in this method of extracting it by the application of scalding steam in three vessels, filled from the liver-chopper on the deck forward. Nor does the speed with which the livers must be, are, processed, within an hour or so of death, that is, impress me overmuch. There are some things I just cannot be interested in: and there are no livers to boil at this moment, anyway. Just a little more am I interested in the towing block, just forward of the liver-house, since this it is which wakes me with its craangking so often. It's a German invention, says Jack, You just pull this lever and your trawl comes free. It keeps the warps free of the screw aft, until you want to haul. Last trip it broke, one of the castings, here, this one, and we had to use a block and chain arrange-
148

ment instead, which wasn't so handy. · · · ·
· From inside we hear the bell of the telegraph,
and are both glad that we are about to move again.
Jack says the Skipper is moving early, taking a
chance that by the time we are out where he wants
to fish the weather will have improved sufficiently
for us to begin fishing again. He moves away, about
forty-five years old, six foot four or five, with the
paunch many trawlermen put on because of the
lack of exercise and the farinaceous food: though
they are tough enough in the arms and legs with all
the heaving and holding, and there is enough protein in fish to fill themselves with if they choose. ·
· · · · I wander up the deck towards the
pounds, tapping the paunch that lack of exercise
gave me on land, reduced now because for at least
half the days we have been at sea I have not been
able to retain what I have eaten to nourish it. It
is one advantage, I suppose, the only effective way
of reducing I have yet come across, but how painful! But I have conquered seasickness now, I feel
as though I shall never again be seasick, I shall be
able to face any voyage I might have to undertake
without any fear of it again: at least this trip has
done that for me. Starfish, red too, like the crab,
perhaps I was wrong to doubt Jack, of course I was
wrong to, bend down to pick—aha! She rolls!
Though nothing much. We are really moving out
now. The starfish rough, sandpaper-like, to the
touch, not very delicate, as the cliché would have
it, but rather crude, clumsily designed, thick edges.
But the colour subtle, the shading subtle, the
roughness pleasant to the fingers. Skim it away into
the sea, star-spread-eagled. What else? · · The
odd gut here and there, caught up by some ob-
struction on the deck, not washed clear by the
thousands of seas which must have beaten their
way across us these last two days: rope-like pink
strands, twisted curlicues of fishflesh, not flesh,
exactly, fishmeat, fish intestines, fish offal: no
doubt all good protein, but no use for it here: I
suppose factory ships process it into fishmeal. But
here it is shot into the sea, discarded, but for these
few relics, sad, no, rubbish! They are washed-out
149

colours, at least the sea has done that to them, faded bloodred to pink, purple to lilac, Oxford to Cambridge blue, fleshcolour to white. This is boring. · · Ah! A ginnie, I must take special care of the ginnies, for her sake, for that is my name for her, I can't call you that, I said, when I first met her, I'll call you Ginnie. Special care: but mind the bony ridge along the back, nasty: is she still alive? I doubt it, but I must give her that chance, must, so carefully, lift, ease, jammed under the pound board, so lift, take the weight carefully, weight off carefully, yes, control, sorry, must kick you, both hands needed for the board, oh, little ginnie, freed now, pick her up carefully, daintily, by the root of your cracking tail, yet, so white underneath, to the rail, over! Yes, floats, does she swim, I cannot tell, no movement, ah! The wave swept her. Little ginnie. Anyway, I did my best, I made the effort to do what was right, as I saw it, as I see it. · · · · · · · · The Skipper is worried about a Norwegian line fisherman in a small boat off to our starboard, who looks as if he may have laid lines right across our course. He tells me of how such as this man will claim months later through his government that on such-and-such a day he lost so many hooks and so much line as a result of a trawler fouling him up: and there is no way of proving it either way, so the trawler owners usually paid up. The Skipper regards the line fishermen as a menace, for their lines often stretch for two miles with nothing to indicate them except a small buoy at either end. · · On such small things do trawlermen build a talking point, making as much as they possibly can out of it. Yet I could stand here for hours, just watching the wash from our bow wave, staring at the way it furrows out, the form of the green-white waves we make, the pattern which is always different for each yet always related to the others, our bow wave wash, and the way the foam boils up furiously, to decline into less than—God, she rolls, I begin to feel sick again! Again! No, not again, I can't believe it! Yet the pattern is as before—accustom, calm, then sick again! Oh, no! No, aaaah, my solar plexus grinds on my
150

ribs, or something! Out, then, don't care if they do laugh, down, the wrong side, I've chosen the weather side, who cares, sick, sick, can't hold it, aaaaaaaaaaagh! · · · · Relief, yet know it is not finished, no, more to go where that went, all staining down the companionway, hope a sea will wash it away, it can do, though the weather is not bad enough for that, yet, no, almost I hope it will be, to clear up my mess on these brass and teak steps leading down: seas were coming higher than this yesterday, at one point I stood on the bridge ladder while the other side of the bulkhead a few inches away a great sea thundered past and parallel to me, a sea that would have washed me a hundred yards astern, if it had caught me, it seemed. Such a sea would rid these steps of my vomit, on its backwash through the lower door, but no sign of that yet, the seas barely flood the scuppers, as she rolls, now: But it is enough to make me heave, the rolling, yes, I feel it again, aaaaoaoagh, nooo, plooogh! A great heave, but far less than last time, down now to the almost colourless stuff, my diaphragm or whatever it is hurts like hell every time, and to touch it hurts, too. I should move, to heave over the rail, at least, one more heave and I can go down below, sleep, or at least lie, though I have only just got up, so down, careless about stepping in the vomit, my own puke, left through the door, gap, there ought to be a shipname for it, pushing aside the rope that is always for some good reason slackly from the top down across, I on to the deck and on to the rail yet again, hard, cold, black-rusted steel, giving off that smell of seawater-corroded iron which, together with diesel oil, makes up that peculiar smell of a ship, which I first remember associated with the nausea of seasickness when I went across to the Scilly Isles. Or so it seems, I connect the smell with seawater corroding iron, but perhaps it does not make a smell, this chemical action, I do not know, I would not know, I was . . . last time, aaaaagh! Not so bad, that time, no, even when so racked with puking I notice I still keep desperate hold of the rail, so it does not appear to be true that one would just as soon die when being

151

seasick, no. Well enough, then, to get back down—
oh, she pitches now as she begins to hit the big
seas, the rough outer water, as that strip of green
land is now a grey line on the horizon, ah, down,
rest, rest, rest.

green · · · · · green · · green the green
pro · · · · · · green green pro · · · · ·
It must be · · No · · that is too painful, I
cannot go over that. · · · · · I must. · ·
· · · · · · Picked her up in a pub, went all
the way to the bank at lunchtime for the money ·
· went back to the pub · · · · · how sor-
did! · · She had on a green beret sort of hat
and a green costume top and I picked her up in a
pub and took her back to my digs, then, in the
early afternoon and she wanted the fire on and
· · · · · · · · I was very low at this
time. · · Excuse myself to myself, but it is not
as though anyone else will ever know about this. ·
· · · · except Terry, I had to tell someone,
who knew already of the depths to which I had
sunk. · · So I put the fire on and she undressed
down to her woolly and stood barearsed and shiver-
ing before the gasfire and with her back to me as I
undressed · · · · · and I · · could · ·
· · · · · · · not · · · · · · · raise
· · · · · · · · · · · What relevance has
this? What use going over such pain? · · · · ·
For I knew this was likely to happen, knew that it
was really no answer, and my body merely reflected
that, oh, that is not to say it did not make some
attempt, did not swell to somewhat more than its
normal girth, for it did, flaccidly, but would stand
no farther, so that it was impossible for it to enter,
no, that is not true, it would enter, once or twice,
but attempts to establish regular movement ended
in it slipping out and no satisfaction was to be had
and she kept on wanting to get it over with and
leave because she did not like it in other people's
places, and kept saying Come on, let's have a do. ·
· · · · · · · And I could not. · · · · ·

Her feet, her dirty feet had dirtied my sheets afterwards I noticed, turned them over afterwards as it was not yet the end of the week for clean sheets. · · · · Though she wanted to leave as quickly as possible she was yet an honest tradeswoman, wanted to give value for her · · two pounds, I think it was, so she worked manually at my flabby member until the teat end of the sheath she had provided filled opaquely. · · There was little pleasure, I remember, obviously, in the circumstances. · · · · And she dressed her smallboned dirty limbs. · · · · · · · · Ah, getting that out of me was a relief! It is a long time since I would let myself think of the green pro, since Terry told me about the drooping left side of my mouth, perhaps, about the twitch, over a year ago now, I was very low at that time, have perhaps come lower since, but did not try that way out again, perhaps through fear of another failure, no, certainly because it is not an answer, I knew it was not an answer before I even did it, but know it now, even better, so trite, really, since Daedalus, yet we move so slowly, so slowly! Ah. · · And Terry was understanding, I could not have told anyone else about this, as I had to tell him about this. And once I saw the green pro in the street, by chance, just once, and she looked at me but did not recognise me, or gave no sign of it, at least, and I looked away quickly, ashamed, yes, ashamed! · · I would not have thought it after Daedalus, no, no.

It was while I was working at the oil company that I had the phone call about my tutor. They had rung me up once or twice before to cancel a lesson because he had fallen ill, and that is what I thought it was this time when I heard this secretary's voice. I have some bad news for you, she said: and I wondered for a moment. Then she told me he had been found that morning dead beside his bed, had had a heart attack getting out of bed. My mind saw him immediately, the gross, short, figure dirty in bursting striped flannel pyjamas, for some reason, heaving himself up out of bed, and collapsing on

153

the floor. I was curiously at the time unmoved by it, disappointed that I was not to have my Greek lesson that evening, and even a little embarrassed. Yet later I felt it, his death, and remembered what he had meant to me. Whether he did it shrewdly or by accident I could not tell, but he had found exactly the way to make me work hard: I came to him with my determination to pass O-level Latin in nine months from knowing nothing, and his pessimism about my ability at twenty-one, when he said the automatic memory had failed, to do this made me all the more resolute. I think I had three lessons a week from him, two in the evenings at six and one on Saturday mornings, while I was working for the oil company during the day. I used to finish at five in Holborn, catch the central line to Holland Park, and have a drink and a cheese roll in a pub called the Castle before going to this large house become a crammers'. He would be waiting for me in his small classroom, or occasionally I would have to wait while his previous pupil finished his lesson. He was short, fat to overflowing inside his great tweed suit and snuff-coloured and besprinkled waistcoat, and the green glossy material of his tie was frayed at the knot where the stubble from his chins abraded it. I never knew his age, though from what he said about Oxford, where he took a double first, and Gilbert Murray, he must have been well over seventy. His desk was often untidy, but the two features which gave it continuity for me were the hierarchy of thick blacklead black and white marking pencils he aligned on his desk in order of the amount they had been used up, and his timetable of lessons given, which represented his piecework record of money earned, and which was kept from being blown away by the weight of two or three small brown and yellow ounce tins of Dr Rumney's Pure Mentholyptus Tobacco Snuff. These latter would be dipped into in a pecking order as strictly observed as that which governed the use of the marking pencils, and, though at first I politely refused his offers, once when I had a cold he insisted that I take a pinch, this being what snuff was for, colds:

154

and thereafter I generally had at least one pinch
every lesson, enjoyed the smell of it, even bought
a small tin of Dr. Rumney's myself: though this I
kept before me when doing Latin exercises at
home as a reminder of what I was supposed to be
doing rather than to take as a habit. Once he had
seen how I worked, he paid me the great compli-
ment of assuming my intelligence in everything,
sometimes even crediting me with more than I
had, so that I had to slow him down and ask him
to explain something yet again. But all the time he
was deeply pessimistic about my chances of passing the examination in the summer: and when,
having entered for three different Boards in the
hope of luck in one of them, I passed all three fairly
easily, certainly with an ease which surprised me,
he afterwards said he had been sure I would pass:
and to my protestations that some of the things he
had taught me were not even tested in the exami-
nations, were not even on any syllabus, he merely
smiled slightly, said it was basic policy to teach
beyond the level required, in order to provide a
margin, and that surely I was not complaining at
knowing too much? · · · · I tried to get
to know him better after lessons. I was generally
his last pupil on my evening lessons, and would
ask him out a for a drink: I both respected him,
and yet needed someone to respect in this way, at
that time, I remember; that is, I suspect my admi-
ration for him to a certain extent, it was impure.
Usually he declined, not even politely, but once—
perhaps it was just before the exams—he did allow
me to go with him to a pub where they knew him
well and where they made him a special welsh
rarebit with beer in it, all sloppy with beer, in fact,
which I had never seen made so before, though he
told me it was quite a common thing. I think we
had light ales to drink. I did not have a welsh
rarebit. · · · · Once I tried to get him to
talk personally, or rather like a father figure to me,
being involved with some woman or other at the
time: but he just said he had never been even
interested in women, had never wanted to be married, and that finished that conversation. He had
155

read no modern literature, and when I asked him to translate for me the Greek epigraph to *Four Quarters* he told me he had never even read Eliot, who I at that time thought of as already a classic, even as being old-fashioned. He also said that nothing a young man wrote or had to say was worth reading or hearing, and added an exception in the case of a genius just as the name of Keats was about to burst from me: this statement, which I now see to be very true, worried me far more at that time than the dismissal of every modern writer by this man I so much admired. · · Yet he was interested in the world outside, in an oldfashioned way: once when a quiet young Indian had finished his lesson and left, the first thing my tutor said to me was that I had just been—he implied honoured —to see the heir, if he lived, for his health was finely balanced, to all the riches of some vast maharajadom or something: I was surprised at his reverence before, and interest in, the aristocracy or wealth, whichever it was. I am sure the Indian did not pay more for his lessons than I did. · · The morning one of the exams was held, about nine o'clock, before going to the centre I went into the gents' just beside Kensington Town Hall, and the attendant there said, Well, that's done for her, then. I nodded, not wishing to make conversation in bogs, and only later realised it was the day that they hung Ruth Ellis. · · · · His own funeral I attended, my tutor's, out at the Streatham cemetery, that vast acreage of white stone where my father's parents are buried. My tutor was to be cremated, however, and I arrived at the chapel just as they were finishing the previous service. A tall, grubby cleric removed a name written on a board, turned the card round, and put it back in its slots: it had my tutor's name on it and I knew for the first time that his Xtian name was Lucius: his parents had directed him towards Latin from his christening. The cleric asked me if I was one of her party, indicating the name, and I realised that he thought the name was the form of which Lucy was a diminutive: I pointed out his error to him, sharply, I could not help it, wondering how a man

156

whose calling, I believed, involved the study of Latin, could make such an error, and then reflected that there must be NCO's and warrant officers in the church, too, that they were not all educated men, if any, the men of God. He conducted the service tiredly, mechanically, this man of God, too, hesitating and looking down when he came to the first gap where my tutor's name had to be inserted, and pronouncing the c in the Xtian name soft, whereas I had said it to myself hard, in the pronunciation he had taught me, and this too seemed to me a slight by this cleric on the man I respected. There were other mourners there: a woman who might perhaps have been his sister, a niece perhaps, and a girl of about fourteen who looked long at me. There too was the director of the crammers', who nodded to me afterwards, after the surprisingly small coffin had slowly slid on rollers through the curtained opening at the far end. · · I regretted that I had known my tutor less well during the previous few months than when I had worked so hard for O-level: he had helped me to Latin in Intermediate BA, as a private addition to my course at Birkbeck, and, when I had passed this and needed to go no further in Latin, had suggested I do Greek, which he had always told me was a finer language with a finer literature: so I did, for this short while, until he died, having given me only half a dozen lessons. · · · · · · · There is a fault in my method, there must be, or so it seems. · · I create my own world in the image of that which was, in the past: from a defective memory, from recollections which must be partial: this is not necessarily truth, may even be completely misleading, at best is only a nearness, a representation. · · I see now there is a lot of sentiment in my memories of my tutor, what I have chosen to remember of him, that is, a short-tempered, self-centred old man who very probably saw me only as an entry on that timetable of money earned. · · · · · · · This is merely to escape: this is not to confront. · · · · · · · Is it

On the horizon, through glasses, Scouse points out to me a battleship, presumably Russian, moving very fast for an object at sea, that is, noticeably moving, at a distance that must be several miles: and while I look there is a flash forward of her, which I excitedly tell Scouse about, and we both hear the sound of her guns, very faintly and seconds later. Even the Skipper seems interested enough to take his eyes off the fishfinder for a moment. I keep the glasses on her longer, however, she interests me more than she does the others. A cruiser, probably, she seems very oldfashioned, somehow, a throwback to the boys' papers and omnibus books of my boyhood during the war. I do not think of her as a threat or as belonging to an enemy: she is merely another ship, out here, at sea.

Refraction or reflection? In this raindrop domed from the outside of the thick glass I from inside see reflected or refracted the deck and sea below, contained in one fish-eye lens view: this even catching the movements as the fish are swung through the air, as they cant down the chute. · · · · ·
For hours at a time I could watch this scene, do watch these scenes, the gutting, the hauling, the shooting, the steaming. The fishing. And the wake, the wake, again and again, constantly, always the same and never the same, the moving, the movement!

A squall: that is, a grey patch at sea level extending high into the sky, from what is probably roughly the east: which I have come to know as a squall, have been pleased that I can thus see the weather from a long way off, in a way that one does not see it on land, in cities, at least, though in the flat lands one might, I suppose, or at least there is more likelihood that one might.

The Russian cruiser has gone, its smokestack and staining smoke last, as in all the schoolboy books
158

demonstrating that the world is round: and it is true, this—not proof, this evidence for the roundness of the world: solipsistically, I have now seen for myself that parts of ships, the lower parts, are below the horizon at one point, and the nearer they come, the more of them shows, from the top downwards: and vice versa, of course, as they go away: there are laws that govern these things, the things accept the governance of the laws.

The tenth day of fishing, and fishing since we left Vardö has been good. But the tenth day: five days out, ten days fishing, five days back makes up the trip. But the Skipper thinks we must make up for the time lost off Vardö: and the fishing is good at the moment, cod mainly, but good-sized fish, and the usual reds, and a few haddock.

Now the grey squall fills a quarter of our seeing, ninety points of our compass: the Skipper stares to the east, ahead of us on this haul, we trawl from west to east, haul, then swing about and trawl back from east to west, keeping just to the edge of a foul patch of the white duff, the Skipper tells me, a narrow borderline where both the useful and the useless are to be found and where it is difficult to take one without the other.

Snow at sea, great white flat flakes that sprawl in the wind, keep gusting out of the greyness which has grasped us, as far as I can see, greyness and the whirling white. Unlike snow at home, on land, there is nowhere here for it to settle, the flakes just vanish in settling on the dark swollen sea, the sea takes them, enfolds them as anonymously as the sprag gorges a codling, each contributing to the greater size of the other, not a good image. Except on the deck, where here and there pockets begin to form even now, tiny drifts, this soon after it has started, snow clings to the warps, and every windward side of nearly everything, chiaroscuro pounds in the afternoon of the short Arctic day. · · The gutting trawlermen too occasionally take snow in their faces to take a look upward at the bridge. ·

·   And the Skipper, too, of course is thinking much the same as they are. ·   ·   ·   ·   Suddenly the Skipper turns to Duff and says, That's it, then: and swings the telegraph over and back to signal the last hauling for this trip.

I ask Duff how much we have, when the Skipper has left the bridge to sleep his first full night for ten days, and he tells me fourteen hundred kit, which is a fair catch: though how much they will make for it depends on how many other trawlers dock for the same market, for the sale on the same morning. They will worry about this all the four or five days back to port, now, for their earnings are directly related to the price the catch fetches, which is not within their control. Scouse on the same watch is glad we are going back, that this will be a twenty-one day trip and not longer, says to me that he is looking forward to screwing his wife again. And then he says, I wonder what she'll ask me for this time? Every time he is home apparently his wife asks for something new for the home, and almost always gets it. Last trip she asked for a griller, he says, And I said, What d'you want with one of them hairy-arsed bastards?

Scouse, Duff and I stare out at the last gutting on this trip: the last few redfish are thrown ungutted into the washer, the last bastard halibut slide rippling down the chute, and the last cod and had-dock, gracefully olivegreen and silver, are dowsed in the seablack water, urged over the edge of the chute by the rough sea's action, go down, down. The snow blusters in the lights directed down from the bridge on to the pounds, in the lights strung above the washer snow skitters out of their ambits into the bitter blackness of the Arctic night. Here on the bridge the snow is not cold, I can afford to enjoy this new aspect of snow at sea: but there on the deck Stagg stands, perhaps bowed by the cold, and soon Festy sends the old man in. There are no more than a dozen fish left now. ·   ·   ·   ·   · None ·   ·   ·   ·   Festy hoses down the deck himself, dismissing the others. ·   ·   ·   ·   The

deck is clear, the pound boards waiting until to-morrow to be taken from their deck stanchions. ·
· · · ·   Seas swill through the scupper doors, green, white, black. · · · · · · · Duff turns to me and says: At least you've seen some weather, at least you're not one of these pleasure-trippers who come out in July and wonder what the hell all the fuss is about!

I have perhaps lost my chance to see the northern lights, the aurora borealis, the farther south we go, now we go south. But perhaps I may see them, per-haps, on the way home. Home. What does that mean to me? · · No. · · · · · I should go to sleep, retire to my bunk, think there, perhaps, if I can, if I am allowed to, as the saying goes. I shall see.

Home. Means her. · · · · · · · Good, for a start, that I think of her, Ginnie, in connec-tion with home, home not in the sense of my home, I have no home: there are the flat I rent and my parents' home: but neither of these is truly my home. I can form the concept of my home, though, I can see the desirability of having a home. Which means her, in that home, making that home: with me. I'll rest there.

Mahogany · · · · · · · the dark red mahogany · · Mahogany Hall Stomp, late Louis, I think · · yes, with some group he called his All-Stars, I think, Bigard, Hines, Cozy Cole on drums, none of them were really stars, not up to the standard of his Hot Five, or Seven, though Hines played in the late Sevens, or even from the beginning, I can't remember, but can ·
· yes, recreate the sound of that Mahogany Hall Stomp, listened to it so many times, it started with four stop-time chords, really stomping, then a chorus you could hear Louis cutting through, clear, still playing well, into his first solo, only fair, for him, that is, then the trombone, forget who that

161

is, but he tries to get such a dirty tone that it becomes grotesque, filthy rather than dirty, ha, to be succeeded by Bigard's weak, mannered clarinet and Hines' trivial oversophisticated piano, and the further descent to some inept banjo riffs: then suddenly Louis' second solo, clean, sharply articulated, knowing exactly where each variation is going, perfect, the tone like no one else's, the sureness delightful in its inevitability, even the longheld high note, which would be showy in a player with less of his confidence, rightness: and the sidemen redeemed only by the drumbreak from which Louis leads into the final chorus, the stop time stomping again, and a perfectly-executed short coda. Worth having in my head only for Louis, how missed are the ensemble virtues of the Five, and even more those telepathic double breaks with Joe Oliver when Louis was second trumpet to the master in his Creole Jazz Band. · · · · · I collected 78s from · · Dorothy's time, it was always a cause of disagreement between us, that I would spend so much of the so little I earned on records, jazz records, that she could not understand and did not like, even once spending three pounds fifteen on transcriptions of Jelly Roll Morton's Library of Congress recordings, playing and talking about his life: which she found quite pointless · · while I worshipped him, Jelly Roll, worked like a scholar on the sexual innuendoes in his creole, in his name and in the titles of many of his compositions. · · Perhaps that is what she hated · · Yet the money was probably · · of course · · And I loved the jazz more than her, I see that now, of course, this was being true to myself, I saw through jazz, or rather through the lives the men lived who played it, what I had to be, an artist, in the broadest sense, though not a painter, not a jazzman · · and that helped · · · · · or perhaps I consoled myself with art · · no, for I wanted this while I was in love with her, the two fought, conflicted · · perhaps · · certainly · · yes, those records showed me, Parlophone New Rhythm Style Series, blue, white, and gold, Hot Fives, Hot Sevens, Meade Lux Lewis, *Boogie-Woogie Prayer*,

Albert Ammons, Pete Johnson, ah, Morton's Red
Hot Peppers on plum and gold HMV, labelled accurately (but not in the sense the labellers meant)
Dance Orchestra, all with odd stamps for copy-
right royalties: most of all the black and gold
Brunswicks of Joe Oliver, just stark labelling, as
though he were any old dancehall musician. · ·
Then later the specialist labels, Jazz Collector, Jazz
Selection, gold, · · Melodisc, yes, purple and
yellow Melodisc, Leadbelly singing *Ain't You
Glad*, others purple and · · gold? That strange
drum solo by Baby Dodds, a whole record of
drums, by Baby Dodds, how well he knew dynam-
ics, can sustain interest on that record! · ·
Tempo, Cow-cow Davenport, piano, · · can't
remember any more Tempo, · · Vocalion Origins of Jazz, a later series, when things began to
move. · · And the French label, with initials
AF ... · · can't remember, had only one,
Johnny Dodd Memorial, with the Chicago Feet-
warmers, *Lady Love* on one side, and on the other
 · · can't remember · · Jazz Man with more
Morton, rare Morton, just before he died, poor sod.
Hot Jazz Club of America · · the odd Colum-
bia · · Vogue · · Esquire · · · · · ·
 · · The jazz of those 78s runs through my head
like the · · · · · never mind the image, the
thing itself, that is important, they stay with me
while the socalled masterpieces of English literature which were poured through me at college left
nothing but the flatulence of disappointment. · ·
 · · · · · Jazz was very important to me, to
my development, though that is somehow the
wrong word for it, yes, the wrong word. It was certainly through Jazz that I began to realise what it
was about, art, that is, through Jelly Roll and Louis
and most of all through King Joe, I began to understand what it was I could do, what I should do,
then, accepted that if I was lucky I would end up
being ruined by success, like Louis, or if I was
unlucky end up being dead of cold and poverty
like Joe: those pathetic letters to his sister at the
end, about his clothes, about not being able to
afford an overcoat, about his job as janitor in a pool

hall, his pyorrhoea, heart trouble, his inability to play any longer: Louis' two sidemen who saw their former leader selling on a street corner and were too overcome to speak, his dignity, the nobility reflected in his name, and most of all his responsibility to his talent, were what the bare biographical details of the life, to say nothing of the playing of, King Joe Oliver gave to me, mean to me, at this time, and have stayed with me, so that now he seems an exemplar for my life, for all of which I am proud and equally for that which I fear: so that now I give to old men selling on street corners, or old men begging, or young men down on their luck, for that matter, if they are reduced to the depths of asking for a cup of tea, or the price of a packet of fags, or a drink, it matters little, I give to them because it seems like giving to myself, there is no charity about it, because that is the way I see myself ending, dying in some street, in the cold, without an overcoat, worst of all unable to play any longer. · · · · · "Soon as the weather can fit my clothes", that was one of the phrases I remember, "weather can fit my clothes", that construction, in Joe's letter to his sister, "Soon as the weather can fit my clothes I know I can do better in New York". And his sister spent her rent in having his body sent to New York, in the end, that was the only way he got there, to New York, in the end. But what he did, the way he did it, too, his loyalty to what he was, to what he contained, consisted of, this was my exemplar. · · · · · · ·
And all the others, the way they did it, totally involved in all that was going on, besides art, in prohibition, the gangsters, Pinetop Smith shot in a speakeasy, Louis marrying Lil, the treatment of sex and love as enormously important, so rightly for me, as I wanted to be just so involved in everything, in all of it, who was a bank clerk at the time and engaged to a bourgeois Dorothy. · · · ·
· · · · This interest in jazz was both a gesture against such as Dorothy and an example of the sort of thing I must do, felt buried in me, something very small and quiescent to which I had to be loyal, could be disloyal to only at the utter ex-
164

pense of self: and this exemplar gave me hope, too, in this situation, in my situation, that these men created where they could, as they could, often in circumstances greatly inimical to their creating anything, while still fully enmeshed in everything else in life, their lives and their art inseparable. ·

· · · · · · Went round the London jazz clubs, then, in search of this life, disappointed, of course, though I still think the jazz was good, the boys trying to play like Joe and Johnny and Honore Dutrey, and making noises far better than any commercial band was, at that time, in that comic cellar in Oxford Street, for example, and a crypt of a church behind Marble Arch, another in Gerrard Street, great times, in their own right, now I think of them, though not what I had been looking for, which were of course speakeasies and bathtub gin and molls. The only girl I picked up there was Jewish, a Jewess, from Golders Green, of course, who thought jazz was great, tried to sing herself like Bessie Smith, fair voice, not the experience to sing like Bessie, of life, that is. Yes, she had an audition for one band, in Great Windmill Street, Rochelle, her name was, and when she arrived the manager said Go into the rehearsal room and warm up first, there's a pianist there, and we'll come later. And Rochelle did, and after she had sung a couple of numbers they came in and said, No, they did not want her to sing with the band: and that was her audition, they had done it so she would not be nervous, but she thought she had been cheated, and cried. · · Rochelle was the only virgin I had, I think, not counting Dorothy, who does not count since somehow it was the only thing she gave me, not that I could see anything in it, for me, in return for my pandering to her bourgeois, there should be a better word for my being disloyal to my self. · · · · Met Rochelle when she was sixteen, kisses, passionate manual manipulations, then a break because her father hated gentiles going with his daughters, of whom there was another, older, who fancied she knew about modern art: and then, three years later, when Rochelle was nineteen, yes, met again through both

165

being in the BM one lunch hour, and came together
for just about a fortnight, ten days perhaps, when
just once I had her on her father's parlour (he
would call it) floor, satisfying touch, that, when he
was out, just before her period, using Gynomin,
and me withdrawing, too, three ways safely. I
looked upon it as didactic, instructing the young,
there was little pleasure in it for me. · · · · ·
Rochelle. She was all right, I wish her well, no
bitterness, there, and I had her once only, no one
would notice, I felt no barrier. I had only her word
for her being a virgin, and what is a virgin anyway,
what use, what significance is it? Not to me, not
to anyone, much, really, perhaps she was not one,
but so what? · · · · · Rochelle: I wish her
well. · · · · · · · But jazz then was important for these things, and also, since adults and
the bourgeois hated it, despised it, ridiculed me
for it, it set me apart, was the first real martyrdom
I went through for a minority, willingly, epitomised
my relative isolation, and I knew I was right about
it, and have since had it more than confirmed, that
jazz is an art form, a great, no, an important ... ·
· · · · that's all over, that fight, this is accepted
now, there are other things, more important
struggles for this generation, for my · · Sleep
· · · · · Never difficult to sleep, for me. ·
· · · · Sleep.

I wake of a sudden, clear, my purpose in coming
achieved. I do not know why. What did I consider
last night? · · Joe Oliver · · · · · jazz
· · · · · · · · Rochelle. · · · · · ·
· · Nothing there to precipitate it. · · But
everything, building up on this voyage, all the
thinking, collectively, accumulatively, must have
led to this sudden freedom I feel now, relievedly,
relieved of all the thinking. · · · · · · ·
I climb through, up the companionway, strongly
hauling myself by the arms, feeling the strength of
my release in the power of my arms, for some
reason, the decisiveness, the resolution, to haul
166

myself through this hatch, by the vertical brass bar, and straight out across the galley alleyway, into the air · · and it is cold · · · · ·
clear, the storm has blown itself out, there is now just a heavy swell, through which we cut resolutely: the snow has ceased, no sign of it out here on the sidedeck, no sign of a squall, either, the weather clear, sharply cold, shall not stay here long, but the way we plough along, twelve knots, fast after the towing speed, is invigorating, yes, that's the word, or re-invigorating, in the cold, here, over the rail, by the towing block, or rather where the towing block was, for I see now it has been dismantled, that it will disturb my sleep no longer, not that it did of late, for I had become used to it, one becomes used to anything, in time, except seasickness. · · · · · Wind on my face, through my hair, rustling beard, beard long enough to rustle through now, less prickly, softer. · · · · · And not so many gulls, seabirds · · · · · I even enjoy or at least accommodate the rolling, the pitching, the increased movement, now, at this speed, at this increased speed, more rolling, more pitching, at our homeward speed, roll, roll, and pitch, roll. · · · · · She rolls, bowls along by a cold coastline through these grey seas under a grey sky, already it must be the Norwegian rather than the Russian coast I see, that much nearer home, ah, honed to one level glacially, not that those were Norwegian or Russian glaciers then, the politics of geology, or something, it does not matter, no differentiation either in the atmosphere above those uniform heights: but the crests stained with snow, made white with the guano of the storm, and, yes, I can see foam beating at the bases of those cliffs, the white different from the snow against the black rock, we must be within the limits to see those breakers, as we may be, that we are no longer fishing, no, but in any case we steam west, from the east, towards the fjords, I hope he will go through the fjords, that the weather is rough enough to make it worth his while to go through the fjords, and oh, particularly to stop at Honigsvag! If that's the right place, yes any land

167

under my feet, still still, not moving, an end to this moving, a fortnight of movement! · · If he stops. · · · · · What's the Queen's favourite television? says Scouse, coming up and leaning on the taffrail next to me. When are we going to get in? I ask him in return. Phillips seventeen inch, says Scouse, and then, If I don't go to sleep with a tit in each hand next Tuesday night, then someone on board's going to have to bend over. · · Tuesday! Today's · · Friday. · · · · · Four days! Not counting today, which is already counted. · · And I may be sleeping with her on Tuesday night! If I can ring her when we dock, if I can · · My mind bubbles! · · · · · I could be lying there, her sweet full breasts cupped in my hands, by Tuesday night! At last I can see the true end to this voyage, to this testing, to this thinking! · · And I have come through! Look, we have come through: Lawrence's words come to me now, I feel that poem! · · · · · Scouse talks on, about what he is going to do this time ashore, I think, as I do not listen to him. All I can think of is Ginnie · · the warmth and the sweet softness of her: · · · · · Tuesday night.

We come upon Honigsvag very suddenly, for me, anyway, just after we enter the fjords, have had for only a short while cliffs, black and snowy, on our starboard as well as to port, which is the mainland: or perhaps it is that I stare too long at, my eyes are fixed upon, the two great silver spheres, part of an early warning radar system like that at Fylingdales, spun on the peak of a mountain, their silver brighter than the snow, the snow streaked by the cable overhead lift running up the side of the mountain: as near Russia as they may be, these threatening spheres, or as they need to be. · · All that labour, all their materials, must have been transported with such difficulty to the top of that mountain: for war they will go to such lengths, will take such pains. · · So that, my eyes on these, I miss the slow appearance of the little town to our starboard, suddenly turn and there it is, the houses stepping half way up a hillside from a waterfront with a jetty, and sheds, oiltanks: the houses painted surprisingly fresh colours, unusual colours, sorrel, terracotta, denim blue, deep ochre: and I realise I have been deprived of certain colours, surfeited with greys and whites and silvers, cold colours, I long for warm colours. As I long again for fruit, too, perhaps I shall be able to buy fruit here: the Skipper says I will, they take English money: I have three pounds, I know, I had not thought I would need money, did not bring much, had not much to bring, fruit will be dear here, I must have fruit, what kinds will they have, though? · · It doesn't matter, though I would prefer the more acid kind, feel as though I could almost eat a lemon, again, would welcome its acidity. Duff says they also have cheap lighters, the men buy cheap lighters and try to smuggle them, a small deception, and who is harmed, why do lighters cost so much in England anyway? Suddenly I see I want to buy something for her, a present, to take home to her, and I feel so pleased that this desire is not calculated, was natural, was spontaneous, the wanting to give, for I have too often calculated, too often been unnatural, unspontaneous: and this is the best thing she has done for me, Ginnie, that I am more natural now, whatever nature is, but I know what I mean, and for any of the earlier ones, others, I would not have felt this, she releases me, Ginnie. What can I buy then? · · · · We swing round, edge slowly into the harbour, bounce gently against the old tyres on the jetty, and one man secures us to bollards as the Chief appears on deck, the first time I have seen him on deck, to supervise the passing on board of the freshwater supply pipe from the same one man: who then comes up to the bridge, greets and is greeted by the Skipper warmly, and I ask how long we have, seeing Scouse and a fireman and Mick and Festy and the deckie-learner already climbing the taff-rail and stepping on to land. Twenty minutes, says the Skipper, No more, no more! · · · · I briefly notice a pipe from the jetty the other side, dripping a trickle of effluent which causes and has caused and goes on causing a great semicircle of

169

ripples right across the still surface of the water. Water still, water which is still, is what pleases me. · · Duff comes ashore with me. I stamp my sea-boots on land, not dry land, for there are pools and slush everywhere, but it is solid, the jetty, and it does not move. Duff smiles at my simple reaction, and leads off across the jetty to a road wet and icy with packed translucent snow in ruts, past cars, yes, cars moving with chained tyres, familiar enough objects for all their chained tyres, three or four of them moving down the cold wide street of this little town, with its so firm earth, not that there is any earth to be seen. · · · · Duff shows me the shop where the lighters are to be had, a gift shop full of eight or ten of our crew, looking very much out of place amongst the neat tables set out with all kinds of small fancy goods. The girl behind the counter looks apprehensive, the man, perhaps the owner, looks as if he is restraining anger. I look round quickly at what there is for sale, and fortunately see what I think would please her: a flat, short knife, a palette knife for serving butter or perhaps cheese, stainless steel and black nylon handle, a pleasing design, I think: so I pick it up, am first to the girl with anything, hand it to her with a pound note. She is the first woman I have seen for over a fortnight, but I feel nothing for her, no desire towards her. She wraps the spatula for me, hands me my change in kroner, how many I do not count, it is not the point whether I have been given a fair exchange rate, for I have enjoyed buy-ing, am pleased with what I have bought. · · Fruit. · · · · · Shop, oranges, yellow apples! Tins! Yes, in, buy, woman, woman sends for man on hearing me ask if anyone speaks English, he comes, asks politely but flatly if he can serve me, and I give him all my kroner and take oranges and apples and a tin of Israeli grapefruit juice, my mouth aches, the back of my tongue goes dry for the taste of grapefruit juice, most of all quenching, most of all able to satisfy my craving for fruit; clasp the oranges and waxy apples and the tin in my arms, smile thanks at the man, who formally nods and flatly says goodbye. Festy and Johnny are out-
170

side, laugh as they see what I have been buying, show me the lighters they have bought for a few shillings each. We walk slowly back to the ship, I eat an apple as we go, not my first choice, I would rather have had the grapefruit juice first, and next the orange, but both these involved trouble in opening, so as I walk I bite into the yellow thick-skinned apple, God knows where they came from, were grown, and they are only passable, as apples considered comparatively, but very welcome now, there are no others to compare with them, does not however satisfy the desire for acid, fruit acid, that I must wait for a tinopener for, back aboard the ship, five minutes early, could have stayed on land another five minutes, but must get this tin opened. . . .

The snow does not lie on certain slopes, obeying laws I do not wish to understand: remark only on the patterns created apparently at random, what I would call random, that is, but which is a pattern in fact obeying these strict laws of orientation and wind, rain and incline, immutable laws except when they are changed, the huge rational mess which is nature, ah, what am I about? Through here she does not buck. · ·   ·   ·   The moun-tains! ·   ·   They change only slowly, but any-thing is worth watching, is new to me, at this point, who have had little more than the sea to watch, for too long. I stare at these rocks, these glacier-ground heights changing slowly as we move down the fjords, not into the land, between the islands and the mainland, really, protected from the rough seas outside, in the clear water, it is called.

A black stain ahead of us drifts across the bloom-grey sky and powder-white gullies, from the black smokestack of a ship ahead of us. Duff tells me she is a Greek timber boat, burning coal, filthily, bound for the Mediterranean after taking on Russian soft-woods. I wonder that he can know so much, she is far away, to me, but do not doubt he is right. ·   ·
I notice for the first time that Duff has missing the

top joint of his righthand little finger, ask him how he lost it, expecting to hear some grisly detail involving perhaps an unbridled warp: but no, he was in a fight in a pub, was knocked out, woke up to find it missing, and eyewitnesses told him it had been bitten off by his Chinese opponent, or one of them. Scouse says he has always told the same story to account for the missing joint: there is no reason to think he is lying: I make an effort to believe him: I believe him.

Sometimes we are close to the shore, to a sandy inlet ringed with sheer rock, with one house on a new moon of grass, there seeming no access but from the sea: or we are twenty yards from a cliff whose fall gives a sense of continuing below the sea's level indefinitely, of being the edge of an enormous drop: at other times the land is a long way off, crags and rock islands, outcrops, standing stark in the sea, with farther off the snow on higher crags, protrusions.

We gain on the black Greek ship. She does half a knot less than us, so slowly we gain on her. The amount is only noticeable after a long while, every hour or so. Always, the forward view is perhaps corrupted by the screen from her smokestack, the smear of her wake.

Now I know these rocks only as shapes, that they are rock is of no point, they drop, but how do I know they even do that, they may climb, everything is relevant only to me, relative only to me, to be seen only from my eyes, solipsism is the only truth: can be the only truth: a thing is so only because I think it to be so: if I do not think it to be so, then it is not so: this must be the only truth: belief does not arise.

I stand near the after gallows, looking forward along the deck (now lined with bobbins like a great string of babies' beads) to our wash bowing out towards this unfriendy coast, the Greek coalburner nearer now, we shall overtake her on her port, if

172

we do not have to negotiate narrow passages, soon.

No one about, the deck strangely inactive, which was the scene of such movement earlier. The deckies sleeping, this first day they have not been on watch eighteen hours a day, for ten days, the deck deserted, few gulls even, as we stalk through these narrow fjords. · · · · · · · Her name in Greek and Latin characters, on her stern, the funnel rolling black smoke to landward, a breeze off the sea, across us as we near.

The sun sets, is towards setting, is now on our starboard, smudged across with black, now the fingers of the fjords point it directly at us, still stained, making a dry composition, then again the sun cedes to the intercession of the black outcropped mountains, fills the air with vicarious redness, bursts, bursts, as we move into clearer water, the red-gold wine of the Greek-black sunset, sun sets, sunset, sun sets.

The black ship drops astern, the last sun now glinting squarely on one port bridge window. · · · · · The light now, just there, placing the darker outcrops from the dark sea, the seadark sky, a white line, a lighter line, for some reason drawn across the sea level at the base of the land on the horizon, and across the gaps, too, strange, a line.

Car lights progress along the haunch of the fjordside. Towards home, someone is going home, perhaps, as we are, as I am. I who have not seen car lights for weeks, see these and am pleased, almost heartened, by these, wherever they may be going, since I do not know where they are going. · · · · · · · The pilot sits quietly, he does not talk as the other pilot did, the one who brought us up through the fjords. He sits, a naval figure, in cap and braided coat, quietly.

Flute and harpsichord gently from the speaker next

to the Sal log, delicate, blended sounds, so strange to hear them here, that Molloy should put them out, in this context, at this time, as the radar glows amber, the music a pleasure, my own, a secret pleasure, I do not reveal I am listening, really, just as I could do when I went to concerts with Martin, who taught me about music, what little I know, tried to · · —No, I need no more of these flash-backs, these autopsies performed on the past, I have all that, no, not all, only a part, there is so much, but what I wanted has been achieved, I have been purged of my past, of those things which have hurt me, or enough of them, to make me feel it has worked, this coming to sea, that I have no need now to shoot again, I am going home now, this music I can enjoy for its own sake, not for its associations, a blessed relief, that I become more natural, that I relax, somewhat, that I— · · · ·
· · · · The piece ends, coda, resolution. I need to take a deep breath. I straighten from the brass rail, feeling its curved impression still deep in my forearm, lean over against the door of the wireless room and ask Molloy: he says it is Tromso radio from some hundred miles south: and this reminds him of the new bridge at Tromso, and that I ought to see it, so he talks to Scouse, and Scouse agrees that this bridge is a wonder, yes, he uses the word wonder, that I ought to see, it is important to see everything that I might never have a chance of seeing again, he believes, then says It'll be worth getting up for, and calculates we'll be under it at about two in the morning, and I am not so keen about being awoken at two in the morning, to see a bridge, in the dark, but what can I say, they are insistent on doing me this favour, on giving to me?

In the crew mess four sit playing dominoes, more watching, money between them, playing intensely, concentrating. Cheese, bread, margarine on another table, and a piedish swilling gently with once-dried apricots, looking like nothing so much as redskins' earholes. Notices on the walls telling me how to extract the oil from livers properly, how to
174

use the self-inflating life raft and mind my mates
as I jump.

Odd things lie scattered around the transom cabin.
I notice Festy's watch on his bunk as I climb up.
There is absolute trust aboard, no stealing by or
from your mates.

A bow of steel or concrete, I cannot tell which,
thin, slender, picked out in red lights, not a particularly graceful shape: perhaps its wonder lies in
its thinness, I cannot tell, of course, what they see
as a wonder. I look round at the city, the hillsides
spattered with random patterns, again, of street-
lights, back at the curve of the bridge, concealing
my disappointment from Scouse.

Almost I could imagine myself on a cruise now,
standing here in the bright northern morning sun,
having risen at the sophisticated hour of eleven,
seeing scenery free which tourists must pay to see
in summer, though now the sight is as good, surely,
as impressive, at least. The passage of the night has
brought us south, into more temperate places, the
mountains less uncompromising, gentler slopes,
and grass down long sunken valleys: thread-thin
larches here and there, and fleeces of firs, ah, it is
a long time since I saw a tree, of any kind, how
different, warm, human, they make the landscape.
· · · · · · · · The humps of land, islands,
outcrops, stumps, fells, the shapes dictated by the
way the glaciers went, the way the icecap melted,
to the south, these shapes tell me, this way the
great ice ground us. · · · · · · · And
now there begin to be more than occasional farms,
there are clusters of wooden houses, again painted
brightly, upland farms, long and single-storied.
And here fresh water runs! The falls we pass now
and again run, this far into November they are still
not frozen, another thing I have not seen which
delights me in its newness, freshness, running
175

water, the falls, the falls! · · · · · · · · ·
Now I stare at the log, see we have come just two
thousand miles, seamiles that is, and calculate we
have about another thousand back home. The
Skipper sees me looking, working it out, grins, now
in his more formal passage clothes, says It's a hell
of a way to come for a bit of fish!

Gulls still follow us, in the expectation of offal: the
Arctic Skua rides fatly on the swell, past us, in-
spects our wake, rises to show the white flash on
its dun-brown wings, beats forward, eyes still on
the wake, to overtake us and settle again: the
Fulmar glides for long periods, following the swell
a few inches above it by tilting as the sea deter-
mines, white head, the eyebrow as though pen-
cilled in: the Herring Gull, no herrings here, nor
little else at the moment, thuds flatly around,
powerful wingbeat to catch up, wheels, heels in
the wind awkwardly, staring-you-out eye, vicious
beak: but most of all the Kittiwakes, smaller than
any of the others, demure, delicate yellow beaks,
some with a smudge behind the eye marking them
as juveniles, the eye itself redringed, the only birds
I have noticed who will perch, not within reach,
certainly, but they will perch on the ship: I do not
see the Common Gull, nor either the Lesser nor the
Great Black-Backed Gull, not the Iceland, not the
Glaucous, not the Ross's, especially, not the Ivory,
not the Black-Headed, not the Slender-Billed, not
the Little, not the Great Black-Headed, not Bona-
parte's, nor yet Sabine's, Gulls: I take these words
from a book the Mate has, the Skipper identifies
for me, suggests I feed them with scraps to see
them more closely, insists I take a photograph of a
kittiwake, his favourite, as it glides near us on the
bridge. · · · · · The Norwegian pilot stares
ahead, not the one who was on duty last night, his
relief, they work in pairs: he stares at the fells, the
openings ahead, the clear waters through the
fjords. I meditate on the rightness of the derivation
of gull: Welsh gwylan, to weep, to wail, the gull a
wailer, from its cry: beautiful, exact.

At one, the BBC news, presented by some foreign
service department beamed at the Middle East,
apparently, picked up by us through some freak,
or by being on the same longitude, or something,
I do not like to ask Molloy: news, preceded by some
martial, patriotic music, and read far more pompously than home bulletins, very conscious of presenting an image of Britain to the world. I am not
proud of this, this seems like deception.

A cleft mountain to pass through, it seems. · ·
· · · Mounting on either side, black, wet. ·
· · · · · · · Then out into clear water, the
land falls back on either side, an island ahead. ·
· · · · · · Now the sea begins to be
choppy, I shall be sick again, I feel it, but not yet:
the sea is breaking against the foot of the cliffs as
far as distance will show, I shall be sick, the inevitability of it, but I can accept it again, I have lived
through it, again, now, before. · · · · · · ·
· A band of cloud emerges from a fjord on our
starboard, held at a height by mannered air currents,
so that I can see the black bases of the wavewashed
cliffs below and the snowcovered heads of the
mountains above, separated by this band of cloud,
this dense drifting mass. · · · · · · ·
One pointed mountain like a triangle on the horizon. Nearer, become three-dimensional, nearly a
cone. · · · · · · · A curiously rural
scene on the deck, as the men pick at the net spread
around them, repairing it with wooden braiding
needles, hung up with nethooks to keep it square,
sorting, checking, a rural craft, seemingly, yet this
is a modern net, of nylon, Japanese, to a certain
extent experimental, trusted to this skipper since
he is known not to lose gear often, some skippers
lose a net or more each trip, and nylon is far more
expensive than hemp: this is the third voyage that
this net has been brought back safely. Duff climbs
the rigging, his great feet steadily finding the
holds, his hands grasping the shrouds, that small
red woollen cap staying on his head despite the
wind. He secures the derrick arm, which has
landed our cod-end all the trip, after it is pivoted

177

upward from its near right angle to nearly parallel
with the foremast. The washer has been dismantled
and bolted against the bulkhead of the net locker
under the whaleback, the fishroom hatches are
secured, no warps to make the deck dangerous with
their sudden grinding movements, the dahn buoy,
unused this trip, leans roped against the rigging,
and the men now work with an easiness that was
not in the gutting, talking and laughing.

I realise suddenly that we are not passing one of
the towns which lie in between the mountains, or
on the slopes, or on a shore, that we are no longer
pointed at the next open sea between the fells: but
are heading towards a town: and a small boat, tiny
standing wheelhouse and motor tyres lashed as
fenders, is metallically putputting towards us. So
this must be the southern extent of the northern
fjords. I should have realised it from the time, that
we were reaching the southern limits. Duff grins
at me, in anticipation, All downhill from here, he
says, arcing his arm over the curvature of the hemi-
sphere and grinning wider as I protest at his joke's
weakness. · · · · Both pilots time their
jumps carefully on to the small railed deck, from
just forward of the aft gallows. Festy lifts a basket
of berghylts over to the captain of the pilot boat,
a tip for the pilots, and receives a fistful of letters
to the ship in exchange. The pilots' cases are
handed over, the Norwegians disappear into the
wheelhouse, the boat revs, and the gap between
us wedges out. We turn towards the gaps again.

Now the last land I shall see for three days left
behind, the short day ending. And we begin to
rock, in the unease of the sea's swelling, I shall be—
I shall not be sick!

Now this cold North Sea morning the trawlermen
move around the ship cleaning her like charwomen,
sousing and scrubbing and burnishing, stoning the
gut-stained deckboards until they come up white
178

again, everywhere swilling with hoses, rubbing brass, sweeping with springy brooms. The ship shines with this honest effort. I go on the bridge, but cannot find a place out of the way since the floor gratings are up: I am in these men's way as I never was when we were fishing, nor on passage out. The deck foams with whitening, even the boatdeck is occupied by men bashing the filth out of copra mats, my favoured place by the jury steering at the stern made untenable by clouds of fibre, dust, dirt. On the whaleback men are busy: when I try to find a place amongst them, I am for the first time cursed for my idleness, the first expressed resentment of my pleasuretripping. Just when I want to be, think of myself as being, one of them, up and around, there is no place for me, no place, I am replaced in my isolation yet again. At least my bunk is my own, I'll go back there, who only an hour ago rose, from my new non-isolation.

No, this is ludicrous, this out-of-placeness is only a reminder of what was. The feeling of having been exorcised returns, rise through me again. Look, I have come through! · · Come through! · ·
· · · It is as though I have at last paid off some vast emotional debt that I had incurred through all my years: that I have earned enough to repay that debt, in these last three weeks. But how? · · ·
· · I still do not know exactly why I felt isolated, how it had come about that I was isolated: but I do know now that I feel it no longer, that, rather, I accept the isolation, such as it was, can encompass it and move on. No, again, I feel as though I have repaid at usurious interest some debt, which has occupied all my thoughts, all my energy, impossible of limitation or definition: and worst of all, I can never remember having had benefit from the loan in the first place. The lifting of this—images fail, and are unimportant, as are the reasons: what use are reasons? To know that one is because, is no more use than knowing one is: and to believe the condition is made any more bearable for knowing why, is to be deluded. It is the condition must

179

be suffered in itself, because of itself, not for any reason. So I eccentrically feel. What use is knowing a reason? I have found few reasons in analysis of my past, so the benefit must have come from the rehearsal of the experiences themselves, like writing an experience down, it fixes it, takes the hurt out of it: one remembers then that one was hurt, but not the hurt itself. Similarly what use is it pointing to this ship as a womb, for instance, as a symbol, these men's refuge as well as their purgatory, and all that balls? What use would it be? All this, all reasons, are in the limbo of the unconscious, the nomansland of the unknown: which perhaps soon may be revealed by scientific advance, perhaps not, but now (the concern is always with now) is not known, cannot be known, and concern with it, with reasons, must always be delusion. It is what I am now that is important.

Full of pity for the boy I was, recalling the girls my women were. Yes, yes, all those loves and wished-for loves, I need never think of you again, have exorcised you, I need never worry about what you did or what I should have done: have distanced you in mind as well as time: you will never enter my thoughts again in the same way, only by accident, by association with the impersonal: I am glad to be rid of you.

And I feel it will now be right with her, with Ginnie, that it must be right with her, that I have cleared my life of the dead weight of its past, can face her completely, honestly. And it must be right, for this is the last chance I give this bizarre structure of thought and laws and impressions called life, called existence, with its absurd problem, which I no more wish to solve than to have posed. · · · · · · · So: towards this vision of a future not more than five years off: Ginnie as wife, a child, a son, perhaps, the chyme sliding down his chin, freedom to work as I have to work, a home: in the far hope of that happiness, I give life one more chance: towards the chance of that future I shall voyage honestly and hopefully.
180

I am only what I am now · · · · · I am not
what I have been · · · · · It is as if I am
free to be what I may be · · · · · I am not
what I shall be · · · · · I am what I am
now.

And things do slowly become better, the vision
does come, as I see it, slowly: only have patience
with the slowness, more and more belong with the
movement forward, which is as well the movement
away from my own isolation, if only it can be
borne, the slowness of this advance. · · · · ·
I should give this feeling form, I should make a
gesture of faith in this future, to the nearest thing,
which is a woman, which is Ginnie: so up. · · ·
· · In the wireless room Molloy tells me I can
cable a pound's worth of flowers from this North
Sea position for another pound: I do so.

Calm today, Bollocky calm, the Skipper says, a
useful expression, I think: and sun, diffused albeit,
but sun, the disc just discernible, the afternoon
brighter than I have noticed it to be for months,
the sea almost blue here, as it has not been before,
and those who say one area of sea is much like
another are quite wrong, the sea can look different
far more ways than I realised. · · · · · ·
· A Belgian trawler hauls across us, slowly, fishing
in a place which is passage water to us. Staring
down into the water, just below the surface I see
a large cod, or perhaps it is a sprag, swimming:
odd, until I realise it must have escaped from the
Belgian's deck. · · · · · · · Johnny
asks me to take photographs of two great spider
crabs he has, their legs spanning at least two feet,
that he has dried out in the engine room and wants
to varnish to take home to his children. He stands
squarely on the deck outside the galley alleyway
door, in his thigh waders with the tops turned
down to his ankles, a rough rag filling the gap his
smock neck leaves, unsmiling in his flat cap, a

formal face for the photograph of him holding his spider crabs.

Duff pummels me on the point of my shoulder, points as I round on him, and I see a porpoise mimicking the waves' shape on this calm sea. You can tell it's not a dolphin because it hasn't got a long beak, says Duff. My arm still aches where he has thumped me.

When you come ashore, says Duff, You feel ten feet tall, all these people on land just don't know what life's about!

Despite that calmness across the North Sea, we are half an hour late for the evening tide. Tugs park us in order first out in the roads. I can see the lights of a seaside promenade to the south, other lights along the river. We shall go in in the morning. I refuse a chance to go ashore, as Festy, Scouse, Stagg and Johnny do not, in the tug, to have an extra night in their own beds.

We start to move, the tug shepherds us. She rolls, very slightly, and I am sick yet again, the final sickness: the bitterness rises in my throat, no bile, no green bile, I retch twice, am almost glad for this reminder of what I have withstood, and then am recovered: it is finished. · · · · · · · I stare from the rail, the sky lightening behind me. Red lights ashore, we head towards red lights with shadowed bulks below them just darker than the sky. And the tower! That square Florentine tower stands high against the sky, its castellations hinted at in outline, its top pointed by a red light. The tug grunts away in front of us, to one side. A clock on a tiny building, between the red lights, which now I see are on diamonds, the lights, their daylight representations, on either side of each lock entrance. The tug eases us towards the lefthand entrance at what seems to be too fast a speed. On the lockside are the shapes of men waiting. They call

out as we fill the entrance, as we dully shoulder the righthand lock wall, call out to Duff, standing honourably, magnificently, at the very point of the whaleback. And then we are through, into the outer basin, the tug casts off and we head for a gap in the long row of sheds along the farther side, under our own power. Duff shouts that we must bear slightly to port: the Skipper beside me says if we do that we shall only hit the other side. · ·
The ship grates slightly on the starboard side. Now we are through and can see our berth, first on the far side of the fish market, open buildings, long, low. And a small group of people waiting where we shall berth, women from the colours of their coats, fawn, red, blue. Mick comes forward with his duffelcoat and suitcase, ready to land. Duff's wife and sister-in-law, says the Skipper, drawing my attention again to the quay by where we shall berth. It is too far to see faces: he must tell by their coats: fawn, blue, red, another blue, the red just like the coat that Ginnie has—Ginnie? Can it be her? She could not know what time I was due in, nor even which ship I was on, for I would not tell her. But she could have found out, if she had tried hard enough, of her own accord she might have tried to break my isolation in the only way it could be broken. Ginnie! But is it she? My eyes narrow, strain to see through the early-morning light, the mist, the shadows on the quay, to the face of that figure in red. It must be of her own accord, to contain, to accept the knowledge, the certainty. . . .
 · · I, always with I · ·   ·   · ·   one always starts with I ·   ·   ·   ·   ·   · ·   And ends with I.

HOUSE MOTHER NORMAL

Friend (I may call you friend?), these are also
our friends. We no longer refer to them as
inmates, cases, patients, or even as clients.
These particular friends are also known as NERs,
since they have no effective relatives, are
orphans in reverse, it is often said.

You may if you wish join our Social Evening,
friend. You shall see into the minds of our
eight old friends, and you shall see into my
mind. You shall follow our Social Evening
through nine different minds!

Before entering each of our old friends' minds
you will find a few details which may be of
interest to you. A CQ count, for instance, is

given: that is, the total of correct answers
which were given in response to the ten classic
questions (Where are you now? What is this
place? What day is this? What month is it?
What year is it? How old are you? What is
your birthday? In what year were you born?
Who is on the throne now – king or queen?
Who was on the throne before?) for senile
dementia.

You find our friends dining, first, and later
singing, working, playing, travelling,
competing, discussing, and finally being
entertained.

age	74
marital status	widow
sight	60%
hearing	75%
touch	70%
taste	85%
smell	50%
movement	85%
CQ count	10
pathology	contractures; incipient hallux valgus; osteo-arthritis; suspected late paraphrenia; among others.

. . . not like this muck, they give us muck, here, I made him
a proper dinner, gave his belly a treat after all that Gas,
but he could hardly eat, the poor boy, what I put before him
was faggots in a lovely gravy, it was something special I
made, for him, just for him, then, not like this slimy brown
muck they slosh on everything here, can't think why they do
it, what the point is, not on my life, no.   And
I could see his eyes light up as he saw it, it was really
like being at home for him, that's when he realised it, for
the first time that first day, I think.
But then he couldn't eat it, the first mouthful and he was
sick, he had to rush out the yard to the carsey and I was
left – Now what's she done wrong?   Mrs Ridge
in trouble again, she asks for it, she must like the twitcher,
really.   I could hear him in there, standing
at the door as I was, looking at them faggots and the new peas

I'd shelled that morning, and thinking of the butter I'd
mashed his taties with and how little Ronnie had had to go
without for a week, though I gave him his Dad's later, he
did enjoy it, that day, for his tea.

   And when he came in from the yard you could
tell he was that ill, by his colour, and he asked me to come
up and lie on the bed with him, and I did, though it was just
after midday, and he just sort of   lie
there, with his eyes shut and his face all

          tight,
without bothering to turn down the counterpane to rest his
head on the pillow, and it was greasy with brilliantine or
something suchlike, but I couldn't say anything could I?

Not that he touched me, he lie there with his hands crossed
across his belly, like he was dead already, not touching me,
just wanting me near him, he said, to feel I was there, and
I don't think he could have done anything with me anyway,
then, it was   months before he was a real husband
to me again, ah.

Clear
up, clear up, it's all on the hurryup in this place.
Now what's she
saying, how can you be quiet about clearing up knives and
forks, how can anyone? Though these cardboard plates
can't make any noise, because if – *Here, Ivy, no, I
haven't finished yet!* Last scrapings of this muck,
muck they give us here, but I'm hungry, there's nothing
else, nothing. There. I'll walk, at least I can still
walk, though that means she makes me do the running about.
I have to clear up and wait on the others, these bent forks
and knives, the knives not sharp at all, down here, I'm
not washing up today, the sitters can at least do that,
sitters can – Now Mrs Bowen's knocked her plate down,
now she'll cop it. Yes.

Her and that
dog, shouldn't be surprised if House Mothers aren't
really supposed to keep pets, could write to them about
it, her and that bloody great dog
Get on with it, help Ivy, get on.
She won't get
it done sooner by shouting at me, I go as fast as I
can, yes I do, can't go any faster.

Nearly done.

There, at last that's done, sit down again, next to
Charlie, later I'll get round him for a cigarette, I
know he's got some.   Oh, not
that song again.   What good does it
do?

                      Better sing, though, don't
want to cross her again, no.

The joys of life continue strong
Throughout old age, however long:
If only we can cheerful stay
And brightly welcome every day.
Not what we've been, not what we'll be,
What matters most is that we're free:
The joys of life continue strong
Throughout old age, however long.

The most important thing to do
Is stay alive and see it through:
No matter if the future's dim,
Just keep straight on and trust in Him:
For He knows best, and brings good cheer,
Oh, lucky us, that we are here!
The most important thing to do
Is stay alive and see it through!

                      Well, I suppose it
pleases Her, at any rate.

Listen to
her now, work, work, I've known nothing else all
my life, who does she think she's taking in?
Good deed indeed, she must make something out
of all this, though it's not sweated labour by
any manner of means, I will say that for her, it's
not arduous, and she can't get much for these
Christmas crackers they make, wonder who does
the fillings, the mottoes, we used to enjoy
crackers that Christmas before he went, there was
an old-fashioned Christmas if you like, it snowed
that year it did, very unusual for London to snow
on Christmas Day, don't remember any other years
it happened, in fact, and how it changed the look
of everything, people started acting differently,
too, people you knew only to nod at suddenly
joined in snowballing in the street outside as
though you'd all been kids together, had grown up
in the same street.   And we had some money for
a change, had a bird instead of a joint, a capon,
the baby had some giblet gravy with roast potato
mashed up in it, very nourishing for him it was.

Knowing he was for the Front made him
depressed, then suddenly he'd be so cheerful, such good
company, he made it a wonderful Christmas for all of
us, him and his brother, they did a sort of act for
us, Jim got up as a woman, makeup and all, we ached
from laughing, they were so comical, the pair of them,
ached from eating too much, as well, I never – *Me?*
Me and Charlie?   Trusties, she talks to us

as though we were doing bird, indeed, one of these
days I'll show her how trusty I am!
What's Charlie got in them bottles, then?
Looks like gin, smells like spirits, too – she
must be at it again, the crafty old chiseller!
Still, what's it got to do with me?
Glad I haven't got the job, anyway, never could
stomach the smell of spirits, I told him that before
we were married, stick to your pint, I said,
don't you come home here reeking to high heaven of
spirits, I won't have it in my home.
Yes?

Little bottles, what are they?
Soak the labels off, I bet.   Use the bowl from
the sink, I'll stand them in that, in water, would
some soap help? *Do you want me to keep the labels?*

My nails are broken, have been for years,
but give the bottles a good old soak and they'll come
off. *Shall I use a knife?*

Good, this is an
easy job, I can get on with that, it helps to pass the
time, I don't mind, get the bowl, fill it with water.

What's in these little bottles? Chloro-benzo. . . .
Can't read it properly, whatever it is. No matter, none
of my business anyway. *Charlie, have you got a fag?*

Mean old sod. And
I know he smokes. Like my Ronnie, always telling
lies, I'd catch him with the fag in his hand
and he'd put it behind his back and drop it and
breathe out the smoke all over the kitchen and
swear he wasn't smoking at all.
And he married a like one, his kind, oh I hated
that creature, bad as my Ronnie was he didn't
deserve her, no, never.   Lie, she would
lie her way black and blue out of anything, you
could catch her out any number of times and she
would still deny it. I gave up in the end, you
just couldn't rely on anything she said, anything
at all, anything even as simple as just meeting
you for shopping, she'd lie about who she'd just
seen and what she'd just bought and how much
money she'd won on the bleeding dogs. I'd no time
for her, it must be twenty years since I saw her,
fifteen since I last saw my Ronnie, too. He came
into the pub we had in Strutton Ground then, I
was so surprised to see him walk in, he had a
Guinness and no more than a dozen words to say to
me, a dozen words, and most of them he could
hardly get out, he was that ashamed, I think,
ashamed of not going to see his old Mum for all
that length of time, months it was, perhaps a year.
Not like Laura's son, twice a week he used to
visit her regularly, once for a cup of coffee at
lunchtime early in the week, and later – There,
that's enough soaking, let's see if these little

labels will come off now.
No, tough little customers they are, it's not
waterproof paper, is it, can't be?

Perhaps it would help if I scratched them a bit,
to let the water soak in better. A fork would
do it.

        Yes, that's easier, let's try doing that
to all of them.

                        I wonder if
Ronnie knows I'm here?   Not that he'd want
to visit me, no one gets any visitors here,
anyway, but I'd like to see him just the once more
before I pass over, just the once.   He
wouldn't have to see me if he didn't want to, no,
as long as I could see him, out of a window,
perhaps, going along the road, just the once.

                        As long as she wasn't
with him, the barren sow, she could never give him
any kids, and I know he always wanted kids, my
Ronnie, he was ever so good with them, look how
he used to go and play football with them until
he was quite a grown man, used to run a team for
them as well, he used to get me to wash the team
shirts each week in the winter, it was a trial
getting them dry, it was, she wouldn't wash them,
I doubt if she washed Ronnie's own things properly,

let alone the team's, she was that lazy, Doris
was her name, yes, Doris, I wouldn't want to see
her again, no, just my Ronnie, once.

                Does he think I'm dead? How could
he know I'm here? Could I find him?   How?
Could ask House Mother.   She'd laugh at the
idea, brush it aside, take no notice, I'm
afraid   of her
                          Not her!
Now let's see if they'll come off   Yes,
nearly there, if I have a good scrape at this one
then by the time it's off the others will be even
more soaked, all ready.
              What does she want with them?
Yellowy sort of stuff inside, yellowy, runny.
Nasty-looking stuff.

In summer there everyone seemed to take life
easily, so easily, it was as though there were
no pain, no work either, everyone had time to
just walk about, go swimming, sunbathing, get
up boat races, and go dancing. They danced a
new dance called the gavotte, or it was new to
me, anyway, being a foreigner. And they danced
in the streets, too, that was new, the streets
lit by paper lanterns in their fashion. And the
sun so hot at midday that the market-women
put up their red umbrellas for shade, and the
men went into these sort of cellar pubs that sold
wine, I never went into one, could only see down

into them that they were cool and shaded, and there
was a lot of laughing and the tables had zinc
tops and so did the bar, a long bar, the bottles
kept in holes, no labels, I was so thirsty I
went to a café down on the promenade with the
children, little Ronnie was all right but that Clarissa
was a little bastard to me, she knew she could
play me up with safety and she took advantage
of it.   I could have been so happy
there, there was so much sun and the life was easy
apart from Clarissa, and she was my job, to
let her parents have some time free, free of her,
that is, for she was a little bastard to them
as well as to me.   I wonder what she
could have become, she was already an Hon., I
think, Clarissa, and it was doing little Ronnie
so much good, the sea air and three good meals a
day, the food was good in that hotel, even for
those in service, and it seemed as though it
would go on for ever, the summer, the sun, and
for the first time since the War I really felt
that things were getting back to normal, though
all the ones who could remember better than I
could were saying that things would never be the
same, never could be, after the War, which I could
understand in the case of someone like myself,
who'd lost their husband because of the War, but
not those who'd not lost their nearest and dearest
in it.   And it was there I
think I first got over Jim's death, not got over

it, exactly, but accepted my lot, that I was a
young widow with a young kid, like lots of
others, that this was what my life was, that
this was what I was. In that seaside town in
France, France where Jim had got Gassed, though
not the same place, of course, and I think
Clarissa's father may have had something to do
with it, it was the first time I had seen a
man's parts when he tried to get me down on
my hotel bed, since Jim's, that is, and I think
that must have made me realise there were other
men in the world, seems silly now, though at the
time it was a frightening thing to happen,
perhaps if he'd asked me, or gone about it in a
different way, I'd have let him, though I knew
it was wrong and I respected his wife, I might
even have enjoyed it, it was two years since Jim
had gone, but he was so rough and arrogant with
it, he seemed to think because I was a servant he
could order me about in anything, order me to do
that like he could order me to clean his shoes,
which I didn't like, the brazenness of it, just
came up to me while I was at my dressing-table,
unbuttoned already he was, and seized my hand and
made me hold his part, and when I drew back,
naturally, he got rough and threw me on the bed and
would have had his way with me had I not yelled and
screamed fit to make the whole hotel hear. And
so he got up and buttoned himself up with his back
to me, swearing all the time vilely at me, and

little Ronnie woken up by all this noise, standing
up in his cot and wondering what was happening to
his Mum. And of course I didn't last long after
that, he couldn't look at me after that.
Clear up now. Nearly finished. Just scrape off
these last two.

There. Now give them all a wipe.

And put them all back in their nice little cardboard
sockets.   One   two   three   four
five   six   seven   eight
one   two   three   four   five
six   seven   sixteen
one two three   four   five   six
seven   twenty-four
one   two   three   four   five
six   seven   eight
one   two   three   four   five
six   seven   sixteen
one   two   three   four   five
six   seven   forty-eight, two cases of
twenty-four is what I started with. The satisfaction
of finishing. A job well done.

Here, Missus, I've finished.

How nice to be thanked.   The warmth.
                    Very pleased indeed, she said.

That pleases me. A job well done. And the time
passed, too. Now what's she want?

Pass the Parcel?　　　We used
to play that, didn't we?　　　Don't want to
play much now. Why does she give us games?
I just want to sit quietly after working so much.
But I suppose I'd better be sociable.

Me to start?
Off. Pass it to Charlie. What is it? Brown
paper, soft.

It's stopped at Mrs Ridge first, but she won't be
able to open it all in time.

Oh! It's stopped at me!
Open, open, get the paper off, I won't be the
winner, there, it's started again.
　　　　　Stink. . . .　　　What is it!

Ron's got it, he'll get it open. *What is it, Ron?*
　　　　　How disgusting!
Why does she do a thing like that?
　　　　　Glad I didn't win, glad I
didn't win!

It was the third husband I'd buried, I was getting
used to it. All the market crowd in Strutton
Ground chipped in and gave him a great send-off,
he was a popular landlord. Flowers, I never saw
so many flowers. And the customers, too, bought
the odd one for Fred, they did.   But
it didn't worry me too much. The brewers let me
take on the licence, and within weeks it was just
the same, as though he'd never existed. That
pub used to have a sort of life of its own, then.
And during the war of course you didn't have to
sell beer, it sold itself, it was getting hold
of enough of it that was the difficulty. Oh yes.
And crisps. There was only one place you could
generally get crisps, then, and that was up on
the North Circular Road. Many's the time I've
caught a trolleybus up the Edgware Road to Staples
Corner and come – Exercise?   Haven't we
had enough?   Oh well, up we get. It's not
for long. She thinks it does us good, perhaps it
does. It doesn't kill me, anyway.
                    I'll push that George Hedbury
round. Not much company, but there you are.

Off we go! *George, can you hear me?* Deaf as a
post, deaf as a post, daft as a doughnut.
One two three four! Round and round, round and
round!

And so it goes on.   That Laura

was a great one for her Guinness. Sometimes I've
seen her knock back thirty in an evening. But
she was a quiet drinker. You'd never know
she'd had too many till she fell down when she
tried to get up. This bloody pushchair needs
oiling or something. But she was a good friend
to me, we had many a good time together. She
pulled me out of many a dark time. Like when
Ronnie married that Doris. And after the cat
got run over, Maisie.

We kids used to run about in felt
slippers then, they were the cheapest, a cut above
the barefoot kids. It was our way of

Tired of pushing. But still carry on. Slog, slog.

They were the good old days, it's true.

And where were we when we were wanted? Oh, we
were there all right, slapping the sandbags on
the incendiaries, ducking down the shelters when
the HE started. All that sort of thing.
That's enough. I can't push any more. I'm going
to stop whether she likes it or not, going to stop.

A sit at last,
rest my legs.

Sport! She certainly keeps us on the go.

Tourney. That means me pushing someone, I suppose.
Up again, Sarah, you can do it.
Lean on George's bathchair till I have to move, take
the nearest corner, Charlie'll have to go further
with Mrs Bowen.
George doesn't seem too well. Prop the mop under
his arm, keep it steady.

Ready!
Go!
Trundle, trundle, not as young as I used to
be, get up speed.   There!
Silly old fool let the mop drop and caught
hers in the chops!
Not so fast this time.
Keep up the mop now, George!
There, that must have hurt him.
You all right?   Seems all right.
I should think it
is the last time!

Ooooh! That surely
hurt him. But he says nothing, George, just takes it.

Wheel him over to his place and sit down again.

                        My legs are getting
worse, I'm sure they swell up with all this standing.
It's like a dull ache.

Poor old thing.   Let her talk
away, I'm not interested, it's a rest for me. And
my poor legs.
On his back for months, my Jim, going slowly, you
couldn't see it day by day, but suddenly I'd
realise that compared with a month or so before he was
definitely down. And he found it difficult to talk,
more and more. For days I knew he was trying to
bring himself to say something, and then it all
came out. He'd been with some girl in France, they
all did, he said, went to some brothel, and he was
so guilty about it, as though it were some great
crime he'd committed. Perhaps it was to him, then.
But to me it didn't matter, because I could see
he was dying, everybody could, nothing seemed to
matter but that fact and that I had to make the
most of what there was, nothing in the past
mattered, neither the good things nor the others, his
guilt was of no interest to me, or the girl, I
just forgave him as he seemed to want me to, and
it did relieve his mind, you could see that, he
just sank back, and very quickly fell asleep.

                      He kept a spit-bowl
by his bed, that was the worst part, emptying that,
the yellowy green stuff and the blood, he couldn't

get out to the carsey, either, but somehow
emptying his spit-bowl was worse, like throwing
away bits that were him.

I tell them
my troubles, they tell me theirs.

We had a good feed at a chip place, before he
went off to his football. I went round the
shops, all excited inside all the afternoon.
Perhaps it was expecting what – Laugh? *Ha ha
ha, ho ho ho.*
I wish I'd been kind to old people then, now I
know how it is. It's always the same, you can
never know until you actually are. And then
it's too late. You realise which are the important
things only when it's too late, that's the
trouble.
However much he made it was
always too little, I always had to watch every
penny so carefully. In the butchers I had to take
what he'd give me cheap, and his dirt and insolence.
No one has ever treated me like a queen.
You'd think every girl would be treated like a queen
by someone at some time in her life, wouldn't you?
But not me. Perhaps I never deserved it, perhaps

I never treated any man like a king.

            Now what's she rucking Ivy for?

                Oh, she's going through that again,
is she? She don't half fancy herself! Well, I
don't, and it's filthy so I shan't watch though
she may think I am.   My idea of a holiday
was never the sea, anyway. On those pub outings
they never looked at the sea in any case, all
they were interested in looking at was the insides
of the pubs along the front at Southend, one after
the other. They went into the first next to the
coach park and so it went on, all along the front.
They'd give the stakeholder half a quid each
and he'd buy the drinks as long as the money lasted.
                             You could get big fat
oysters on one stall, only time I ever enjoyed them
was down there. My dad would never eat shellfish
but once a year down at Southend, said they were
never fresh anywhere else. Cockles I'd have, too,
and those little brown English shrimps, very tasty,
but whelks I never could stand, far too gristly
and tough.   The Kursaal bored me, but
all the men used to love it when the pubs were
shut – What a disgusting spectacle!   Why
does she do it?

                  Disgusting!

Ugh! Never did like it, had to
pretend, all my life pretended to like it.

Listen to her!

No, doesn't matter

age	78
marital status	separated
sight	50%
hearing	80%
touch	80%
taste	95%
smell	30%
movement	85%
CQ count	10
pathology	contractures; bronchitis; incipient leather bottle stomach; hypertension; among others.

I have always liked a lamb chop.   Even in the last
days I managed to have a lamb chop once a week.   Welsh
lamb I found the best, though New Zealand is a close second
in my opinion.   Even Betty knew that to please me she
had only to give me a lamb chop.   Here the lamb chops
are mutton, I am certain.   They are too big for any
lamb.   Where does a lamb end and a sheep begin?
                              I used to see them in the
fields.   I know these are mutton. Sometimes they are
tough.   They are not always tough, though. They are
always stronger in taste than lamb.   Lamb has a delicate
flavour. The best lamb, that is, of course.   Mutton
tastes – again, every mealtime, that Mrs Ridge.
                              Strong mutton is not
without its own special attraction, of course.   Perhaps
if I had not tasted lamb first I would have come to like mutton

more. One day she will go too far and someone will report her to the authorities. Whoever the authorities are.

Yes, perhaps I would now like mutton if I had tasted it before lamb. It is an accident.
Perhaps. I can understand that they have mutton here rather than lamb.
It is for cheapness.
I am fortunate to be here. And mutton keeps me going as well as ever lamb would. That is their point of view, I am sure. Mutton has enough of the taste of lamb to make me remember.

I do not miss lamb now.
I do not miss anything now. There is no point.

It is hard. Harder where there's none, as my old Mum used to say.
Harder where there's none.

I still enjoy my food. I am lucky in that. Some of these poor old souls here do not even have that pleasure.

And it is a pleasure to me.
I am lucky to be here.

Some would revolt at some of the things that woman
says.   I do myself.   But I keep my feelings
to myself.   It would not do to be seen to
revolt, I am in some ways revolting in myself.
     Sometimes I have to be changed, like a baby.
Is that revolting?   I finish my food cleanly,
a clean plate.   I place my knife and my
fork as I was taught to do as a child.   It is
easy for Sarah to pick them up with one movement.
I am a tidy man.   I have been called fastidious
by some.   Betty had another word for it,
     what was it? She hated my tidiness,
anyway. As one gets older it becomes more and more
difficult to control the ordin. . . . Now there'll
be a fuss. Just over dropping a plate.
     I noticed it first with spitting, for sometimes
I would spit when speaking. And not always when
I spoke with some vehemence, either.   Sometimes
I would spit without any warning.   Even without
there seeming to be any reason for it, too. I found
it disturbing, but it was as nothing compared with
what there was to come   I found myself
not wanting to . . .   not minding about spitting
when I spoke.   Is that
worse?   Sometimes I cannot worry about things
like that.   Yet there is always a worse.
I have only to look at some of these poor old things
here to know that.   I am not as bad
as some.   I am lucky in that.   I am always
more than ready to count my   blessings.

Life has taught me at least that.   I can at least say that I was not a slow learner as regards life's lessons.   As though anyone should ask – the Song. She wants us to sing, as usual. Well, singing is something I have always enjoyed. The music teacher asked me to sing in his choir, outside school. It was a church choir, in Haggerston. Not because of your voice, he said, but because of your ear. You have perfect pitch. It was something unusual about me others did not have.

The joys of life continue strong
Throughout old age, however long:
If only we can cheerful stay
And brightly welcome every day.
Not what we've been, not what we'll be,
What matters most is that we're free:
The joys of life continue strong
Throughout old age, however long.

The most important thing to do
Is stay alive and see it through:
No matter if the future's dim,
Just keep straight on and trust in Him:
For He knows best, and brings good cheer,
Oh, lucky us, that we are here!
The most important thing to do
Is stay alive and see it through!

      There was word amongst the boys that the music teacher was bent.   I never saw it myself.

                     Work? I'm retired,
I'm not here to work.   Though what she
calls work is not what I would call work.

Fancy goods, fancy goods.   She
thinks she's a pretty piece of Fancy goods!

            Not my fault. I wasn't on Fancy
goods last time.   That is a relief,
she can't blame me.
          Relief.

                   Crêpe paper.
      Crêpe?   Crêpe, crêpe, what a word.
crêpe.

                Crêpe.

Reason, I have always believed in reason.   It
was only necessary to be reasonable to be saved.
          But I have found many in my time
who have   disagreed.   It is
not important.

        Ah, now what does she want me to do tonight?

Good that she relies on me, that she –
                          Pour about a quarter
into   these empty ones. How many
empty ones?   Several dozen. I see. What is
it in the bottles? No colour, like water. Even
when I open one I shall not necessarily know, since
my sense of smell is not – *Yes, I understand.* What's
it say on the labels?   BOAKA, BOAKA? Can't
understand that.
*No, I'll be very careful. I haven't let you down
yet, have I?*

     What's she going to give her to do?
Nosy. I should mind my own.   But she's
got bottles, too. Little bottles. They look snug
in their little cardboard compartments.
                          Messy. Glad I
haven't got a messy job.   She'll get all
messy doing that.   I shan't, just pouring.
I am a very careful pourer. That's why she
chooses me to do these special jobs.
Let us apply reason to this job. If I stand a line
of empty bottles up, with a line of full ones in
front of them. . . .   No, that wouldn't be
very efficient because I'd have to keep moving the
full ones anyway. Try again.
                 If I fill the empty
ones a quarter-full with water, then I can pour
from three full ones to top it up. Yes. A dozen
at a time might be a suitable number to – Now

what's she want?   *No, Sarah, you know*
I haven't got a cigarette. Disturbing my
reasonable deliberations. Now then, let's try
filling a dozen empties a quarter-full with
water. When Sarah's finished at the sink.

Line the dozen up, and a dozen full in front, and
pour . . .   yes, a quarter each from three full
ones   and I've got a finished
one. But what does she want me to do about
the corks?   Does she want them corked? I haven't
enough corks to go round. Still, that's her problem.
She'd have told me if she'd wanted them corked. Now
another – no, wait a minute, mate, here's a better
way. If you pour water from three of the quarter-
filled empties into the three you quarter-emptied –
better still if you'd filled the empties right to
the top with water, but for one or two. Then you
could have. . . .   That's it, Charlie
boy, you've got a scheme now. It's all sewn up. Off
you go, back to the sink for more water.

Easy now. Filling and pouring.   Straightforward
for a careful person with at least some intelligence.
Like I am.   Straightforward. I can do it
without thinking after a short while. Even might get
to like it without too much trouble. Same as during

the War. Soon learnt to get on with it and
like it. Got out of being sent on one draft
because I was the aerodrome pianist, but couldn't
dodge the second one. The first one I actually
left Dover aerodrome and was at Walmer
preparatory for leaving for the Front. But the
officer at Dover rang up and said Have you got
Edwards there? And they said Yes, he's doing a
good job clerking. Well, he'll do a better job
playing the Joanna here, he said, send him back
at once. So I went back in a staff car. Just
as we arrived there was a general alert throughout
the whole Dover Patrol and everyone leapt about.
Either bombs or shells were exploding as we drove
across the approach roads. But no one got hurt.
It was remarkable like that. So I was back to
organising socials and dances and concerts. By
the end of '15 I was pianist and leader of an eight-
piece. The personnel changed, of course, as people
got drafted, but somehow our officer always avoided
sending me until the autumn of '16, when I had to go.
But the year and a bit I was there stood me in good
stead. If it hadn't been for the experience I got
then I don't think I would have become a pro after
the War. I found I was better at it than I thought
I was. And I was making a tidy bit on the side
from it, too. It was then I first realised that
there was money to be made in this music game, far
more money than in the clerking I had been doing
up to then in the Civil Service. My disability

pension wasn't much when I came out, but it was just
enough to keep me going until I got myself a job
playing in a cinema. A white sheet hanging up by its
four corners in a church hall in Kingsland High
Street. They didn't listen to what the pianist was
playing. They only heard you if what you played
didn't fit in with what was on the screen. I'd
never really been to the pictures until then. But
I soon enough picked up what was wanted. You had
to keep on playing no matter what. They noticed if
you stopped. Sometimes they would applaud. Since
I was the only one live who had anything to do with
it it used to amuse me. I would take a bow as if
I were Paderewski or someone like that. Sometimes
we had a drumkit and other sound effects. The new
films came in twice a week or sometimes oftener.
I did not usually get any chance to see them before
the first house. That was the worst house, too.
They booed and yelled as if they were at a prize
fight.   There. That's the first
dozen. Put them into their crate.
Suppose this must be liquor of some sort. My sense
of smell is nearly gone. I'd be lost in a fire. But
don't ask questions. That's why she puts her trust
in me. But can't help wondering to myself what it
is. Or where it's going. Perhaps it's going to one
of those clubs like I used to play in in the twenties.
Before the rift came with Betty. Like the famous or
notorious Mrs Marshall's All-Up Club in Frith Street.
All that dust-up in the papers over bribing a

police sergeant. They were all taking. It was not
only the sergeant. Mrs Marshall was just the type
who would buy watered whisky. Or stolen whisky. Then
she'd water it down herself. The customers were
always complaining about the drink. She was very firm
with them. She tried to run it as she would her own
home, silly as it may sound. That's what she said
to anyone who complained, however. One night the
place would be full of gangsters, and the next you
might even have royalty there. There was no telling.
And it was all Mrs Marshall's doing. She was that
kind of powerful   phoooooooor . . . rt! that's better,
woman. No man could dominate her, no indeed. She
had her man, or rather men, of course. But one at a
time. I've seen that woman set a man quivering with
fear just with one look. That was enough. And he
went sneaking out of the door just like a whipped cur.
Yet she was kind enough when she wanted to be. She
was very kind to me in her way. She could see that
I was dotty about Betty at the time, so there was
never any question of my wanting to make advances to
her. So really right from the start it was purely
a business association. I could get her the quality
players she needed for a place like that. And at
the same time those boys were the souls of discretion
itself about who they might see there and what they
might see going on. And they needed to be.
To people like us she was a good payer, too. I had
no gripes. The only bandsman I really had trouble
with was Ronnie Palmer. Later he made a name for

himself, of a sort, on the wireless as a kind of
poor man's Harry Lauder. But then he was violin
doubling saxes for me at Mrs M's All-Up. Ronnie
was ill-bred anyway, and a bit too fond of the
ladies with it. So fond that he was arranging for
them to be available during band breaks and other
odd times. Mrs M. wasn't keen on this on her own
premises, especially when it involved several of
the girls she had as cashiers and so on. But
when she spoke sharply to him about it, he answered
back. But he only just began to say something
that I think meant he could blackmail her in some
way and she was on him. First of all she thumped
him, and how he knew he'd been thumped, too, then
before he could think what he was doing she'd got
an arm-hold on him and had bounced him all the way
to the back, where one of the kitchen porters took
over and bounced him out to the dustbins. We
had to get through that night without Ronnie. It
was too late to find anyone to dep. for him.
Perhaps it did him a good turn in the end. Next
I heard of him he was in the BBC's own dance
orchestra. Perhaps I should have tried to get
into the wireless end of the business then. If I
had had foresight. Then I'd have had all the trouble
and all the jealousies and a hundred to one I
wouldn't have lived to be the age I am now. I should
count my blessings. Where's Ronnie Palmer now?
Dead, I should think. And he was younger than me.
It would have pleased Betty though if I'd managed to

be on the wireless. She was a great one for
that kind of thing.   Finished them
just in time. All full. What about corks?

                    Here she comes,
down. *What shall I do for corks for these, Miss?*

Yes, I put those back afterwards.

Right, Miss. I don't know about the lifting, Miss. . . .
She's not listening. After that so-and-so dog again,
hairs everywhere.
Cork up. Dozens here in this box. Where does she
get them?   Anyway, they fit, won't
take me long to finish this lot.

Fingers can do this easily enough. I still hear
pieces in my head, but I couldn't play them even
if she had a piano here.

                    Now she's having another go at
that poor old soul. Though she asks for it in some
ways, I'll admit.   There, that's
the lot. I won't lift them. I don't want to strain
my gut.
                    Praising that Sarah. I've done
just as well. *What about me?*

I should think so, too.

Now what is it she's going to get us up to?
Pass the Parcel. Pass the
Parcel. This is stupid. Who wants to play silly
games? But we all do. We all do as she says.
Always.   Stupid.

A lovely surprise. I can imagine.

For me?

Pass it on to Ivy.

          Mrs Ridge   She's about
half opened it.

Coming to me   Now to me, it'll come to
me!   Not quite.
Sarah's got it. Not fair. Injustice again.
What's in it? There, she didn't have time to win.
Hold on in case it stops now.   Have
to pass it now.   Not fair.

Pass it on!

Ron. It's that Ron.
          Ha ha ha ha ha ha ha ha ha ha
ha ha!   *Ha ha* I shall
choke! That serves him right! *Ha ha ha ha ha ha*
ha ha ha ha ha!   Oh dearie me, dearie me, *ha ha!*

Ha ha!   ha ha ha ha ha!

It's like in Verdun. That fellow who couldn't
speak Flemish, or French was it. He was having
dinner in some café. Lamb he thought it was. He
enjoyed it so much that he tried to say how pleased
he was to the proprietor by pointing at his plate
and going "baa-baa" with a pleasant, questioning
look. But the proprietor grinned, shook his head and
said "bow-wow!" It's just a story. It must be just
a story. Though anything could happen out there.
You could believe anything. And though they said
that cities were bad places to live, they certainly
produced the best fighters. That's what I found.
Paris, too. They had more guts. They had had to
fight all their lives. It was natural. We were
attached to the French there. Rum once a week if
you were lucky. Once it didn't get through. Next
day we found the rum rationer dead on the road, not
dead drunk as we thought at first – Travel? I've
done enough of that in my time, if you don't mind.
Her name for the exercise session.   Stretch my
legs. Could do with a stretch.
Ah.   *Mrs Bowen,*
shall I give you a turn round?

         Yes, I feel fine. Just for a few minutes,
eh? I'm sure she won't want to keep us at it too
long tonight, eh, Mrs Bowen?

It was the guns all night. Then over the top at
dawn. Why wasn't I killed like most of my mates?
It's a mystery. No one can know. I had the new
shrapnel helmet on for the first time anything
came near my head. Left me a little concussed,
that's all. Another time a Jerry got me across
it with the butt end of his rifle. But it didn't
affect me and I got him with my bayonet while he
was recovering from the swing. I'd got used to the
noises people made, by then. It was him or me, I
knew that.

I saw a Jerry using
his spiked helmet as a weapon. Hand-to-hand it
was by then, in some attacks. When there were
gas shells about you tried to get a Jerry's gasmask off.
Some of those old songs still turn me over.

March, march, left, right, left right, left right,
left! *Don't feel nervous on the corners, do you*
Mrs B?   *Good.*

I also saw gunners chained to their pieces to
stop them running for it. I saw officers urge
their men on from the rear with revolvers in their
hands. A man shot dead for answering back one of
the officers. Two weeks before the Armistice my
own cousin told me his officer had it in for him
and would certainly see to it that he got sent up

to the Front right to the last. He was blown
up with his gun. Serving his gun bravely to the
end, that so and so wrote to my poor Auntie.
Sent her the bits and pieces left, his brass
numbers all buckled, a tiny wineglass not broken, a
present for his daughter, she decided. And there
amongst the – Tourney?   Right.
                              Right, Mrs Bowen,
sport now. You won the tourney last time, didn't
you?   You can do it again!
                              Thanks, Ivy.
Take the soggy mop.

                              Oh, this is a right
lark!

                              Off! Thunder
off!   Better start than Sarah,
faster top speed, better knight, harder *IMPACT!*
Very good, Mrs Bowen, right in the face!
Round we go.   And back again,
we'll have another go.
                              BOMPF!
Right in the shoulder, Mrs Bowen!
                  And again. We'll be the win-
ners, two-nil up.

Tiring.   *THUMP! Well done us, Mrs*
Bowen, we deserve a rest, eh?
                              Well done!

I don't want to listen to
all that rubbish again. Who does she think I am?
Bill and Glory asked
me to come and play in their pub in the city. I'd
never played in pubs before that. Because of my
disability I could not be called up. I was too
old anyway. But I had to go into industry, everybody had to do that. I had nothing to do at night
times only go down the shelter or hide out in the
suburbs. So I was quite pleased to have something
to do. Shortly afterwards America came into the
war, and they used to pour out of Liverpool Street
station straight into this pub right opposite.
Somehow it seemed that the way I played was just
their handwriting. The word got around the
aerodromes in East Anglia and the pub did a roaring
trade. They would come in there with their five
days' leave and lots of lovely money in their
pockets and say 'Sing us the songs the old man sang in
the last war.' They used to have a good time, I
was better off than I had been for a long time.

Nothing comes from nothing, I was
taught. But what about plants? The space occupied
by the growth must have left a space behind?
A field of wheat must surely have sunk by the volume

of the growth? If not, why not? These questions
should be answered.   House
mother up on the dais again. Surely she's not going to tell us all those jokes again?

      Yes, she is.

         Groan, not laugh.
Heard it before. Shan't listen.   The
places I can't reach. They must be getting very
dirty. Can't scratch them properly, either. They
might be festering. They get wet when I bath, but
not washed. I am not allowed to be as fastidious
as I was. Or rather I am unable – Laugh! On the
word Laugh! you will laugh as ordered. *Ha Ha Ha!*

        I went too far after the
rift with Betty. I just walked out on a job the
day after, and walked and walked all over, not knowing – *Groan, groan!*   I didn't
care whether I lived or died. As it happened, I
lived. I don't know how, at first. We had met too
many well-to-do people on our tours, and the girl
became dissatisfied. I can understand that now. At
the time it seemed bound to happen and very painful.
I went hungry once or twice, but soon found how to
ask for things with a fair chance of – *HA HA HA!*
      I also offered to do

little jobs to help people out in return for the
odd meal or place to sleep for the night, and I
usually managed – Now what's Ivy done?
                              Poor old girl. Just reading
her book quietly.

                                        Who
wants to see hers? I've seen plenty of them in my
time, enough to last me a lifetime, thank you very
much. As for that great hairy dog. . . .
                    One day I thought to myself
I can do better than this, so I went into a shop
and bought myself a penny whistle. It was a brass
one because they told me a tin one was illegal.
And as the fingering was the same as on the little
fife I learnt to play at school, it was quite easy
for me to pick out a few tunes. So from then on I
used to go drifting about all over the country playing
my little whistle and picking up enough coppers
to keep me going. But there were times when it was
hard. People wouldn't give money to a young chap
of thirty-three or four or five who looked so hale
and hearty. They thought I should get a job, not
go begging around the streets with a penny whistle.
Some of them told me so, too. One man went so far
as to knock me down in the gutter, saying he hadn't
fought the war for beggars, or something like that.
So I showed him my disability, and then he – Oh,
filth, utter filth! Even in France in the first
War I never saw such filth. In front of everyone, too.

Filth.   Though she looked as
though she enjoyed it.
                         Not me, no feels.
                    Listen to her!
                                        No, doesn't matter

age	79
marital status	widow
sight	65%
hearing	55%
touch	65%
taste	80%
smell	70%
movement	75%
CQ *count*	10
pathology	contractures; asthma; osteoporosis, mainly of limbs; inguinal hernia; bronchitis; osteo-arthritis; among others.

. . . we had then, good friends, who used to come and see us,
just drop in there and then, never mind what was happening,
once they nearly caught me and Ted on the job, oh, that was
comical!   We had to shout to them Hang on! while
he got his trousers up, but I went out and talked to them
without my drawers on, I just didn't put them on, and all
the while we were talking there was Ted sitting across from
me, knowing I had no drawers on, on tenterhooks as to whether
I should uncross my legs too boldly, but Len and Enid knew
what we'd been doing, I'm sure, though not that I'd left my
drawers off, and we all laughed and had a good time, oh, we
enjoyed ourselves in those days!   The
cocktails we used to get through!   Every week there'd
be a new recipe for a cocktail in my women's book and we'd
try it, invite the friends round to try the new one, oh those
were good times, the friends made up for not being able to

have children, and soon I began to prefer them, all the
trouble that children can be, I saw, and at least the
friends didn't have dirty nappies, though they were sick
in the bathroom sometimes, the friends, that was a mess to
clear up, wonder I'm not sick like that after food like
this, then she'd have another sort of mess to clear up
after me, then she'd have something to complain about, the
old bitch!

I've a good
mind to make complaints about her and this food she gives
us, to my friend on the Council, I still have friends –
all the treats of our Social Evening, indeed, just like
any night is what it'll be, as usual, give me a good book
any time, I just want to read.

There she is
again! Hurrying us up, I'd leave some of this if I wasn't
so hungry. Never mind, Ivy, Doctor's coming
tomorrow, how I love him touching me! Let
me try to work out a way so he has to touch me a lot when
he comes.

Difficult.

I'll think of something, come the morning.

Last scrapings, horrible plates, not like the good
china I used to keep for best, not even like the everyday
stuff, either.

There, finished.

I'm finished, clear up, must help Sarah to clear away and
then I – oooh, my arm, the creaking, it gets set one way
and is so painful to move any distance at all after that,
aaaah   picking up these plates

         She's left more than usual.
                   All right, Sarah, don't wet your
knickers!
As soon as I've cleared up I'll get my book out and have
a good read, I do enjoy a good read, we are allowed books
here. If that Sarah will let me read, that is, chatter,
she does chatter, all emptiness, on and on. Not like my
old friends, all of them, dead now, as soon as we've cleared
I can get down to a – Now she's dropped it! Now she'll
be in trouble, I'm glad.   That's it, give it to
her, silly old thing thinks she can move, ha ha ha ha ha!
the idea!

         That dog. She's dotty over that dog.

               Right, last things, clear
up, let's get started on the washing up, three volunteers
are better than an army of pressed tongue, as they used to
say, off we go, how's your father.

                       spoon,   spoon,
fork fork   spoon,
       knife,   fork,
  knife   here's a sticky one, who's been
doing what with this one?   The joys of
life, music while you work, used to listen regularly,
funny how radio's just died out, really, no one listens
like they used to, so quick, too.   Used to sing,
too, when we had friends round, to the piano, Ted could
vamp a little, we used to enjoy *strong*

        Throughout old age, however long:
        If only we can cheerful stay
        And di-dum welcome every day.
        Not what we've been, not what we've done,
        What matters most is that we're errrr
        The joys of life continue strong
        Throughout old age, however long.

        The most important thing to do
        Is stay alive and see it through
        No matter if the future's dim
        For dum di dum, di dum di dim
        Oh, di di di, di di di deer
        OH, lucky us, that we are near!
        The most important thing to do
        Is stay di dum and see it through!

She didn't notice, did she?   No sign!

Ah, a good sing-song does
you no harm, no harm at all.

Yes, yes. Ivy this, Ivy that,
why do I do her running around for her? Get the
fancy goods boxes. Over in the cupboard. Right.

This glue is nasty. Paste rather than
glue. Attracts the mice, I shouldn't wonder.
And the rats!

Easy for her. Not so easy for
some of us. Though I can do it all right. I can
do more cracker cases in ten minutes than some of
these can do in a whole evening. Not that I'm
proud of it. Won't be able to read
now until after we've finished work. What a pity.
I do enjoy a good book.

Yes. I'll give out the work,
carry round the boxes. *What were
you doing yesterday, Mrs Ridge?*
Yes, this must be yours then.
What about you, Ron?

Here you are.　　　　　　*I can't help it*
if you don't want to work, Mrs Ridge! Tell her,
not me. She's the one who makes you, not me.
　　　　　　　　　　And you! The cheek of it!
I don't have to do this, you know!

　　　　　Here.

　　　　　　　　Wake up, dear.
Yes, I knew it, there are mice dirts in the bottom
of the box, rolling around, sound as though they're
hard so they must have been rolling around here for
some time.　　　　Filthy mice! Ugh! Mustn't tip
them out in front of this dotty old bugger George.
He'd only go out and eat them.
Though why not?　　　　　　*Here you are,*
dear, stick this paper like she says, you know,
and here are some little sweeties for you, ho ho.

Yes, they've all got them now, madam.

Kept back the best brush and glue for myself, well,
I'm better at it than them. I can do more.

Now let's get two of them organised as I did

yesterday. A team or syndicate. That's the best
way, then we all get the most out of it. *Ron,
shall we do it the way we did it yesterday?*

*I know all about your arse, Ron, I know, I weep
for your poor old arse, but what can I do? If
you do the gluing at least you don't have to
go reaching all over the table for the roll
of paper, do you?   Come on now, Ron darling,
you know you'll only dwell on it otherwise, what
have you got to lose?*

*That's it, Ron, that's the ticket. Look, you have
this brush and glue, it's the best one, my one.
          Yes, the best. You'll be all right
with that, you'll do a good job, Ron.*

*Now what about you, Mrs Bowen, are you going
to join us as you did yesterday?*   Hope so, as
I'm not speaking to that bitch Ridge again, and
the other two are dummies.
*Certainly you can do the rolling again, dear,
Ron will do the gluing and I'll do the cutting.
So we've got three rollers between us and they
can keep going round, or rather back and forth
between you and Ron.
I'm sorry to seem to be ordering you around, but
someone has to do the organising, don't they?
Off we go, then.*
Hope Ron is going to be able to do the gluing

properly, it was his fault last time, he's the one
who should take the blame for what she was saying.
Keep my arms working and moving, so that they don't
get still and stiff and set, ah.
My book will have to wait until after this work has
finished, have to wait.

My eyes are not what they were, still, I collected
over seven hundred pound for the Blind Club, they'll
see to my eyes, for that, not seven hundred all at
once, of course, over the years, over the years,
silver paper from chocolate and milk bottle tops
and   other things.
That was when we were living near Southend. I could
have collected for the Lifeboat, but I preferred
to collect for the Blind. Ted did, too, he didn't
want me getting mixed up with that lot who collected
for the Lifeboat, there were some
unpleasant women amongst that lot, and men, too, and
Ted said he couldn't afford to get in with the wrong
lot, what with this new job that we'd gone down there
for in the first place, it was such a good job, a
chance in a million, and I thought he might be right,
and it turned out he was, after not so very long.
And he did so well as a rep for Stevensons, Ted, you
have to cultivate just the right sort of people in
that sort of job, and he was so successful at it that
within five years we moved out of Southend and had our
own little bungalow out at Thundersley, a new one, up

on the top of Bread and Cheese Hill, funny name,
all our friends used to remark on it, and laugh,
we had lots of friends then, they'd call round
just when they felt like it to see us, life
seemed so busy then, I joined the Women's Institute,
and did the flowers for the Church on the
rota, time seemed to fly by   doesn't
now

                        I'm getting so annoying
fat, through not working, not getting enough exercise
in this place. Still, all my life my weight
was slowly going up, all the time, all the more to
love, Ted used to say, bless him, oh!
Only time I came down a bit in weight was when they
cut my womb away, God knows what they didn't cut
away as well, saved my life, they said, but I've
never felt the same again, I've heard others say
that it made a new woman of them, but not me, I've
never been the same, I can truthfully say I miss
what they cut away, I'm not the same woman without
it. Oh, I'm alive, that was successful, yes, they
would call it a success.

*You're doing famously, Mrs Bowen. What a rate
we're going!*   *Oooh, I've made a rhyme!*

Ron, dear, could you please be a little more
sparing with the glue? You heard what House
Mother said about being careful, you know!
                                    His hands now,
I thought it was his arse, arthritis sounds like
it ought to be a disease of the arse really.
That's a comical idea, my Ted would have laughed
at that one!
Well, just try, Ron, you know what she's like
if she's crossed. For your own sake, not mine.

                         Good for you, Ron.

It was still like country out there then, that
was why we chose the bungalow there. One Sunday
afternoon while it was still being built we went
to a fair, it was a real country fair with local
people, not one of these shady travelling affairs,
here today and gone tomorrow, it was real old-
fashioned, it reminded me of when I was a little
girl. They even had that competition for children,
bobbing they called it, where they had to find a
sixpence with their mouths in an earthenware dish
filled with flour. Their faces, how everyone
laughed at their faces! I remember going in for
that myself when I was about six, and crying at not

winning, tears running through the flour on my
cheeks, until the man who was judging it sorted
out the sixpence with his fingers and gave it
to me to make up for not winning the prize,
which was half-a-crown, I think. A lot of money.
They also had a grinning match through horse-
collars, very old-fashioned that was, you don't
see that nowadays. It was so good to be back in
the country again, I was so glad that Ted had got
himself that job. I tried to be a good wife to
him, did special things for him to show that I
loved him, special things.

Then there were more bungalows
built, the country was creeping farther and farther
away, soon it meant getting in the car if
we really wanted to see the real countryside, we
were luckier than most in having a car at all, a
little Ford. We'd go out of a summer evening to
a country pub and have a drink, be quiet for a
change. You had to go quite a way, anyway, for
a drink, in Thundersley, as when they were building all those bungalows they forgot to build any
pubs, or shops too for that matter, I did hear the
land had belonged to some religious people or other
in the first place, who wouldn't allow the thought
of drink on their property, but that doesn't
explain why there were no shops. Soon people
began converting their front rooms into shops, and
Ted and I toyed with the idea at one time, to give

me something to do, as I was free of children, but
in the end we decided against it, no need, we were
comfortably off.
Clear up? That means Ivy clear up . . . I thought
so. *Yes, I will.* Here we go again. Don't finish
the one I'm doing, just bung it all in the box,
glue and all.   *Can I have yours, Ron, please?*
                          And Mrs Bowen?
                                    Ta muchly.
Let's put the finished ones in this empty box,
shall we?

                    Good. We've done a good
day's work, our lot. What about that old cow
Ridge's stuff?   Not much here. In fact
nothing at all.   Say nothing. Just collect the
glue and the paper and the scissors.
                    Oh! I wouldn't touch
you with someone else's bargepole, you dirty fat git!
                    You say that louder
so's she can hear, and you'll get the twitcher
again! Move away, quickly.

What about the dummies, what have they done?
Next to nothing. As usual   *What a mess,*
Mr Hedbury! As usual for him, too.
Yes, that's it, give her the twitcher, the slobbery
cow, the twitcher!
What a mess, Mrs Stanton!   Nothing. Ah well,
Ivy to clear up, as usual, as usual.
                    Pile them away in the cupboard, anyhow.

Ah – that's
where the mice get in, through the wainscot there.
They must like this glue. Shall I tell her about
it? Not now. What's she on about? Pass the what?
I just want to sit down and get on with my book and
have a nice feel.

No chance of that now.
    Oh, a relief to sit down again, a relief.
Scratch it, scratch my fan, relief too.

Now then, we're ready to
go.   Sarah, then Charlie, then me.

I never win these things,
never have.   *Here.* Don't even talk
to that cow Ridge.   The lucky cow! The
music's stopped and she's got first go at opening
it! Music again. Snatch it and give it to Ron. *And
you! One of these days. . . .*

Sarah's got it. *Go on, Sarah, undo it!*
        Not quite there.

Here it comes. Quickly to Ridge, quicker it goes the
sooner it'll come back to me – not while she's keeping
it though! *Pass the parcel!*   That
shithouse again – wonder she's allowed in a good clean
House like this. Oh – Ron's got it undone. *What's
in it, Ron?*
Ha ha ha – shouldn't laugh, really.   But
can't help it, ha ha.   *She said you'd get a lovely
surprise, Ron!   Ha ha ha ha ha! And you have, too!*

Ho ho ho!
Didn't we used to go at it!   What jousts we
had! Jousts, Ted used to call them, his prick a
great lance he'd charge me with, more like a pink
rubber truncheon it looked with its mackintosh on.
                              Takes a long while these days.
                                        Longer and
longer.   But we get there in the end.
                                        Always!

On the Readicut rug in front of the gasfire, that
was a good one, a particularly memorable one.
Long, that took long, but it was extra special
good when I did come. Chintz we had on the chairs
then, chintz was all the go in Southend at that time.
And making rugs at home. I'd made that rug from a
kit, they sent you all – Exercise?
Like a prison, this is. Exercise time. I like a
good walk, a tramp over the moors. Oh well, I can
finish later, I wasn't nearly there, anyway. Mrs
Stanton would like a push round, I'll do her,
sacrifice myself and feel good, because she
smells the worst.
Off we go!   Yes, she
does stink! *How are you, Mrs S?*
No answer. I've never heard her speak since I
came here. *CAN'T HEAR A THING, CAN YOU,
MRS STANTON?*   Poor old
girl. Wonder what she was when she was young?
Didn't prepare herself for this, obviously. I did.

When my Ted went I knew what was coming, so I
prepared myself for it. They say women live
longer than men because they never retire. Men
don't prepare themselves for retirement, as a
rule. It's their own funeral. Women are better,
anyway.
Push, how she's a weight. *DON'T GET ANY
LIGHTER, DO YOU, MRS STANTON?*
                                        Puffs you out.
Ivy won't end up in a place like this, I said, Ivy
won't.
There we were, stuck on this little railway station,
in the middle of nowhere. Oh, you could read the
name of the place well enough, there were lights
on, I'll say that for them, but it didn't tell
you anything that mattered. And Ted blamed me
for not looking out for the place, and I blamed
him for wanting his little bit and tiring me
out so that I fell asleep. It was a carriage
with no corridors and we had a compartment to
ourselves, it was tempting at the time, we thought
why not, we were young then. And the only train
stopping at that time of night was going in the
opposite direction, so we had the choice of
nothing, since he had to be at work at nine sharp
the next day, but sleeping on the wooden benches,
and damn me if he doesn't want another bit there
and then, because he couldn't sleep, he said, and
it was so funny we both burst out laughing and it
was all right again.   Now she's dropped off.

The things I remember!   Push
her over there.   *All right, Mrs Stanton?*
Yes, she's all right.

Sport! More effort! No, I'm going to sit this
one out, she can't make me take part if I don't want
to, I'm going to read my book, here it – Ivy again,
fetch and carry, get the mops. All right, I'll get
the mops but then I'm going to sit down and get on
with my book.   One, two, wet. There.
                         And at least she thanks me.
Now where's my book?
                                        Here.
              My marker, torn newspaper.   Ah,
"A bus is not caught by either my father or myself,
a number eleven, that is, the one we came by, on
our return. We walk down the whole length of North
End Road. We always do this. We enjoy the street
market. Occasionally my father buys something.
Usually it is vegetables. Today he buys some Felixmeat for the dog. The dog is a perverse dog.
Felixmeat is his delight, nothing can make earth
seem more like heaven than Felixmeat, in his view.
I feel it is fortunate that not more of us have
views like this.   I catch with my father a
number twenty-seven bus several minutes after arriving
at the bus-stop in Hammersmith Road at the end
of North End Road. The northern end of North End
Road, that is. We could have caught a number nine
or a number seventy-three, to place them in numerical

order, had either of these splendid numbers been
opportune. But we catch. . . ." What a load of old
rubbish! No story about it. Boring.

Where's my other book?

Ah.   "There was no doubt that Polly
Mallinson was dead. Indeed, there was no doubt that
Polly Mallinson had been murdered. But the mystery
was why anyone should have gone to such enormous
pains to murder her in such a complicated way and
to have her found in such a crowded place.

Ascot racecourse lies about twenty miles
to the south-west of London in pleasant wooded
country that is, alas, fast being eaten into by the
commuter octopus that is the metropolis. Each year
in the month of June the Ascot Gold Cup meeting is
held there, a race which attracts horses of the very
best bloodstock in the world to compete against each
other. It equally attracts the best human bloodstock to be found in London during that sunny month,
the cream of which clusters into that holy of holies
called the Royal Enclosure.   On this particular Gold Cup day the race was won by Garlic
Clove by a head from Hiatus with Noseylad three
lengths behind, and as Sir William Scadleigh, KCVO,
PC, DSO and Bar, relaxed from the tension of watching
the finish at the crowded rail he became fully aware
of a pressure on him from behind which was natural
during the race but hardly necessary now it was over.
Reacting firmly but in a manner befitting an officer
and a gentleman, he gently eased back. The pressure

ceased, and as Sir William turned he was astounded
to see what had caused it. It was a young girl,
scarcely out of her teens, and she was falling. As
he automatically reached out to grasp her arm and
save her he became aware of several things simultaneously: that she was wearing very nearly nothing,
that *rigor mortis* had set in anything up to forty-
eight hours previously, and that before she died
someone had been treating her very inconsiderately
indeed." This is better, know where you are when
it's telling you a story.   "It was not
possible to tell what colour Polly's eyes might
have been, for they were now only enlarged, bloodied
sockets. Sufficient remained of her hair, however,
to establish that it was almost cert –" Laugh! Now
what's she on about? Stupid. *Ha ha.*
"Sufficient remained of her hair, however, to establish
that it was almost certainly red-gold. It was also
fairly certain that whoever Polly had annoyed enough
to cause to treat her in this way was a smoker, for
he or she had stubbed out innumerable cigarettes all
over her.   Not normally a man who could be
easily shocked – he had seen too much of war and its
horrors for that – Sir William gasped as much as any
other member of the crowd which quickly gathered
round what was left of poor Polly Mallinson. Their
idle curiosity was quickly ended by the arrival of two
St John's Ambulancemen who covered the body with a
blanket and summoned the racecourse police.
                    There was another reason why Sir William

was more shocked than perhaps he might
otherwise have been: for Polly was his –" *Oh!*
        oh!   oh!   House Mother's angry!

Sorry, I'm sorry, I'll pay attention! Have to
be careful now, or I'll be out. Don't want to
cause trouble. That's why I'm here, they transferred me from Ravensholm because they said I was
a troublemaker. That wasn't all.   Can't
look after myself, can I? Nearly froze to death
last time I was on my own. Would have done if that
young fellow from down below hadn't come about the
wet coming through the ceiling.   Fair pair of
knockers on her.   *Hooray!* That'll show her
I'm still paying attention.   Could have
had one together if I'd started again sooner.
        In London one summer, it was one of the times
he was on leave, very hot day, he took me to a
night club, forget where it was. Didn't see much
in it, myself, nor did he. Did a strip for him
myself that night in the boarding house, much more
for him to enjoy. Oh, I was keen on it then! What
would Ted say if he saw me today? He's well out
of it, that's certain, well out of it. And he
didn't have to bear much pain, either, except
right at the very end.
                        Doggie, doggie,
doggie. Must cost a lot to feed a great brute
like that.   How much? Pounds and pounds a
week.   This must be it now.   Yes.

I could do it like that, once. Used to, often.
Don't really miss it now, any more. What is it?
What is it to miss?
      Listen to her!
           No, doesn't matter

age	81
marital status	widower
sight	30%
hearing	45%
touch	55%
taste	40%
smell	40%
movement	45%
CQ count	8
pathology	contractures; dehydration; incipient hypochromic anaemia; incontinent; inguinal hernia; inoperable rectal carcinoma; among others.

... again. The same again.   It's
not as though they tempted me
to eat and risk the agony down
below.

                    Cutting down
has helped, I was right. The
only way not to inflame the piles
is not to eat. Found that out
first time I had them. Don't
feel any weaker, I was weak to
start with. Must eat something, though, to show
them, told them I was not a big eater, don't want to be thrown
out, not on the streets again, couldn't take it, the ramp, those
dirty   Soup is what I should have, a man in my –
She's taking my dinner!   She can have it. . . .
                    No, the House Mother shouldn't hit

her like that, that twitcher is a wicked

     t w i t c h e r
Say nothing, hurts to m o v e,   p e c k   a t   t h i s
               I   d o n ' t   w a n t   i t,
w e a k e n s   y o u,   AH!   m y   r i v e t e d   a r s e,
aaaa!   f e e l s   l i k e   n o t h i n g,
              I   c a n   t h i n k
o f   n o t h i n g   b u t   t h e   p a i n   a t   t h e
v e r y   c e n t r e   o f   m y   a r s e.

S a y   n o t h i n g

       K e e p   q u i e t

      B e a r   t h e   p a i n   w i t h o u t

s a y i n g

Soon have to move
again

aaaa!

Dropped it, she
has.   Mess, mess, it's all a mess. I'd let
the dog eat it, easiest way to clear up that sort of mess.
Tad would
have cleared it up in no time, Taddie would.
He was a fine dog, Tad, broke my
heart when he had to be put to sleep, there was more of
me in that dog than there was in myself at that time.
They could never understand
it, the w a y I l o v e d t h a t

Oh, the song, must make
some   effort
she   must
see   me singing
of life continue strong
Throughout   old age, however long
If only we can   cheerful
stay,   And   every day.
not what we'll
What matters most   that we're free
joys of life continue strong
Throughout old age, however long.

Important   to do
stay alive
No matter if   future's

knows best, and brings good cheer AAA!
the pain shoots again
again!

Work, no, that
will mean moving. No matter how still I try to
keep my arse, if my hands are moving then it
gives me gyp, *aaaa*, there.

Careful?
How can you be careful with her scrappy bits
of paper when your arse is giving you gyp all
the time? You can't keep your mind
on anything, can you?

Just a smear
along one edge, sounds
easy, but she doesn't take
into account my fingers
aren't what they used to
be, with this arthritis
liable to finish them off
altogether if – *Yes, I don't care.*

That woman's
language! They are the gentle sex, they say.
                                        Some of them.

                                        Oh. I'll
try to work, then, it may take my mind off of
it, my arse, though I doubt it, I doubt it very
much.
                    The red paper, this isn't the
roller I had yesterday, mine was newer than this,
this is grubby.   That slimy old
woman must have been using it, getting her
filthy spittle all over it!   Ugh!
But   don't   complain,   never
complain   about   such   a
small   thing.   Never   complain   about   the   small
things.   Get   on   with   it.

aaaaaaaaaah, the pain shoots, shoots!

*I can't Ivy, it's my arse, I'm in constant pain
from it.* There's no words to describe it.

Whether I work or not I still get it, nothing I
can do makes it any the easier.
                                        Nothing to lose.
You're right, Ivy, I've nothing to lose, nothing.

The best one? Can't think what state the others
must be in, then. Have a look.
Yes, the others look pretty lousy, all glued up
and bristles coming out and dirty. For small
mercies.

I'll just finish this one on my own.

There's no satisfaction
in it, in any of it, now.

                    Off we go.

Sloppity glue.
                In the mind, mind the
pain shooting up my! Went to the doctor. Piles,
he said at once. No, I've had them, not the same
this time. No, he said, doctors know best. Must
ask her if I can see the doctor sooner than Thursday. Can't wait till then. She'll not like it,
she hates anyone making a fuss. I can't do it!

      I can't wait, either, till Thursday.

K e e p   q u i e t   a b o u t   i t,   t h e n.

     Ivy understands about my problem, would make
someone a good wife, still, Ivy. Nothing to look
at, of course, she doesn't even seem to have that
look of peace that some of the other women have.
Did she have a hard time of it?
               There's no telling.

Still hurts to glue, I still have to move even
ever so slightly. How can I think about anything else, it's constant, the pain, what else
is there to think about, it goes round and round
in circles, my mind, off it, on it, not very
often off it.

Luxury bed, downy pillows, none of your plastic-
filled articles.   Out,
out, he said, and out he took it, left a gap
at the back of my mouth, felt like a bomb
crater, kept poking my tongue in it, all salty
blood, you can't help it, can you?
                              S t r a y,
s t r a y, s t r a y.
And then you don't know where you are. Still
don't understand how he swindled me on that deal,
just know he definitely did swindle me. I paid
him three hundred for the whole consignment, and
somehow when I got it it was only a consignment
for which I would have paid one-eighty, if that,
two hundred at the most.   His
name was Flannery or Chinnery or something like
that, a sharp one he was, he could swindle you
so's you had no way of getting back at him, offices

he called it – *Yes?*

       More careful still?
My hands, this arthritis, Ivy, I'm being as
careful as I can, really I am. Not very
interested, anyway, balls to it, nothing makes
the pain any better, don't make one any better
concentrating on the other, aaaaaaaaah!

Yes, I know what she's like when she's crossed.
Yes, Ivy, I'll try. Don't want to cross House
Mother.

                  Then there was that
sneaky little sod who also had one of the railway
arches down there behind the Broadway, he could
drop you in the fertilizer too if you weren't very
careful, though with him you could see it coming
and you could watch out for it. And never deal
with him unless you had to. The best way was to

play safe and sell before you had bought. Make
sure you had a sale before you paid for whatever
it was. Even then you could get caught sometimes,
find yourself *aaaaaaaaah!*
Not again, I could do with a better cushion than
this, she ought to provide an air cushion for
people in my condition, I've even seen people take
them on buses, if they were in this painful condition, what can I do, only ask, and I'm afraid to
do that.

More glue
*Mrs Bowen, can you pass me
your glue, please? This one's finished.*

*Thanks very much, Mrs Bowen.
Yes, all right now.*

There may be others
like me. I hope so. I hope
not, on the other hand. I
would not wish it on
them.

                              Finish,
finish now. Didn't do much to take my mind
off of it. A little. A very little.
Still, it's something. A little something.
                         She's all right,
that Ivy. A good sort.   Finish this last
one, nice and tidy.
Yes, here it is, Ivy. They're nice and tidy
today, aren't they, Ivy?

      Try again. *They're better today, Ivy?*
                         No proper answer.
Well, I think they're better than yesterday's.
And considering all the circumstances, too. Let
them complain. That's it, until they complain
then I don't care.

Ivy and that Mrs Ridge are always having a go
at each other. Stupid bastards, the pair of them.

                    We're the best, we are.
That's all right, then, that's a relief. Forgot
my arse for just two minutes

aaaaaaaaah!

Pass the Parcel! What a
waste of time, more movement, but
Pass the parcel, up my arcel!
ooooooooooooooh! My arse again, keep still,
keep still   A fart would be a
blessing   D a r e n ' t.

Ooooooh, *no!* The pain, pain!

Pass the parcel.
Chuck the bleeding thing.

But what's in it? Sarah's getting it open. Now
it's off again.
Curiosity.

It's my turn, that old woman's cheating! *Pass it on!*
No need to chuck it at me!   It's stopped,
it's me, I can get it undone, I'll win, what is it?
SHIT!   It's a parcel of shit! Is that
what I've won? Is that all?   Stinking shit!
shit shit shit shit shit shit shit shit shit shit shit
shit shit shit shit shit shit shit shit shit shit shit

shit!

w h y?

                         Get up,
she wants us to take exercise. Take up thy
arse and walk?   I'll try,
the pain can't be worse
                    aaaaaaachk! Yes it can!

                    B u t   t r y   a g a i n.
T o   w a l k.   The pleasure of it. As
I stroll along the promenade. It must be a tidy
middling.   The trouble
with business is that you can think you're doing
so well and then you get caught for a tidy
packet. Right into the middling, right into the

fertilizer.   It may be something to do
with the way I walk, of course. That may have
something to do with it.
Haemorrhoids or piles:
just as though you could
choose!   *aaaeh!*
I shall try again to remember my first fuck.
The first is the one you never forget, they say.
They are not right in my case, not for the first
time, either. Yet I remember it was when I was
seventeen, because that was what I said when
questioned about it some time later. But who it
was is difficult to remember.   Who did I
know at seventeen? It must have been someone from
the town, I would not have been stupid enough to
shit on my own village doorstep, as we say in the
trade. In that case, it might have – No, I can't
walk any more, I must sit and be damned to her
and her dog.

If that seed had borne fruit, I should have a child
of over sixty now. It might have been a son, a
competitor. Tom was never a competitor, none of
them. I was their father, and I saw I remained so,
oh yes!
Who could it have been? My memory's playing me up
again, so she was redhaired, ginger-eyed and had
a pair of tits on her like twin mountains and an
arse as broad as East Anglia. Her fanny was like

a red ravine, dry and dusty, not so dusty.
                                    Her face?
I can't remember her face.

                                    Ah, yes,
that was fun last time, the tourney. I enjoyed
it. Wonder if I can get a bet on this time? Mrs
Bowen won easily, I'll back her.   *Mrs Ridge,*
I'll bet you my breakfast milk that Mrs Bowen wins.

          But what will you give me if I win?

                              Right, you're on. Shake.
Now I've got a bet on.
                              They're at the tapes!
Come on Mrs Bowen! Lot depends on Charlie pushing,
too.   *They're*
off!

Hooray! One up to me!

                                    They're off
again! *Come on Charlie!*

Rah! Two up!   I shall win!

                    They're off! Last time, I must
win two-to-one at least!
                                          Rah!
Cheers for Mrs Bowen and Charlie! You owe me a feel,
Mrs Ridge, a feel, tonight!

She gets it both ways, she does. If she'd've
won she'd've got my breakfast milk, as it is she
gets a feel she'll enjoy just as much as I will,
more, probably, with my arse in this state. That's
funny, forgot it during the tourney. Just goes
to show, just goes to show.
                        But it's getting worse now, it's
paying me back, aaaaoooh!
                oooooooooh!   *aaOOh!*
No, try to think of something to take my mind off
it, the feel, that's something to look forward to,
ooooooooh, but it's no help now,
what shall I do?

                S t a r t e d   w h e n   I
w a s   f i f t y - t w o ,   i t ' s   a
p u n i s h m e n t   f o r   t o s s i n g   o f f
t h a t   l i t t l e   b o y   w h e n   I   w a s
i n   t h e   N a v y ,   i t ' s   a
p u n i s h m e n t ,   b e   s u r e   y o u r   s i n s
w i l l   f i n d   y o u   o u t .

He asked for it, he was a saucy little sod, and I
paid him a few piastres.

                aaaaooaoaoah!

aaaaaah!
                        oooooh!

oooaaaeh!

eaeaell!

oooooooh, oooh, aaaah!

eh!

oooooooooch!

ooooooooooooeoeososoaoeo!

aaaaajjja!

    we never did think we'd live to see him grow
up! I'll force myself to think of something else.
     we never did   to see
think we never did
            we'd live
     a few piastres seemed
so little at the time, for what
it   was
     years after, that smell

City of galloping

knobrot

oooooh!

oooooooaoah!

this can't go on surely
something must bust it must give the pain over
it must make me bust   *ooooooooh!*
oooooooorh!

one two three four one two three four sheep **over**
the edge one three six ten fuck them all *oooooo*

nothing comes
of it, nothing seems to
help, you'd think they would
be able to do something
for you, people have been
suffering from sore arse-
holes since time began.

no, *oooooh!*

ooooooooooooh!
Regular, it
comes in waves.

ooooooooooooooooooooooh!

oooooough!

                                     oooodh!

                   OOOOOOOH!

      Listen to her!

                  No, doesn't matter

age	85
marital status	not known
sight	45%
hearing	55%
touch	30%
taste	20%
smell	60%
movement	45%
CQ count	6
pathology	contractures; plantar fasciitis; mental confusion; progressive senile dementia; cholecystitis; osteoporosis; among others.

. . . me and then   get this down me and
then I'll   be all right
                    spuds and mashed and   with knees
try hard   peas, peas, peas
shovel peas in, more   then I'll be all right
            more?

                                        more
        general sold his   cockerel
                the meat is good, more meat, that's
the thing, must eat to get right, get this down me and then
I'll be all right, that's it, ask for more meat. *More meat?*

He's not going to eat his, no, I'll have his, must eat, how he
can leave it I don't know, here Oh!   twitcher!
            no . . .   *eee!* my hands,

the backs of my hands!   Hurts   not for long, I've
got over worse, I'm the toughest.
                   They said it was just a craze,
wanting to eat, it would never   catch on, la la la!
Catchy.
                  I always did believe
in ruining your own work, it was one of my fondest beliefs,
if you do that then you don't have to beholden to somebody,
do you?

  Scrape the plate, the mash off, mash off corners

                   Swinging on
ropes, nothing much on, just something round his
                unmentionables, as we
used to call them, into all that mucky water and crawlies,
out in the bare colds or   rocks was it,
only a picture after all.
        Another one I saw had Charlie Chimpanzee
in it, when I was that high.   Then we had Gilbert
Harding being rude, we enjoyed it! Diving into the
crawlies and the water all covered by scrum, those jungle
creepers!   How we used to laugh!
       She ought to show us films here,
though some would abuse the privilege, they never do.
       It would never do.

                da-da, ma-ma

      Brisket and taters, brisket, brisket

atrisket, my love bisquit, brown bread and waistcoat,
crumbs to his watch-piece.

　　　　　　　　　　　My name's Gloria, Glory
for short. It's too far this time.　　　　May I never?
My true love went once round fingering, blue hair he
had with his long black eyes, four foot　　　　three
in his bloomers, I remember him so clearly, it was in
a pub we first met, I was with my mates at the time, he
was with his.　　　　Yellow jumper and pale skirt
　　　　This for two or more I was with him,
standing in the dark. Milk stout was all our tipple, then.
　　　　He was my first, it was raining at the time.

She's in trouble this time, not me, House Mother'll hit
her, not me, this time

　　　　　　　　　　　　　No, she's
not, that's not fair, she's only getting a tonguelashing,
not the twitcher, it's not fair　　　not fair!

me
me me meeee memememememememememe! say it aloud
ME!   The twitcher, lucky
she didn't hear, lucky me!

                    A gallon of gin I must have
drunk last night, this won't do, where's the money
coming from?   It doesn't get him anywhere.
I must cut down on the food, supporters and sus-
penders, it won't do, I won't have his drinking though
I'll have his drink *been, no twat you'll be,*
    What matters most is what we'll be
    The joys of life continue strong
    Throughout old age, however long.

    . . . MOST IMPORTANT THING TO DO
    IS STAY ALIVE AND SEE IT THROUGH
    NO MATTER IF THE FUTURE'S DIM
    JUST KEEP STRAIGHT ON AND TRUST IN HIM
    FOR HE KNOWS BEST AND BRINGS GOOD BEER
    OH LUCKY US THAT WE ARE HERE!
    THE MOST IMPORTANT THING TO DO
    IS STAY ALIVE AND SEE IT THROUGH!
                        Now she ought to be
pleased with me, no twitcher, no one can sing louder
than I can, not even that fat slob Ivy, cow.

                        Work! The people must
work if they are to earn their daily bread!   Life
is not all butter, someone has to earn the guns as
well, ha ha!

                        What's she
giving them two to do? I could do it, whatever it
is. *Here!*   Twitcher! The twitcher!

It's not only that, there are tripes and lazy
breeders for supper, summer in a sauce made of milk
and parsley.

               I think, I think!

                    Careful,
I'm always careful, never let them stick it up me
without a rubber on, very careful all my life,
never had no kids, never!   Very careful,
very clever, that's me.
             I can do that easy,
that crinkly paper's not very good for it though,
not very good at it.   Nasty work,
only fit for the Ivys.   *Nothing, nothing, nothing.*
Nothing!   Not my box, hate this
work, nothing here, who makes me?

Don't want this work. *Don't want this work!* Or
this Ivy, cow she is, slummocky old cow.

Slummocky old shit cow! That annoyed
her, that'll teach her to order me about, I'm
not here to be ordered about! Except
by the twitcher, that's all that keeps me quiet,
the only thing.

I'll just sit here, that's what I'll do, just sit
here, and only work if I feel like it. Start one,
roll the paper round the roller, here, this isn't
as easy, roller roller penny a paint, painy a
pent, old cow, I'll roller, red paper, red paint,
red roller roller roller.
And just leave it like that. Then anyone who
sees me will think I've just broken off for a
moment. Oh, I'm clever, you know, I
know all the dodges, I learned them, all the
dodgers, when I was working, you learn all the
dodgers to work as little as
This way I won't have to touch
the horrible glue, no, not even to touch it.

The twitcher's
gone up the stage with her, the twitcher has, bye

bye the twitcher, good riddance twitcher! If
I just sit here and keep quiet and do nothing
then she won't come down here again with the
twitcher for me, the twitcher for me, If
ye're no a garlic, the twitcher's for me.

If possible keep on going where   they
are all like   Mind you, if I was her I
would not put up with any of it, any of it, myself

It pays to keep up with your payments. Sometimes
we wouldn't. They were all away. The girls had
it away. No one played at home, then.

She's going to team up with those two! Now they
won't talk to me. It's not fair. Yesterday she
did it, too. She deliberately doesn't ask me. I'm
sure of that. I can do this as well as anyone,
round the roller, the glue. I could be part of the
team.   **It hurts.**

Where are they all gone? I had them here, all of
them.   And now they're not here. It may

be my true love, my one true love. His hair was
golden, his eyes were blue, he stood six feet two
in his bare socks, the first one. My one true.
One two, dozens since then. He bumped into me
coming out of the four ale bar into the corridor,
there I was scrubbing near the milk stout. I was
a young girl then. He was my first. Swept me
off my feet. Swept my chimney, he called it, my
black chimney. What could I say? It was a
frosty morning. Frost clears away the flu and does
good for England. Everything's in a mess

That time they let me play. Let the piccaninny join
in! that Bobbie yelled. I enjoyed it more than my
tapioca.
                        What would you say if I
took off my arm and gave it to you in a stew?
              Got you there, got you there!
                        Why not?

It was the milkman and his wife who ruined it.
What made him marry a mad woman?   The cream
curdled all, she would and all.

                              So instead of
doing nothing, you would rather do nothing! I
spit at you. That Ivy is a slummocky swine.
Her tits hang down. In really, you can't see
her tits, she just has a bulge. She's got no
tits, a long streak of gravy. What that Ivy
has done to me! How many times have I had
hot dinners than hot times? Where do they all
come from? She pinched my last piece of meat,
the piece I had been saving, she did, that Ivy.
But jesus will come for my end. He will lift
Me up into his heavenly boudoir and I will sing
with the angels all the night long. The stars
will shine down on Me when he comes, his Milky
Stout, and the sun will come out and beam upon
the starry firmament. And we shall all live
happily ever after ever until the end amen.
Aah, isn't that nice.   Except for Ivy,
she'll not have an end, she'll go on with her
gravy tits and sticky fingers all her life
until she dies and

Well well well! They can talk!

And what about the price of candles! A girl can't
go on and on burning her wick at both ends, can
she?   When
will we be allowed to see what really goes on?
Yesterday they won the war, all the Tommies came
home raving for it. Their only pride was between
their legs, like a dog's tail. We worked over-
time. No fear of that, I said, when he came, I've
been a good girl, after my way, always fashionable,
I was, wore a hooped crinoline sort of dress,
starched sleeves, bare arse. Oh, we were proudish
then!

Now when I try to brush up my brushing, it hurts
under my armpit, hurts. I should go to the doctor.
He'll help me, the doctor in Margery Street. Walk
up through Exmouth Market, buy some priest shoulder
at a stall, then up past that place in Amwell
Street that always smells of flux, opposite the
other church, and down into Margery Street, rest
my feet. Good doctor, he is, he'll heal my armpit,
nasty nagging pain and then it comes sharply, ouch!
Or some smoked salmon scraps, not shoulder, only

a tanner a quarter, bits off the edges,
bones, scraps, one of my fondest favourites,
smoked salmon scraps from Exmouth Market, chew
them, get the bits out, just as good as they
pay earth for, lots more.
                              Hungry again, nothing
more till breakfast, there's worst to come.

My one true, love. His hair was ravenblack, his
eyes were green, he stood four foot three in
his bare, the first one. My one two. One true,
several since then. He jostled me in the public
bar when I was a scrubber. I must have been
forty by then, a mere. The milk stout I remember
coming out of quart bottles. No one must know.
How many beans since then? There must have been,
one after one after one after one after one after
one, no   *No!*

These things make us all. Try for the sky. Jesus
will. Not in here you won't. Was jesus a shep-
herd? Did they have sheep in the desert? He could
make food for them, fish and bread, wish he could

make me some now, I'm hungry. They don't feed
us here. In my day I'd pop down the shop on the
corner for a quarter of Wall's luncheon meat and
a tin of peas. That's a good feed.
What's she at now? Is she coming down here again,
yes.   But not the twitcher, ha, she's left
the twitcher up on the stage.   Good.

Here comes horrible Ivy creeping down the table!
Ivy the creeper, after the work. They must be
finished. Haven't done any. Who cares, who cares?
Can't make me work. Just try it!
                         Ivy the creeper-
crawlie, can't touch me!

You are a stinky woman!

          Twitcher's up on the stage, meeeeahr!
Now she'll come to me next, without her twitcher.
                  Now.
                  Why should I work?

                              Leave
me, leave me!   While there is no pie
we make hay, six times seven sends you to heaven,
whompot, whompit, whampit!   It was a lively
leading lido when we first could greet groaning the

great dawn green with grassy longings, if only I
could now, how now how how?

   This must be enough to be going on with,
there's always tomorrow, after all, always – Pass
the Parcel, what's this, I love games. Pass the
Parcel and I'm the winner, the postman brings me
a parcel, brown paper, must be mine, I'm a winner,
post today, late for Christmas, make sure I'm the
one who gets the lovely surprise at the end. Something to look forward to!
Off we go!

   Next to me, me! Parcel for me!
     Open it, the music's stopped. Feels
soft, strip off the paper. What can it be?
Music. Oh. *You bastard sod!*
Cow woman Ivy, answering back, she always on my
back! Get off my back, you cow Ivy!

       Next to me!
Here again. Stink. What is it?
Hold on to it. Unwrap some more. Yes, stink.
Rules?   *All right, have it!*
I won't be interested in your game any more, won't
play any more. Stinking rotten game. Whose
game do you particularly, the long ones, I could
always give rise to a long long one, it was my
speciality in those days. Madam had four in
her room, she would give one to us girls as a

favour, she would, and I was always the most
special favourite, I was, I was, I was, I was,
I was, I was, I was, I was, I was, I was, I was,
I was, I was, I was, was, was,

                                        was!

All the bees, bottom, bum, behind, buttocks,
                              ARSE!
I know what killed him, I know what killed him
that night, too much of a good thing, that's
what killed him, heart attack during the night
the doctor called it, but I know it was too
much of a good thing that killed him.
                        He was a good husband to me,
I had eighty children by him, too much of a good
thing done for him in the – Now what?
                                        Travel!
            I hate exercise.   But
the twitcher!

Ooooh, so fat I can hardly move. Waddle,
waddle, what's it matter now, don't have to
attract the fellers any longer, so what's it
matter? More a job to keep them away, ha ha!
Ha ha, that Ron, ha!

Round.   Round. Keep away from that
stinking Ivy. One of these days she'll bring
me to such a point that I'll forget myself and

dot her one where she won't like it at all, no.
Where no one likes it.

My true love's hair was red, red as the dawn,
my one true love. His eyes were brown, he stood
four foot umpteen in his boots. My one two,
three four, who's counting? Ha ha! I bumped
into him as I was sloshing the floor in the
Gents. He stumbled over my bucket and there we
were on the floor, at it among the Jeyes and
Lysol. He swept me off his feet. I was quite a
young thing then, stout with it, I enjoyed it,
who'd have thought it, in those days?

That Ron has sat down, so
shall I, twitcher or no twitcher, she must give
it him first, if she's fair, the twitcher, he
sat down first, Ron.

We waved and waved as he went by, King George the
Sixth, they let us off dirty to wave from the
upper windows, it was so exciting, us girls, it
turned me over, truly it did, waiting for hours

we were in the hot sun, it was late December.
And the banners were out, we waved our union
jacks, and cheered and cheered. It was quite
good. That was at the time when I was afraid I
might become Queen myself one day – no
twitcher if she's going to run a tourney, good.

What's that? *Your breakfast milk? Yes, I'll bet
you, Ron.* *All I've
got that you'd want, Ron, is a quiet feel in the
toilet before bed.
Shake.*
    Two lots of breakfast milk for me, yes,
always too many cornflakes and not enough milk,
that'll be nice, something real nice to look forward
to. There they go.

Silly old fool   got himself hit.

And again! Won't get me two lots. Never mind.
I'll get a feel.

Three times! Ron certainly backed the right one.
    You shall have it, Ron, never fear, you

shall have it. Wonder what he'll feel? My
twat is favourite, or at least it used to be.
Or perhaps he wants me to hold his horrible.
Or bag of creepy skin? Anyway, it'll
be short, Ron, I'll promise you that.
No, shan't listen! Bung
my ears up!

This big meat pie, so big
you could hardly get yourself round it. So big.
Three of us made it together, for the Club. In
those days they let you, and my friend Edie got
me together with all this lard and flour. It
must come soon. Bought lots and lots of meat,
very expensive. For the upper crust we had sea-
gulls, and this tower like the Eiffel Tower it
was in the middle. It held up the crust very
nicely with just a little point sticking out.
Ooooh, it did taste nice! Wasn't there none left
over for the curates?
We were good in those days, in spite
of that rationing. You had to be good to get
anything off of grocers and suchlike. They had
a marvellous time of it, having it off in the
back stores.
Where are they now, the martins and perhaps?

All dead. No Edie, Frank, Johnnie, Doug, Maeve,
Dil, no, none of them.

Where do they all go? Where are they now? Where
am I now?　　　　How can all these things be here,
and not them?　　　　　　　That would be a
curious caper, as he used to say
　　　　　　　I asked for a job once, where are
your references, they said　　　　　　　You've
got to have the right pieces of paper, you see,
at the time you want the
I want a jobbies

It is very confusing, laughing

　　　　　　　　　Laugh! Laugh,
laugh, I nearly　　　died
　　　　　　　We went round the halls
one night, lead in his pencil, more like a great
big　　　His blood pressure was high, laugh,
you never saw anything like it!　　　We
were in a box, boxes of chocolates, programmes,
as many cigarettes as you could eat. A very good
show but I know what he was after with his great
purple pen!
Like a lick of my seaside, he would say.

　　　　　　I would

　　　In the first place there were too many
there, in the third it was neither here nor

there but underneath, where we all liked it,
underneath, pass me the deeoyleys, she would say,
just like that, pass – Good! That Ivy's getting
it! It's a change, give her the *twitcher*, House
Mother!   Now she's in trouble, bitch Ivy,
fat slummy greasy Ivy! Fatty Ivy chop, buy them
at the family butcher's.

                    So what?
She's giving us the benefit, again.   Lovely,
have it off, let's all see

                        Oh, she
threw her clothes over the dog!

             Now the other
      that's it
             Oh, I always enjoy this
bit, it reminds me of the old days when I was out
working. . . .   How far now?

         Oops!
         They're all off, all,
Hoorah!
          Never with a dog, we went to the
Dogs' Home to choose one but came away without one,
I couldn't have kept it   anyway
      My new dress is stained with custard.
Who did that, now?   It must have been that
Ivy, I know it was that Ivy!   *Cow!*
Custard cow, taking no notice, getting her own back
because my tits are better than hers, custard cow,

cowardy custard cow.   Truc love, blue
eyes, green, six foot if an inch, he was tall as
well with it, scrubber I was, the first, first
          Listen to her!
                         No, doesn't matter

age	89
marital status	widow
sight	50%
hearing	40%
touch	35%
taste	55%
smell	45%
movement	20%
CQ count	8
pathology	contractures; diabetes mellitus; colonic diverticulitis; benign renal carcinoma; lesion of alimentary tract; paraplegia; among others.

. . . **tasty**

                   meat then
             that house, the kitchen itself could seat
twenty of us, did at Christmas before we served them, it
was warmer than the   servants' hall, that word worries
me still, always hated to think of myself as a servant, he
didn't, almost revelled in it, he did, knew his place and that
was a servant's place, indeed   this custard,
slop   and greens, how can she, in that   kitchen
there were great bowls we broke the eggs into for custard,
real custard, the arm you needed to beat that many would fell
an ox, two of us girls would take turn and turn about, sometimes my arm hurt so much that   that kitchen
was so big twenty of us could   the
mahogany cupboards, sets of drawers with brass handles, how
I hated brass, a waste to have brass to keep clean, but then

he would say it was good

                 my soul indeed,
what he was interested in was not my soul
          the old sod
with his great stomach, the stomach he had on him
                  Why not, he said,
      Because not, I told him

         The stomach on him, he'd be round the
kitchen spooning out the leavings in the big oven trays,
laughing if Cook or anyone tried to stop him, dodging round
and knocking things over with his great stomach and fat
                  arse.   I know.

There was too much room in that kitchen, Cook used to say,
even when she had to cook for sixty, there were that many
guests there on occasion, oh dear me   yes

       The mahogany cupboards, the whole range to
blacklead, eggs to beat, the meringues the sisters liked
too much, we used to put the yolks in scrambled eggs the
next morning, it was the best way to use them up.

           Years afterwards

went into Town one week and there he was, years after,
outside the Bear, his great stomach even bigger
          grinning
      I felt my insides twist, I couldn't help

myself, he had the effect on me.

In summer the sun used to beat down
on the range, it used to make it that hot
working there, double.

My name is
Sioned, I work here, you're a pretty thing

How could I see it coming?

Clear up now, I'll help, I can still move, you know, push
at the wheels, I'll help, get the plates together, there,
lift – Oh no!   *I didn't mean*
to drop them, Miss!

I wouldn't try to
feed the doggie, you've told us not to.

Yes, I deserve it.

cah, cah, cah   Goats
in the paddock, there. We had goats, then, never ate it
ourselves, but the sisters did. I never liked it, I wasn't
squeamish, no, but the sisters

No,
I won't sing her song. I think it's silly, so
she can do the other thing.

As though it mattered, it wasn't my fault,
no, they can clear up on their own, a little mess
like that.

What matters most

                 old age   *long* ha ah ah!
ha ha ha ha ha!

            future's dim
             hymn

      most important thing
                 through
ha ha! Nearly choked then.
          I think it's so silly, they
can all go and do the other thing, I'm tired.

Oh! Must have dozed off. Ivy's giving out the
work, that's good, always liked something to do,
never idle, keeps you going, idle hands make
idle work, get down to it, I can do this, fancy
goods again, it's hard for me with my fingers but
I can do it if I set myself to it, yes, where's
the glue, ah. Roll it round nice and smooth, hold
it tight, snip it off, glue, glue, loverly glue,
and bob's your uncle!
Oh, I can do these. I'll beat Ivy today, I'll do
more than she can, if she lets me have enough
paper. Roll it round, nice and smooth, hold it
tight, snip snip and it's off, paste the glue along
the edge, press together, another one done.
Roll it round, nice and nice, hold it tight, snip it
off, off it comes, good paper this, this time,
press the glue, too much that time, never mind eh,
it's not as though she's paying us, eh, snip snip
go the scissors, I can do this without thinking, easy,

got it off to a fine art, like I used to when
I was at Fuller's, packing, we used to have
races amongst ourselves to see who could fill
most cartons first, I'd usually win, there was
only one girl who could give me a run for my
money, not that we ever bet on it, her name
was   Fair
hair, rosy cheeks she had, a bit cheeky with
the men from Bakery she was, too, given half
a chance, what was her name?

One afternoon I remember it was so hot that she
undressed right there, took everything off under
her overall and sat there in just her overall,
bold as a knocker, any of the Bakery men could
have come in just then and seen her stark naked,
we were all holding our breath at the nerve of it,
there she was, right in – *Yes, dear, what do you*
want?
Yes, I'll join you, if I can do the rolling again
like I did before. Yesterday, was it yesterday?
Forget, there must have been one day I was
beating Ivy and she kept on keeping the paper
from me so that I wouldn't beat her, but Ivy
seems to think it was yesterday we worked together,
perhaps it was, her memory may be better than mine,
mine is getting shocking.

             Yes, someone has to do the organising.
And it always seems to be you. If it's not House

Mother it's Ivy.　　　　She's welcome.
Roll it round now, nice and easy, that's the way,
smoothly does it.　　　　　　There.
　　　　　　　　　Easy.

　　　　　　　the still-room next to the carved
room　　　would wait on my own and listen
the company　　　　　　　　lords and ladies
　　　　　sometimes　　　　　　　the carving
I did not like, it was heavy and dark, it did not
reach to the ceiling because it had belonged to
the older house, over the doors it said 1636 in a
shield, but the house itself was more modern, the
rooms were taller and bigger, the carving was
patterns and crests and shields of families they
were related to, or wanted it thought that they
were related to, the way
　　　　　　　　mirrors opposite the back lawn with
a sundial
The house itself I loved from the first moment I
saw it, though it meant servitude to me, it was
the people who made me a servant
walking from the village with Megan Williams along
the galloping drive, miles of rhododendrons,
suddenly you could see a top corner of the house,
black-and-white, but big, bigger than any other
black-and-white I'd seen, though when you were
nearer you could see it wasn't wood, it was a black-
and-white pattern in plaster or something like
that　　　　　but it was a lovely house, I forgave

it that   cheating.

            the hall   Hall
         the portrait of Miss Eirwen   and the
tiny   the panelling was oak, it took
some polishing   and a great brassbound
trunk, with studs   it broke my heart
            that place died in 1939, died,
they told me

Even took away my name, didn't like Sioned,
wouldn't call me that, or even Janet, gave me
a new name to suit them, Emma, that I hated
most of all, I think.

Alyn Llywelyn said fuckit in bead-threading. I
did not know what it meant then. I don't think
he did, either. Miss Jones made a fuss about it,
she washed out his mouth with soap and water. We
did not understand, but he was careful what he said
after that. In fact, from that day on he was never
a great talker, was Alyn Llywelyn.

            Bowen gowen. *Yes, Ivy, you made a*
rhyme. No one's ever made up a rhyme about my name

before, never. Yes, we are doing well. I'll
have to catch up or I won't beat her.

      Mr David worked in the Small Library.
I would take coffee to him, with biscuits on a
tray   from the still-room   or the
kitchen   He would speak to
me in Welsh, which I did not usually use among
the other servants.   His wife had
died before I came to the Hall, he had spent
much of his time at his sisters' place since then.
               He would be working at
the Welsh books   the Small Library
was a cosy place
        sometimes he liked to talk to me,
made me feel proud of being Welsh
              the other servants were all
trying to ape being English, there was very little
Welsh spoken in the kitchen
The Factor hated to hear Welsh spoken, he swore
and bullied us if he heard us.

May we receive   that which for
grateful   until ever   after
             no one came
    was to be successful

in the fullness, the first place

The Lyons over Hammersmith station. Would go
there for tea in the war, no meal could cost
more than five shillings. Essential warwork,
indeed! Better than the British Restaurants
or the canteen at Fuller's. But even in the war,
Fuller's gave you your wedding cake if you were
getting married, free. Told him that, but he
said he wasn't going to get tied down just for
the sake of an unrationed wedding cake. We're
happy as we are, he said, Aren't we?

What's he want now,
filthy old man always fingering his backside.
Glue?   *Yes, here.*   *And have*
Ivy's, too, then you won't have to stretch over
and hurt yourself so much.   *All right*
now?   Have to be.

How many of these does she want us to do?
     on and on   Still, Ivy'll
tell me when she thinks it's enough, Ivy's doing
the organising here

                  Finish at last
I'll say we've done a good session. Worked my
poor old fingers into an ache. Glad that's
over for one day. It makes a difference.

I've worked harder than Ron, I'm four or five
ahead of him, spare, all those. I'm good. *Yes,
here's my bits and pieces, Ivy, and good riddance!*

            *Yes, pack them neatly in, crackers
for Christmas.*
Why can't we have some different coloured paper?
I'm fed up with this sort of red, rotten red.

I may not be very   but I am

Here she comes. I hope she'll like what we've done.

             Ron is stupid. *They're not
bad, are they, Miss?*
            Better than hers, anyway –
Oooh – she hasn't done any, Mrs Ridge!   How
does she get away with it?

So tired now. I'll drop off
in my chair soon if she doesn't watch out.

Pass the Parcel.
Haven't played that since I was a child. Sweets it
was usually, very small packet of sweets wrapped
round and round and round with lots and lots and
lots of paper and string and brown sticky paper.
It was such a let-down in the end, but that made
it all the more fun and it meant that all those
who didn't win were less disappointed when it
turned out to be next to nothing.

Oh, it's my turn.
Parcel feels exciting. On to George.
Marvellous, he moves. Passed it to Sarah, as well!
He must be getting better, old George. You never
know, he might even say something next. That would
be a miracle!

She shouldn't keep it, you can't trust that Mrs Ridge
to be fair in the slightest.   Oh, the
music's stopped, and Ron's the one to open it. I
wonder what it can be?
Eh? Not very nice at all! Why did she do that?
Poor old Ron, I feel sorry for him, his backside in
that sort of state, too. It's not right at all.

The Factor was a swine,
a swine. And he was a villain, too. He came
there with hardly a penny to his name, and died
worth twenty thousand. How he got it is a long
story. He would tell the sisters things had been
done on the estate when he knew very well they
hadn't. And he'd pocket the money, of course.
One day Miss Mary called me in to her in the great
drawing room and asked me if I knew where the Factor
was. He's gone to Birmingham, I said. To pay
the coal bill, she said, but he could have done it
by post, I gave him a cheque. I think she knew
then he was taking a backhander and had gone to
collect it. She would never hear a word against
him until then, that day I think she realised what
a villain he was, but it was too late, she was –
Travel, no, what she means by that is

Don't mind, passes the time.

But who's going to push me?

*Yes, that
would be good of you, Charlie. A gentle turn
round the hall. Sure you really feel up to
it, though?*

When the Factor retired, he made a bonfire of
papers from his office and it burned for three
days. He built his own house, how he ever did
that I'll never know, out of their money. How
could a man on his salary ever save twenty thousand? The family knew, of course, and tried to
tell Auntie Mary, but she would hear no word
against him. He even had his own electricity line
from the big house, a mile across the fields,
so he got his light free. Though he did good work,
I'll agree, but he never did it unless there was
a backhander in it for him. But you could never
prove anything against him, that was the difficulty.
And he had the power of life and death over some of
us, by dismissing us. Not that I ever wished to
prove anything against him, I got on quite well
with him apart – *Not at all, Charlie, not at all.*

It must have been some time after I came across
his only cousin in Rhyl, near the front, she
looked well and was well off. She would be, of
course.

We're the last to be exercising. All
the others have given up – Tourney, oh yes, I
won that last time, beat old Ron hollow, though
he does have his troubles down there. *Hang on a
minute, Charlie.* Lift, adjust, myself.

That's it, over to the corner by the cupboard. *Yes.*   *Yes, Charlie, I can.*

Here's my mop. *What's she soaked it in this time?
Smells like what you were mixing, Charlie.*

Lark is right, Charlie.
Let's get hold of this mop properly. Now where shall
I try to land it first?   *Off!*
He's a good pusher, Charlie.
George's let his mop fall, get him right in the PUSS!
One to me, very pleased.

Off we
go again. I shall win again, I know. George is hope-
less. Aim at chest this time, oh flinch! SHOULDER!
Still a solid blow, his hardly flicked me with wet.
Good, eh?

Last time. I'll aim for his breadbasket
this go.   Carefully, carefully.
GOT HIM!
Mrs Bowen the Champion, she
should have said. Twice I've won now, I'm the Champion,

I've never won many things in my life, but I'm
the Champion here.

There   it comes over me
                 again
                                        faintness

                                                    won't last
long

                 not long

                                        It just takes
some   time   before   you're
back to yourself   again.

Auntie Mary did leave me something in her will.
They were good like that, remembering. It was very
little. They didn't used to give pensions to their
staff however long they'd been there, they left a
lump sum in their will, the sisters.   Fat
comfort to some.
A little use to me now, I can buy myself the odd
Guinness if I can find anyone to go out for it for
me.   They had their own
bread, we baked every other day. But no brewer,

though, they were teetotal, very strict. Not Chapel,
church, but very teetee just the same. They
knew the gardeners drank ale with their dinners,
but woe betide anyone who brought it into the
Hall!   I did once, felt ever
so guilty. I was low at the time and I bought
myself a small bottle of gin from the Bear. Normally I felt so safe in my little attic room, well,
it was not so little, it was a reasonable size,
but all the time I had that bottle in the room I
felt as though I were a criminal.   My little
room. The washstand with the plain green jug
and bowl, the window, quite big really, looking
down on the lawns and across the bridge to the
warren. I had some happy hours there, it was not
all hardship. Most of the time I didn't have to
share it, only if we had Company and they had
servants.   My bed
along one side, and an old easy chair, the high-
backed sort with wings, donkeys' years old, a
picture Miss Eirwen had painted herself, brown
lino on the floor. I was content – no, at the
time I hated every minute of being a servant,
only now does it seem
                        pleasant.
                        The lilac
curtains, my own flowery jerry under the bed,
but clothes behind the curtains in the alcove.
They may be like it still, the Hall is still there,
I should think, but now it is probably a guesthouse

or something like that, perhaps they've sold it to
build houses on, chopped down all those lovely
trees.   Everything changes,
nothing gets better.

                                      I was going
to read myself, but daren't now she's given Ivy
a taste of her tongue.   But I'm
not going to watch this filth again, why she does
it baffles me. Surely she can't think it stirs
us up?
                  Summer we would go down the
bothy, where the single gardeners lived, next to
the walled garden and the greenhouses. They'd grow
all sorts for the sisters there, figs and peaches
you didn't get anywhere else in the county, or so
they said.   A boilerhouse
in the basement of the bothy, coal down a chute,
the long winters. I can remember it exactly, why
can't I remember what happened yesterday?

               My friends would say I was forward,
just because I used to look men right in the eyes.
None of that shy retiring for me. That's what men
and women's eyes are for, I would say to them.
They knew what I meant, they would giggle.
                    Rabbits were common, we
had trout out of the stream, too, poached, the
sisters did not make a fuss about that sort of
thieving like some of the gentry around those parts.
Why trout were thought so special I could never

understand, anyone who'd had them as often as I
have would prefer a good fresh herring any day.

Listen to her!

No, doesn't matter

age	89
marital status	bachelor
sight	10%
hearing	15%
touch	25%
taste	20%
smell	10%
movement	15%
CQ count	2
pathology	contractures; incontinent; advanced inanition; chronic rheumatoid arthritis; Paget's Disease; advanced senile depression; muscle atrophy; fibrositis; intermittent renal failure; among many others.

Lame

source

unfr

they'll

for

why?

oughter

eh!

schools

       consuls

           how are you? in the

pink

straining

Cox's Orange   pippin!

No matter if the future's dim
keep right on and suffer hymn

Work!   work   Fancy, aaah

crépe paper, créper   crêpep   crêper

crêp

créper

créper?

crêper!

crêper, yes

Stick   she says? *Eh?*
                  crêper
    glue   little round
                     Sweeties are they?

glass

spitting spitting spitting

maybe, ah

Thorban, thorban

seal

floors

with

full

continued

of, of, of

some

gilli

grim

at

point of

in

does

there are

in does

in does

will

,

sake

best

my

my

149

hoarse

which

to

  still

                                              my
name   Eh!   anger at me,
she   no more!   no more meat and gravy
and?   oh.   it's   oh dear, what have I
been doing?   she goes
               there
                         there

a mess, *yes.*   but she's not   no
            fear

      cheek

when I get better

Package

for me   pass, parc

what?

                quite

three and six nine and six fifteen

                            name   it

             moving   moving!

everything's moving!

                            ?

moving

stopped   good

    what's this?

               jerk

    moving   this

stick

             oooooooooh!

splashash   what was?   smell

   mop   not   this   mop

      what?

              aaaagh!

   shoulder!

         blank

   aaaaaaaaagh!

No, doesn't matter

age	94
marital status	not known
sight	5%
hearing	10%?
touch	5%
taste	15%
smell	20%
movement	5%
CQ count	0
pathology	everything everyone else has; plus incipient bronchial pneumonia; atherosclerotic dementia; probably ament; hemiplegia (with negative Babinski response); to name only a very few.

Galluog

lwcus

ynad

noddwr

Teg

enwog

geirwir

arabus

iachus

Hacl

uchaf

grymus

hwyliog

eofn   sylfaen

Math

addien

reit

gorwych

anianol

rhyw

ethol

ter

Huawdl

uchelryw

graslawn

hoyw

eirian

serennu

Afal

llu

uned

nesaf

Teilwng

egniol

gris

arlun

171

ieuanc

Hogyn

uthr

gogoniant

huan

epil

syber!

Disglair

addurno

fyny

ynni

digrif

drud

Tirion

eisen

gwron

atodiad

ifanc

Hadu

unol

golenad

haul

eryr

safon

I am

terrible, Ivy

Now I can every
word you say I am a prisoner in my
self. It is terrible. The movement agonises me.

Let me out, or I shall die

No, I do
n o t g e t   a n y
l i g h t e r,   I v y,
I   i n –
t   e   n   d
n   o   t
t   o   g   e   t
a   n   y –
t   h   i   n   g
a   n   y
m   o   r   e

n   o

m   o   r

age	42
marital status	divorcée
sight	85%
hearing	90%
touch	100%
taste	40%
smell	95%
movement	100%
CQ count	10
pathology	mild clap; incipient influenza; dandruff; malignant cerebral carcinoma (dormant).

They are fed, they are my friends. Is that not enough?
And what would be enough?   Some of them indeed are not
capable of differentiating between meat and bread – no, that
is not an argument for not giving them meat. A balanced
diet is essential to the health of the aged. I know that.
I know what is best for them. I am a trained House Mother.
Did I not work under Frau Holstein of the House in Basle?
Ah! Sunny days sitting on the slopes of the Moron, or walking
by the green river, with that good, good, woman.
Yes, I know what I am talking about, friend, as regards
diet and everything else to do with the efficient running of
a tidy. . . . *No! You can't have any more meat, you gutsy greedy
old slobbery cow!* The impertinence of it! And what does she
think of next? I can read her like a book – she is after Ron's
meat, a birdlike eater, Ron, the twitcher will stop her. *No!
Three from the twitcher for thieves, Mrs Ridge, one! two! three!*

There! That will teach you, Mrs Ridge!
Treat them like children: they are children, aren't they?
       This is truly their second childhood, isn't it?
          Oh, do not think I justify
myself! I have no psychological need to do that, friend, none
at all. Do not deceive yourself: deception is a sin if not a
crime.

*Now come on, finish up like good second children. There's
all the treats of our weekly Social Evening to come.*

      So many of them look beautiful,
manage to keep some beauty, even acquire some beauty. I use
the word advisedly. Even the bearded Stanton lady, in her
way.   *Come along now!* Chivvy chivvy chivvy. Daydreaming, most of them, they remember years ago far better
than they remember to change themselves, or ask to be
changed. They admire the past, think so much of the past: why
therefore do they expect treatment any different from that
they would have received in the workhouse of the past?
Ah, you can bet, friend, they prefer at least this aspect of
modern life, do not want to return to the good old workhouse
days!   Oh dear me, no, no!
    Isn't that a not unpleasing paradox?
       This may be a
charitable institution, that may be the form of words, but
it is as remote from what was known as a workhouse as my
Ralphie is from a

    dingo.

Right now! Clear up! Quietly,
if you please, this is not a bandhouse or bothy! What d'you
imagine you're at? Quietly!

At least we
don't have washing up to do with these cardboard plates.
Just shoot the lot for pigswill, sell it. Must see if I
can get more off that swine Berry, ha, though he gets
enough off me one way or the other, besides the odd
bit of the other. I give him a good class of swill for
his pigs, they must enjoy the cardboard, I think. Pigs
eat anything, they say. No complaints, anyway, and it's
all good for – *You dirty old . . . person!*
What a mess, dropped the lot!
Thought you were feeding Ralphie, did you? I tell you
Ralphie wouldn't touch it after you had! He
has only the finest dogmeat, two tins a day, two large
tins, that is. *Come here, Ralphie my darling, did*
they try to tempt you with muck, Ralphie?
There, there. Feel the flowing of
those muscles, how tense he strains. Five
times! *What a dog!*
Mrs Bowen, I think we'll make that
your last chance to drop anything, shall we?
Come on now! Last one to clear up is a cissy! Really
must get on to the office again about help. Can't run
this place any longer with just a part-time cook. And
I'm not cooking once more in that place when she's off
sick or drunk. They'll have to give me help, have to.

                              Right, at last
we've finished clearing up our mess, haven't we, and
so now it's time for the House Song.   *Not*
to say the House Hymn!

                                        Are we ready,
then?   *Altogether now, let's be hearing*
from you in the Balcony as well, one,

                                   two,

                                        three!

            The joys of life continue strong
            Throughout old age, however long:
            If only you can cheerful stay
            And brightly welcome every day.
            Not what you've been, not what you'll be,
            What matters now is that you're free:
            The joys of life continue strong
            Throughout old age, however long.

            The most important thing to do
            Is stay alive and screw and screw:
            No matter if the future's dim
            So long as I can use my quim:
            For I know best, and bring no cheer,
            Oh, lucky me, that I am here!
            The most important thing to do
            Is screw and screw, and screw and screw.

                What a delightful song that is!

Now it's work, everyone, work, and then play, play
later. Our little good deed for the day, work.

                          Ivy,
fetch the boxes, please.   *It's Fancy Goods*
again tonight, my dears, Fancy Goods except for
Sarah and Charlie who I've got something very special
in mind for.   *Now my little Fancy Goods man*
wasn't too pleased with the work you did yesterday,
I'm sorry to say – sorry for your sakes, that is, not
for mine, of course. Can we just be a little
bit more careful tonight?   *Not get the*
sticky glue all over our fingers but only where it's
supposed to go?   *Ivy, give me one of those here.*

         You see, it's quite simple: you
just cut your crêpe paper to the width of your little
wooden roller,   *roll*
it round   *like this*   *and very carefully*
glue all along the edge – very carefully, mind you,
very carefully.   *You don't need*
much glue, just a smear, just a smear along one edge.
         Is that all clear?
So do let's do our little good deed for the day, but
do it well if we're going to do it at all.   *Ivy,*
give out the work then, please.

         Sarah and Charlie,
my trusties, I have something special for you tonight.

Charlie, I want you to pour about
a quarter of each of these bottles into one of the
empty ones here until it's three-quarters full –
three bottles pour a quarter out of, that is, until
this one's also three-quarters full, and when you've
got them all three-quarters full then top them up
with water from your tap.   All right?
But please be careful not to stain any of the labels
with drips, there's a good trusty, my old Charlie?

No, I know you haven't, I
know, Charlie.   Now Sarah, I want
you to do a similar job for me, though not quite the
same. You see these little bottles? I'd like you
just to soak the labels off, make the bottles quite
clean afterwards.
No, I don't want the labels kept for
anything, no, so you can get them off any way you
like, tear them, scrape them with your nails, oh?
Yes, by all means
use a knife from the washing up.

Everyone happy, then?   Ivy, see that everyone
has a pot of glue and enough to get on with.
All right, friends?
I'm going to work, too, get on with my own
work up on the stage.

Talk by all means, but let's not have too much
noise, eh?   Bless you.

My children. From this dais
I am monarch of all I survey. This is my Empire.
I do not exaggerate, friend. They are dependent
upon me and upon such minions as I have from time
to time. Nothing is more sure than that I am
in control of them. And they know it. They
vie with each other for my attention. This is
especially noticeable on the tablet round
each night and morning. On the weekly medical
round their attention is divided between the
good doctor and myself: they are undecided as
to whether to play for the once-a-week prestige
of his attention, or for mine that it may
perhaps be available more than once a week,
perhaps even daily. Oh, how comic that is!
For I love only Ralphie, Ralphie is my darling!
Where are you, Ralphie?
Ralph, come here at once!   The dirty doggie,
licking at that mess under poor old Mrs Stanton!
Hope it's only water. Perhaps it's gravy from
dinner. There, there, Ralphie, there's a good
dog, that's my hairy darling.

There are always complaints, of course. Complaining
is one of the few activities into which they put
some genuine feeling. It is good for them, of course.
I listen very carefully to their complaints. And then
do nothing. There is nothing for them really to
complain about here. They would be so much worse off
if they were not in here. The hazards of hypothermia,

falls, neglect. But it does not worry me if
complaining is their favourite occupation. It is
also a way of vieing for my attention. I fondle
Ralphie in front of them and that keeps up their
interest. It frustrates them and gives them a
reason to be going on. What would become of them
if I took this away? Oh, I did not study for five
years for nothing, friend, or waste my time as an
abject disciple of Frau Holstein, no! It gives them
something to worry about instead of worrying
about their reactions not being as sharp as they
were, their voices not quite so resonant, that
they are forgetful, and confused, and so on and
so forth. And then there are the diversions I
provide, as well. The Sally Army comes round
collecting several times a month. They enjoy
that, it is one of their favourite treats. Come
and join. Then we have the Olde Tyme Evening
provided by the Council once a year, too, when
they're not too busy. Oh, to them it must seem
like one mad merry-go-round! And a schoolchildren's
choir every now and again. Then there's always
the telly, when it's working – that reminds me,
must get it repaired again: it's over two months,
now. In return, they do these little jobbies for
me. Handicrafts, felt toys last month. And now
Christmas crackers, in due season.
They seem to be getting on reasonably well. Of
course, I can't expect Mrs Stanton and George to
do very much. But the important thing for them is

that it is there in front of them to be done if they
do wake up or otherwise become capable of doing
it. That really is the important thing, we all agree.
All the books agree.   I give
Mrs Stanton about three weeks, and George could
pop off any minute.
But I must get down to my work, too. *Here, Ralphie!*
                    Come and lie comfortingly on
my feet while I work on my accounts.

Have to be careful with these, no names, no initials
either, or at least not the right ones.

                    Frederick, first names will do. Do I
need to keep accounts? Yes, for my own benefit.
Frederick, then, 350 boxes filled with felt toy bits,
how much, at fivepence a box, five hundred pence a
hundred boxes, a fiver a hundred boxes, three-and-a-
half fivers are seventeen pounds and a half, fifty
pence.   So.   That he still
owes me. When will he be round with another lot?
Can't tell. It's that sort of business. He must be
on some big purchase tax fiddle. Income tax, too,
I shouldn't wonder.
Then there was the penicillin. Lump sum for
altering that lot. Twenty pounds. Shipped abroad,
no doubt, as something or other that it isn't. But
that's none of my business, it doesn't worry me,
either. My job is to keep my friends happy, and,
if it makes money, then so much the better. Do

you not agree, friend? Oh, again, do not think
I have to justify myself!
Seventeen plastic ashtrays: one pound exactly,
a job lot.   Contacts are all-important
in this business. It is not enough just to ad-
vertise in the trade papers. I must write to a
number, a large number, of likely sources of
employment. I must point out to them the unique
advantages of my methods of outworking. This
should – Ah, Charlie, my old trusty, I can tell
when you have that lost look on your face that
you are not puzzling over some problem of
philosophy, or even of filling those bottles, but
merely and genteelly trying to fart without Sarah
or anyone else noticing. Charlie.
      Ralphie warm on my feet.

      What you do not understand, I think,
friend, is that what we imagine they want for themselves is not actually what they do want. I do
not know what they want, either. But I do know
that they are certainly not as we are, and that
therefore by definition they do not want what we
want.   How does anyone know
what anyone else really wants?   Multiply
that by the diffusing effect of time, friend,
which alters with every day, every minute,
virtually! When I was eight I wanted to be a fairy
in a ballet, ho ho ho! he he he! ha ha ha! heh!
heh! heh! and similar printers' straitjackets for

the gusty, exploding liberation of laughter.
But I forget myself.   Where was I?
Yes, the Divisional Officer asked me whether I
would like to undertake a week's exchange with
a seaside House. Really, I said to him, don't
you think that would be rather absurd with my
group of friends? Besides (though I didn't tell
him this) I had my Stationery Goods quota to
meet that week. Which reminds me: how many
sets of pens and rulers was it he still owes
me for? Look it up.

        Yes, 230. I'll have to mention that to
him when he comes, whenever. Can't be too careful. That shows the value of keeping accounts.
It's certain he wouldn't have remembered it, con-
veniently, unless I'd mentioned it.

Don't think I do this for the money, friend. The
Council takes all their pensions and allows them
back one pound each for their personal expenditure.
That is too much, to my way of thinking. They have
no need of that much pocket money. No, friend,
not for their money: you can see there is little
chance here of the quick oncer.

Ah, Charlie has nearly finished. He'll be asking
me about corks soon.   I'll go down now.
The rest might as well finish now, too.

*Right now, everyone. You can finish now. You've
done a good session of work, and so now you
deserve to play.*   But let's clear up first,
shall we?   *Ivy, please collect the boxes for
us.*   Descend from my throne.

Charlie, yes, I knew you'd ask. *You've got corks
from the ones which were full, haven't you?*
                              Good. Then here's
*some more for the others. Just stand the boxes
in the corner if you will, please, afterwards.*

*Ralphie! Come away from that! You all right,
Mrs Stanton?* Right as she'll ever be. Done no
work at all.   *George, you've just been
daydreaming!* And screwing up the bits of
paper and getting the bleeding glue all over the
place! Ugh!   Still, what
did I expect?
*How about you, Mrs Bowen? You've been working
with Ivy and Ron, have you? Very nicely, too.
You've done a lot between you.*   Yes, yes.
                *And greedy old Mrs Ridge,
you haven't done any!*   Don't you cheek
me or you'll get another taste of the twitcher, the
twitcher!   *Now then!*

*Very good, Sarah, my old trusty, what a lovely job
you've made of those!*   I'm very pleased with you,
very pleased indeed.   Yes, and you, Charlie.

Now let's have some relaxation. Attention please,
everyone!   *Stay where you are,*
sitting round the long table, and we're going to
play Pass the Parcel. You pass the parcel from
one to another, and when the music stops whoever
has it tries to open it. When the music starts
again, the parcel must be passed on. And so on.
And what a lovely surprise the last one's going to
get, the winner! Here we go then. You start off
with the music, Sarah.   *Off we go!*
Music on.

                                        Stop
at Mrs Ridge.

On again.

                    Music stopped at Sarah. Give her
a treat, she's worked well, give her a bit of excitement. On again.

            Oh my darlings, how I love you!

Pass it on, Mrs Ridge! While the music's playing it . . .
I should think so.   Stop the music.
Who's won, then? Yes, it's Ron! Ron's the lucky winner!
            You're right, Ron, first time. It's SHIT!
But whose shit is it? That's the question! I'll sing it
for you: *Pass the parcel, pass the parcel,*
                See what comes from RALPHIE'S arsehole!

How disgusting! you must be saying to yourself,
friend, and I cannot but agree. But think a bit
harder, friend: why do I disgust them?
I disgust them in order that they may not be
disgusted with themselves. I am disgusting to them
in order to objectify their disgust, to direct it to
something outside themselves, something harmless.
Some of them still believe in God: what would
happen if they were to turn their disgust on God
for taking away control over their own sphincter
muscles, for instance, and think, naturally enough,
that He must be vile to be responsible for such
a thing?   Far better for them to think
handling and smelling and seeing doggie's turd is
disgusting!   Do you not agree?
Right, everyone! Attention please! The game is
over and now it's our Travel Time.   It's so
much more tasteful an expression than Exercise,
don't you think, friend?   *Travel Time. Yes, I*
know your old bones protest, but you know it's good
for you. Those of you who can walk push round those
in wheelchairs, those in wheelchairs move everything
you can move as you go.   *Off we go now!*

There are worse conditions and worse places, friend.
I have worked in geriatric wards where the stench of
urine and masturbation was relieved only by the odd
gangrenous limb or advanced carcinoma. Where confused
patients ate each other's puke. Where I have seen a
nurse spray a patient's privates with an aerosol

lavatory deodorant. Even worse, people like
these can be put away in mental wards and homes
when they are perfectly sane, simply because they
are old: they don't stay perfectly sane long.
They are stripped of their spectacles, false teeth,
everything personal to them. They are shut away,
visits are rare and discouraged anyway, no one cares;
they are forgotten and wholly in the power of nurses
who have been known to make them alter their wills,
to scatter the ward's pills for everyone to scramble
for, and to put Largactil in the tea unmeasured.
This is a happy House, friend, a holiday camp,
compared. Here I give them constant occupation, and,
most important, a framework within which to establish
– indeed, to possess – their own special personalities.
Here we respect their petty possessions, so important
to them but rubbish to us.
This is the time when the bearing surfaces of the
joints begin to wear seriously, when the walls of the
veins and arteries harden, when the nervous system
loses much of its subtlety. It has always been so.
Today we can give them more time, by nylon balls and
sockets, drugs to thin the blood, Largactil to lift
nervous depression: but ultimately these are nothing.
                         You should understand the
simple fact that they are all approaching death very
quickly; and one must help them to do so in the right
spirit. It is what used to be called a holy duty. I
did not invent this system: I inherited it. And in
the end death will come to me too, probably.

There. They enjoy it. Sometimes for a change I
have them doing Travel in the form of bizarre sexual
antics. As-if-sexual, that is, in the case of some
friends.   And now I give you – *SPORT!*
Yes, it's Tourney Time again, friends! Remember how
you enjoyed the last Tourney we had?
Of course you do! Get the wet mops, Ivy, please. And
Charlie, you wheel Mrs Bowen to one corner, and
you, Sarah, wheel George to the opposite corner.
                    That's it. One mop each,
Ivy, thank you.
On the word, then, steeds and knights, you thunder
at top speed towards each other, never flinching,
like bold and parfait gentil knights, and try to
lance each other. No stopping! Straight on, turn,
and back for another joust. Ready then? And may the
best knight win!   One!   Two!   Three!

          Well done, Mrs Bowen! A palpable hit!
One more time, then.   Off you go!

Another hit for Mrs Bowen! Sarah, see if George is
still awake, will you? He doesn't seem to be trying
very hard.   Last joust, then. Away you go!
                    At various times in the past we
have had Balloon Races, Polo, Folk Dancing and Archery.
Mrs Bowen the Winner! Back to the table, now. The
Knobbly Knee Competition was very popular, too.

So after all our exertions let's just have a quiet
discussion session, shall we? And as always our
subject is HOW I WANT TO GO *and its related topics* MY CHOICE
OF COFFIN *or* WHAT I WANT DONE WITH MY EARTHLY
REMAINS. *First of all, let us remember first principles.*
Death may be seen as the price paid for what the body
is – that is, the very biological functioning of
the body, its very nature, inherently implies and
contains death; this debt is paid in instalments;
and the period of old age is that in which all
arrears must be settled. Death indeed may often be a lot
less painful than life: the actual dying, that is.
There are various ways of facing this death. Whether you
believe in God or not, there is still the possibility
he or she will be there waiting for you after death: those
of you wishing for a coin to be placed in your mouths or
victuals to be provided for a postulated journey have only
to let us know. Again, you may see death as the ex-
change of individual life for biological improvement
and conservation as part of a scheme for higher ful-
filment on the part of some life force. Or you can
simply see yourselves as potentially a heap of rather
superior manure: there is, in fact, no dishonour in
that. However you look at it, someone has to decide what
to do with what you leave behind you, and as this is a
democratic institution we give you this opportunity to
decide, for yourselves, between burial, cremation, acid
bath, remote moorland exposure, or whatever.

      No replies. Never are.   I just hand them over to an
undertaker who probably uses them for meat pies, anyway.

And now at last what you have all been waiting for:
Entertainment! Up on the stage for this, so that
they can see better.
Here's one you'll all enjoy. A little girl, let's
call her Dottie, was sitting on her grandad's knee
and said: "Grandad, were you in the Ark?" "No, of
course I wasn't!" said the Grandad, somewhat taken
aback. "Then why," said delightful little Dottie,
"weren't you drownded?"   *Isn't*
that a funny one? Laugh, you stupid old twats!
                    Here's another one, even better.
Most of you are at the metallic stage of your lives:
silver in your hair, gold in your teeth, and, in the
case of the men, lead in your trousers!
                    Laugh!
            I'll give them just one more. *There was a*
very old couple. The husband was ninety-eight and
the wife was ninety-five. One day their son died,
aged seventy-two. The husband consoled his grief-
stricken wife by saying: "There, there, dear, we never
did think we'd live to see him grow up."
                            All right, so it's
a rotten joke. What do you expect, professional comics?

But I must just tell you this last one. A man lying
on his deathbed was asked if he had made his peace
with God. "I didn't know we had ever had a row,"
said the man, wittily.
Isn't that screamingly funny?
            Mind you, he didn't get into heaven either.

A slight laugh. How curious that
heaven does concern some of them in the way – *Ivy!*
How dare you read a book during Entertainment! Who
do you think you are? How dare you?
                              I should think so too! You'd
all better watch now, it's the Piece de Resistance.
          Turn on the sexy music.   *Ralphie!*
Here, boy.   Here we go, then, sway, that's
it, just right, slowly unbutton my overall, so they
can see I have only a bra
then only tights   underneath
                  cast off the overall over Ralphie. Up
on the table   slowly down with my stocking
tights   one leg   the other   *I can*
see you're enjoying this!   All watching, except
Mrs Stanton, asleep or dead – does it matter? Now
my bra, tantalise by appearing to have difficulty.
                    Wouldn't they all rather be dead?
Ah, friend, that is where we make a mistake! For
they would all rather be alive! All!   Tights,
gossamer, off   stand! And the music swells to
an early climax.   *Here, Ralphie! Up on the table*
with Mummy!   That's it, you know what to do with
your long probing red Borzoi tongue, don't you, Ralphie!
                              Lovely!
          ooooh!
                    that's it!
     Oh, Ralphie! Faster! we're getting near the
end of the page, Ralphie!   ooooh!   oh!
iiiiiihl!   ooooh!   nearly!   *YES!*

There! Wasn't that wonderful!
I know you too have your little feels in the
toilets. Good luck to you! I hope you enjoy
them as much as I do.   And now we must be
in just the mood to sing the Jubilate before we
all vanish up our own orifices.
All together now!   One   Two   Three!

Death comes to all, no matter who,
No matter what we bloody do:
Despite lacrosse, P.E. and gym,
Our lights at last will surely dim.
For this we should stand up and cheer
And please ourselves while we are here:
Death comes to all, no matter who,
No matter what you bloody do!

And here you see, friend, I am about to step

outside the convention, the framework of twenty-
one pages per person. Thus you see I too am the
puppet or concoction of a writer (you always knew
there was a writer behind it all? Ah, there's
no fooling you readers!), a writer who has me at
present standing in the post-orgasmic nude but
who still expects me to be his words without
embarrassment or personal comfort.   So
you see this is from his skull. It is a diagram
of certain aspects of the inside of his skull!
                    What a laugh!

Still, I'll finish off for him, about the sadness,
the need to go farther better to appreciate the
nearer, what you have now: if you are not like
our friends, friend, laugh now, prepare, accept,
worse times are a-coming, nothing is more sure.

But here's something he found in the Montgomeryshire
Collections and thought you might like to have
for yourself, friend:

> F for Francis
> I for Chances
> N for Nicholas
> I for Tickle us
> S for Sammy the
>   Salt Box